D1252701

School health and health education

Fifth edition

School health and health education

C. E. Turner, A.M., Ed.M., D.Sc., Dr.P.H.

Professor of Public Health, Emeritus, Massachusetts Institute of Technology; formerly Chief of Health Education, World Health Organization; recently Consultant to the United Nations Educational, Scientific and Cultural Organization and the World Health Organization in School Health Education; formerly Director of Health Education Studies, Malden Public Schools; sometime Associate Professor of Hygiene, Tufts College Medical and Dental Schools; formerly Visiting Professor of Health Education, School of Public Health, University of California

C. Morley Sellery, A.B., M.D.

Formerly Director of Health Education and Health Services, Los Angeles City Schools; formerly Lecturer in School Health Administration, University of California at Los Angeles, Summer Sessions; formerly Assistant Clinical Professor of Preventive Medicine and Public Health, College of Medical Evangelists, Loma Linda, Calif.

Sara Louise Smith, M.A., Ed.D.

Professor and Head, Health Education Department, Florida State University, Tallahassee, Fla.; formerly State Consultant in Health and Safety Education, Florida State Department of Education; formerly Associate Professor of Health Education, Georgia State College for Women; formerly Principal, Peabody High School of Georgia State College for Women, Milledgeville, Ga.

Illustrated

The C. V. Mosby Company

Saint Louis   1966

To *N.C.T.*

Preface

This book seeks to give to the teacher in preparation, and to the school health team in action, a clear picture of the school health program and the way in which the health education of pupils and students is achieved. It reflects many years of experience on the part of the authors, in teaching teachers, in health education research, in school health administration, and in local, state, and international consultation service. It takes into consideration the instruction that student teachers receive in general education, psychology, and methodology as well as the limited time available for the study of school health; and it seeks to meet the further health education needs of teachers completely but concisely. It presents a clear statement of functions, duties, and relationships; and it suggests procedures, methods, and materials for health education in succinct and usable form.

For suggestions and assistance in connection with this revision, we wish to express our thanks to Dr. Harriett B. Randall, Medical Director, Los Angeles City Schools; to Mr. Donald R. Caziarc, Hearing Conservation Specialist, California State Department of Public Health; to Mr. Kenneth E. Brown, Director of Safety Education with the Massachusetts Safety Council; to Naomi C. Turner, Ed. M.; and to the many professors and instructors in health education whose correspondence has been greatly appreciated.

C. E. Turner
C. Morley Sellery
Sara Louise Smith

Contents

Part one

The nature and development of school health and health education

Chapter 1

The place of health in education

School health and health education represent an important part of your professional life. Many teachers will tell you that no part of their teaching experience has been more pleasurable or rewarding than having a part in the promotion of the health of children. But your contribution to school health will be of more importance to your pupils than to you.

A few years ago a thoughtful parent said to me, "Yes, John has improved wonderfully in health and appearance in the last year. I credit most of it to his teacher. Her influence upon his health habits, courtesy, and his work habits, too, has been almost miraculous."

This statement reflects the fact that the heart and center of formal education is the relationship between the teacher and the individual child. The school exists to provide for the child those organized learning experiences which will best develop the concepts, knowledge, skills, habits, attitudes, physical and mental vigor, personality, and character needed for desirable citizenship in a free country. The teacher is close to the child and most directly in control of these childhood experiences.

Good teachers have always been concerned with the health and welfare of their pupils. The promotion of pupil health is a privilege and an opportunity as well as a responsibility. It enriches teacher-pupil relationships. It increases the value of the teacher to society. It is a part of good professional practice. The teacher often acts *in loco parentis*. In helping to shape the child's health behavior he has special understandings and skills.

Primary responsibility for the health of the child rests, of course, with the home; but that responsibility is shared by the school and the community. Outside the home only the teacher is with the child constantly enough to promote habit formation effectively. In respect to mental health it has been said that the future mental health of society depends in no small degree upon the role of the school as a social unit and upon the teacher as a leader in that unit. The school helps pupils and students to feel secure, appreciated, courageous, and resourceful.

What can you do for the physical, mental, and social health and well-being of your pupils or students? The extent and effectiveness of your

3

Fig. 1. A knowledge of personal health and the health of the child is important to those in preparation for teaching.

participation in school health will depend upon your knowledge of what constitutes a good school health program, your appreciation of its value, your knowledge of and attitude toward your own health and that of your pupils, your ability to understand and cooperate with the other members of the health team, and especially upon your interest in children and your skill in contributing to their health knowledge, attitudes, and behavior.

Responsibility for school health

Every government recognizes its responsibility to protect and promote the health of the people. This responsibility is met in two ways: (1) through health services or what it does for people to protect health and (2) through health education which develops intelligent responsibility on the part of the individual for maintaining personal, family, and community health.

School authorities, with the collaboration of health authorities, carry basic governmental responsibility for the protection and promotion of the health of that important fifth of the population which is of school age. In requiring school attendance the state assumes an obligation for *health protection*. Suitable environmental sanitation and an adequate program of communicable disease control are clear-cut responsibilities. But the school should also see that the health of children, individually and collectively, is not retarded as a result of unhygienic conditions met while attending school. It must maintain surveillance over pupil health.

Where physical defects and departures from normal health are found, the school must be interested in their *correction*. Society is making a large expenditure upon the education of each child and, in the interest of its own investment as well as in the interest of the child, it must do what it can to make the child ready to profit by its instruction.

As an educational agency, the school does not have the responsibility for providing medical care. It does have the responsibility to tell parents what is found to be wrong, to encourage the prompt use of medical or clinical service for the treatment of such defects as those of tonsils, teeth, nose, throat, eyes, ears, lungs, and heart, and to provide a modified education program for children whose health status demands it.

Health education seeks to provide and utilize all possible learning experiences contributory to the development of desirable health habits, attitudes, and knowledge. It seeks to help children to achieve and maintain a quality of mental and physical health which will add zest to life and help to produce vigorous, self-reliant, courageous, and public-spirited citizens.

Schools, when adequately staffed and administered, provide experience in healthful school living and give the pupil an opportunity to become acquainted with good sanitation and health services. He learns the value of health advice and supervision. He has a chance to learn something about the care of his own body, the maintenance of health, and the prevention of disease.

The importance of health education

Professional leadership in both health and education recognizes the importance of health education in schools. International recogniton was reflected in a recent communication sent to Ministries of Health and Ministries of Education by the Director General of UNESCO, Dr. Maheu, and the Director General of WHO, Dr. Candau. This communication was sent in connection with the preliminary draft of a publication on *Planning*

Fig. 2. School health and health education are receiving attention all over the world. This is a Joint Expert Committee of the World Health Organization (WHO) and the United Nations Educational, Scientific, and Cultural Organization (UNESCO) on the preparation of teachers for health education. (Courtesy World Health Organization.)

for Health Education in Schools and contained the following sentence: "The United Nations Educational Scientific and Cultural Organization and the World Health Organization, as the specialized agencies concerned with education and health respectively, recognize health education in schools as an important part of general education and a vital means of health promotion."[1]

The International Advisory Committee on the School Curriculum stated that the first objective of primary education is "to stimulate and guide the child's physical development and establish in him sound health habits."[2]

This same report proposes that the fields of instruction in the primary school should be:

1. Health and hygiene
2. Movement and physical education
3. The mother tongue language
4. The basic skills: reading, writing, arithmetic
5. Moral and spiritual values
6. Social studies: social and civic relationships
7. The natural world
8. The use of artistic and creative materials
9. Other fields, such as aesthetic appreciation.

Parents also consider health education important. The *World Survey of Education*[3] reports an interesting study carried out in Brazil among 3,000 parents who were asked to rate sixteen subjects in the elementary school curriculum as important, unimportant, or useless. Teaching "the care of health" was rated as much more important than any other subjects except reading, writing, and arithmetic. These subjects were rated as "important" by the following percentages of the parents: reading, 98.9; writing, 98.7; arithmetic, 98.6; care of health, 81.4; geography, 58.0; history, 30.0; natural science, 32.0; religion, 54.6; singing and music, 16.0; drawing, 31.8; gardening, 18.0; horticulture, 33.3; physical education, 42.3; manual work, 30.0; artistic appreciation, 30.0; and domestic work, 70.0.

Some needed definitions

We have begun to use some terms which may suggest quite different concepts to different individuals. In the interest of clearer common understanding, it may be well to stop at this point to define some of the terms frequently used in our discussion of school health.

Health is that complete fitness of body, soundness of mind, and wholesomeness of emotions which make possible the highest quality of effective

---

[1]The above statement is reproduced, by permission, from *Planning for Health Education in Schools,* a work prepared for UNESCO and the World Health Organization by C. E. Turner. Copies are available in the U.S.A. through the UNESCO Publications Center, 317 East 34th Street, New York, N. Y.

[2]Reproduced, by permission, from the "Report of the International Advisory Committee on the School Curriculum," Second Session, 1957. Report UNESCO/ED/ 157, Paris, 6 May, 1958.

[3]*World Survey of Education: II, Primary Education,* Paris, UNESCO, 1958.

living and of service. The World Health Organization has defined health as "a state of complete physical, mental, and social well-being, not merely the absence of disease or infirmity." The term "positive health" is sometimes used to suggest that there are different degrees of health, just as there are different degrees of illness.

Public health is the science and the art of preventing disease, prolonging life, and promoting health and efficiency through organized community efforts.

The *school health program* includes all of the activities carried on in a school system in the interest of health.

Hygiene is the science of preserving and promoting health.

Sanitation refers to the establishment of environmental conditions favorable to health.

The *health education* of the individual takes place through all of the learning experiences which favorably influence his knowledge, attitudes, and habits relating to health. It is not limited to formal or direct health instruction.

The above statement defines health education in terms of the life experiences of the individual, affecting what he knows, how he feels, and what he does. Grout[4] defines health education in terms of community action and social objectives as "the translation of what is known about health into desirable individual and community behavior patterns by means of the educational process." (Note the implied emphasis upon sound facts, healthful behavior, adequate instruction, and effective motivation.)

Public health education helps people, individually and in groups, to help themselves to better health, through gaining a desire for health, discovering their personal, family, occupational, and community health problems, acquiring essential knowledge, and, with appropriate use of consultation and community resources, taking needed action.

School health education is that part of health education which takes place in schools or through the efforts of school personnel and provides learning experiences for influencing attitudes, knowledge, and conduct relating to personal and community health.

We find two different definitions for *curriculum* in educational literature. Sometimes it refers to a course of study which outlines the subject matter to be taught. Other writers use the word to include all learning experiences, out of class as well as in class, which are under the guidance or influence of the school. This book follows the latter, broader and more functional definition.

Objectives of general education and health education

The objectives of general education are often said to lie in the realms of (1) self-realization, (2) human relationships, (3) economic efficiency, and (4) civic responsibility. Health is related to each of them.

---

[4]Grout, Ruth E.: *Health Teaching in Schools,* ed. 4, Philadelphia, 1963, W. B. Saunders Company.

The reports of the Project on Instruction[5] of the National Education Association suggest that the following are ends toward which the school should be directing its efforts: using rational processes, developing social responsibility, learning to make more intelligent consumer choices, building international competence, increasing understanding of complicated issues confronting voters and taxpayers today, learning through discovery, developing self-direction and self-responsibility, and analyzing mass communication and propaganda.

Certainly the development of sound concepts in the field of health is a challenge to rational thinking. Social responsibility is not more challenging in any field than in health. Consumer education in health is an important facet of health education. Students give specific study to the international agencies for the promotion of public health. Complicated issues facing the voter range all the way from the fluoridation of water supplies to the provision of medical care. Surveys, experiments, and library research are constantly used in the discovery of health facts. Health education is a continuing process of helping the pupil increase his responsibility and his powers of self-direction in the interest of his health and the health of others. Press, radio, and television are filled with health propaganda and communications on health subjects. The evaluation of such mass communications is given careful attention in health instruction.

The school seeks especially to develop the capacity for critical thinking—to help children learn how to learn, how to attack new problems, and how to acquire new knowledge. Decision-making in health matters offers a prime opportunity for the development of these capacities.

A classic statement of the objectives of general education is to be found in *A Design for General Education,*[6] prepared by the American Council on Education, which says with reference to health:

In the committee's judgment, general education should lead the student:
1. To improve and maintain his own health and take his share of responsibility for protecting the health of others.

In further elaboration of the *health objective,* placed first on the list, the committee says:

In order to accomplish this purpose, the student should acquire the following:
A. Knowledge and understanding
    1. Of normal body functions in relation to sound health practice.
    2. Of the major health hazards, their prevention and control.
    3. Of the interrelation of mental and physical processes in health.
    4. Of reliable sources of information on health.
    5. Of scientific methods in evaluating health concepts.
    6. Of the effect of socio-economic conditions on health.
    7. Of community health problems, such as problems related to sanitation, industrial hygiene, and school hygiene.

---

[5]National Education Association: *Schools for the Sixties,* A report of the Project on Instruction, New York, 1963, McGraw-Hill Book Co., p. 9.

[6]*A Design for General Education,* Washington, D. C., 1944, American Council on Education.

8. Of community organization and services for health maintenance and improvement.

B. Skills and abilities
1. The ability to organize time to include planning for food, work, recreation, rest and sleep.
2. The ability to improve and maintain good nutrition.
3. The ability to atttain and maintain good emotional adjustment.
4. The ability to select and engage in recreative activities and healthful exercises suitable to individual needs.
5. The ability to avoid unnecessary exposure to disease and infection.
6. The ability to utilize medical and dental services intelligently.
7. The ability to participate in measures for the protection and improvement of community health.
8. The ability to evaluate popular health beliefs critically.

C. Attitudes and appreciations
1. Desire to attain optimum health.
2. Personal satisfaction in carrying out sound health practices.
3. Acceptance of responsibility for his own health and for the protection of the health of others.
4. Willingness to make personal sacrifices for the health of others.
5. Willingness to comply with health regulations and to work for their improvement.

Reasons for school health education

Modern health education rarely needs to be defended; but, as school people, we should understand why it is needed and be able to explain both its need and its value, to parents or others. Let us review the need for health education and its possibilities.

We need school health education, first, because medical and public health records show clearly that present *health practices are poor*. Innumerable instances reveal the development of both organic and communicable disease as the result of unhygienic living or lack of hygienic precautions.

Second, our *attitude toward disease* has not led to hygienic living. We have traditionally blamed Divine Providence for the illnesses which our own negligence has caused. We have thought of health as merely "not being sick in bed" and we have acted as though the responsibility for our health were our physician's instead of our own.

A third reason for undertaking systematic health education is the general *lack of basic information* in health matters. We have at present, among the medical and public health professions, information that, if it could be applied, would appreciably lengthen human life. Our knowledge of nutrition, of immunization, and of many other phases of public health is growing rapidly. There is a considerable amount of such recent information that needs to become the possession of the average citizen.

A final reason is that *habits affect health and schools can help to develop health habits.* The relation between habits and health is clear. Athletic training gives us evidence of the effect on health of a change of habits. Read the training program of boxers for reducing weight and getting into condition. Follow the conditioning processes of baseball players.

The football coach can do things with his team in November that he could not possibly do with them in September, because late in the season he has them in condition. Many individuals have developed appreciable athletic prowess from bodies that were frail in youth.

There is also ample evidence of the beneficial effect of improved nutrition upon health and growth. No animal can thrive upon improper food. An improvement in the health of the undernourished child when he is placed under the care of the pediatrician or under some hygienically organized program of living with suitable food and rest is a matter of common observation. Holt's early studies showed that Japanese children in the United States, both boys and girls, were taller and heavier than those of corresponding ages living in Japan.[7]

There are many examples of frail persons who have reached an advanced age through taking good care of themselves.

Evidences that the school can improve habits

The first reason why the schools may hope to be successful in this field is that *youth is the time of habit formation.* Health habits, among others, are being formed at school.

Second, *the school furnishes the kind of training that is needed for habit formation.* Only by repetition can desirable practices be established; the school can provide such repetition.

Third, *the school works harmoniously with the home.* From this point of view we may divide children into two groups: those who are receiving good health training at home and those who are receiving little or none.

The following illustration shows this relationship with the better type of home:

One day a woman came to the teacher and said: "I don't see why you are carrying on this health training with my child. Don't you know that George's father is a doctor? He knows a lot more about health than you do."

The teacher replied: "Of course the doctor knows more about health than I do, but we are not presenting facts that are under dispute in the medical profession. We are training children in those fundamental habits upon which there is universal agreement. Very few children are as fortunate in their parents as George. I am sure you would not object to having him hear those things here at school that he hears at home, because otherwise some children would not hear those things at all."

"I never thought of it in that way," said the mother. "Of course it is all right so far as George's father and I are concerned."

She came back to visit health classes occasionally after that. A couple of months later she said to the teacher: "You know there is something I can't understand about this business; George will do things for you that he won't do for his father."

Then we have the other type of home. A teacher in a poor district recounts the following experience:

---

[7]Holt, L. Emmett: *Food, Health, and Growth,* New York, 1922, The Macmillan Company.

A mother who had learned that her boy, Sammy, had failed to measure up in cleanliness came to school and accused the teacher of "picking on" him. Sammy was as clean as any of the other children, she averred.

The teacher suggested calmly that her visitor walk up and down the aisles of the classroom and discover if this were actually so. The mother did this. When she returned, she turned immediately to her son and, with disgust in her voice, she exclaimed: "Why, Sammy! you Dirty fellow! You go and wash up!" And then she said to the teacher apologetically: "He never told me how clean the other children were."

Such a child finds a program of health training only when he reaches the public school.

Fourth, *the schools reach the whole population.*

Fifth, *the school can use the force of public opinion,* and, in the last analysis, that is the factor that is perhaps most important in determining behavior in ordinary matters. How carefully people plan their social conduct to conform to what society expects! The child has the same feeling about the boys and girls in his class that we do about our social equals. The school is to the child the source of authority. He accepts the advice of the teacher, but he is influenced, perhaps even more, by the opinion of the children in his group.

There is a suspicion on the part of the child in the home that perhaps father did not do all the things that he is urging son to do, like the boy who said, "Dad, you say you always went to Sunday School when you were a boy? Well, I don't believe it will do me any good either."

Sixth, and finally, various *specific studies* early demonstrated the value of health education. Investigations conducted by one of us (C. E. T.) showed by a controlled experiment that the introduction of health education without any other changes in school procedure can improve both health practices and health itself as reflected in physical growth. At the same time the health education program commended itself to school authorities, teachers, and parents as a desirable school activity.

We may quote here the conclusions from that study. The reader who is interested in the health education methods used and the statistical evaluation of growth data will wish to refer to the full report.[8]

Given a fair but experimental and critical trial, without any initial investment of funds from outside sources, health education commended itself to the school authorities, teachers, and parents as a sound procedure, contributing to general education and worthy of adoption as a part of the public school program. In the judgment of physicians and nurses, health education was a benefit to medical and nursing services. The program resulted in an improvement of habits, attitudes, and knowledge.

Over a period of 20 months, growth records were carefully and accurately taken of 273 children under the influence of a reasonably intensive health-education program and of 202 children in a comparable control group who continued the usual school program without any special training in health beyond that previously given.

The rate of gain in both height and weight for the children receiving health education was measurably and significantly greater than for those in the control group.

---

[8]Turner, C. E.: "Malden Studies in Health Education and Growth," *American Journal of Public Health* 18:1217–1230, 1928.

More healthful habits of living, resulting from the health-education program, produced an improved rate of growth, but not a fundamental change in the height-weight ratio.

General principles underlying health education

Our understanding of health education will be aided by a review of certain facts and principles which underlie the development and administrative conduct of the program.

1. *One's health is determined by both his heredity and his mode of living.* Because of differences in constitution, two children with the same program of living may not maintain the same health. Neither teachers nor children should expect health education to produce *uniform* health. A particular individual, however, will have better health and greater efficiency with good habits than with poor ones.

2. *Health education is the joint responsibility of the home and school and, less directly, of the community.* The school does not expect to supplant the home but rather to allow the child to find at school support for the program of healthful living which is being taught at home. Many children, unfortunately, are not adequately taught healthful living at home and the responsibility for their health education rests largely with the school. In these cases, the school should attempt to influence the home through the child and through the other means at its disposal.

3. *In the elementary school, health education is principally in the hands of the classroom teacher.* In dealing with the modification of habits, we recognize the importance of repetition. Children will form habits, not by learning a fact, but by doing things repeatedly with satisfactory results. The classroom teacher is the only member of the school personnel who is with a small group of pupils sufficiently long to carry through a program of habit training and to give day-by-day support to the health practices carried out at home. Nevertheless the principal, nurse, doctor, dentist, custodian, and others make a very important contribution, by example and by using every opportunity for incidental teaching.

4. *Health education must be accepted and fostered by the administrative authorities of the school as a part of the education program if it is to succeed.* One can usually tell by talking with the principal, before going into classrooms, whether there is a real health education program in the school. It is almost impossible for a teacher to develop a health education program without the support of the principal, general supervisors, and superintendent. It certainly is impossible to develop a graded and well organized program without such support. If principals and superintendents do not expect health education to function in the classrooms, few teachers develop it properly. Certain phases of the school health program are direct administrative responsibilities. These include schoolhouse construction, school sanitation, supplying ample toilet and hand-washing facilities, the provision of scales for the monthly weighing of all elementary pupils, and the arrangement of the teacher's program so that he has op-

portunity to talk with the nurse, doctor, and parents in regard to the child's medical record.

5. *Effective health education demands the understanding, sympathy, cooperation, and support of health specialists in the school sytsem.* Physicians, nurses, dentists, dental hygienists, physical educators, and nutritionists understand, contribute to, and cooperate in the program of health education. Criticism, dissension, and aspersions will weaken the best of programs. The experience of medical examinations, physical inspections, nurse-pupil conferences, and dental corrections can be made more meaningful by the teacher and the teacher's effort can be substantiated by the medical specialists. The use of the cumulative health record serves as a tangible medium of cooperation.

6. *Health instruction and the development of health attitudes and habits contribute to the easier and better accomplishment of the medical, dental, and nursing services.* Children who know health facts commensurate with their age and grade, and who are conditioned to practice good health habits, are more desirous of taking fullest advantage of the opportunities for learning their health status. These children, likewise, will be more cooperative in securing the necessary correction of defects. Pupils who might otherwise need endless prodding from the nurse before acting upon medical advice are stimulated, by the force of social approval in the classroom, to obtain corrections with a minimum of follow-up. A class with a health education program tries to get a perfect record in the correction of physical defects.

7. *The promotion of teacher health is important to the health education program, as well as to the quality and cost of education.* It is obvious that a well teacher will do better classroom work than a sick teacher. The instruction will be more effective, more continuous, and hence less expensive. Moreover, the well teacher finds its easier to maintain the serenity, optimism, and enthusiasm that contribute to the mental health of children and to their success. An enthusiastic, well, strong, and energetic teacher has a subtle effect upon the children as an example of the effectiveness of healthful living.

We may assume, then, that the various administrative measures which contribute to the health of the teacher will also contribute indirectly to the health education program. Conversely, we recognize that the health education program contributes to the health of the teacher as he follows his own precepts and sets an example of hygienic living for the children.

8. *The professional skill and initiative of the teacher constitute a most valuable element in the health education of the child. The health program must be so arranged that constructive and creative contributions of the individual teacher may be fostered.* Health is a way of living, not a subject that can be taught mechanically. Unless the teacher has initiative, interest in the pupil activities he develops, and ability to adapt them to the needs of each particular group of children, the health education program in that

classroom will fail to be fully effective. The health project or activity that is planned wholly or in part by the class and the teacher is most likely to succeed.

9. *It is necessary to develop health practices on the part of the child before he is old enough to understand the scientific reasons upon which these practices rest.* Practice is needed before knowledge is possible. Health training begins in the home. It is supplemented at school. We begin the organization of health training in the lowest grade. As the child develops, we gradually present the knowledge upon which health practices are based, adapting our instruction to his interests and capacities.

The pupil begins school with the acceptance of a few fundamental health habits, the propriety and value of which he does not question. He finishes his public school education with an intelligent application of the fundamental principles of health to his own particular physical needs and activities.

10. *Correct attitudes are important.* The desirable *attitude toward health* regards it as a means of enriching life and not as an end in itself. Health contributes to happiness, to comfort, to enjoyment, and to the maintenance of friendly social relationships. It contributes to the accomplishment of the fundamental aims of life. It is sought for what it helps us to be and to do. Health is a means toward such fundamental objectives as character, citizenship, and service.

The child should develop an *attitude toward health practices* that recognizes them as related to growth and immediate accomplishment, not as ends in themselves. He must see that health practices contribute to some objective that he is striving to reach, if he is to be interested in going into training for health. Health objectives must be in terms of everyday life. As an abstraction the word "health" means little to elementary school pupils. They will not be easily influenced to undertake a program of healthful living because of its beneficial results in middle life.

All children can succeed to some degree in improving health practices. The recognition of these individual successes and the provision for every child to participate in health activities go far toward making the program enjoyable. The child comes to feel that health habit training is an activity in which he can succeed.

In aiding the development of any health habit the teacher is of course concerned with the development of specific attitudes which will help the child to recognize the value of the health habit and desire to practice it.

References

American Association of School Adminstrators: *Health in Schools,* Twentieth Yearbook, rev. ed., Washington, D. C., 1951, the Association.

Anderson, C. L.: *School Health Practice,* ed. 3, St. Louis, 1964, The C. V. Mosby Company.

Grout, Ruth E.: *Health Teaching in Schools,* ed. 4, Philadelphia, 1963, W. B. Saunders Company.

Joint Committee on Health Problems in Education of the National Education Association and the American Medical Association: *School Health Services,* ed. 2, Washington and Chicago, 1964, NEA and AMA.

Kilander, H. F.: *School Health Education,* New York, 1962, The Macmillan Company.

National Conference for Cooperation in Health Education: *School Health Policies.* This 1956 revision of a 40-page pamphlet is available from the American Medical Association.

National Education Association and American Medical Association Joint Committee: *Health Education,* ed. 5, Washington, D. C., 1961, National Education Association.

Natonal Education Association, Project on the Instructional Program of the Public Schools: *Deciding what to Teach: Education in a Changing Society; Planning and Organizing for Teaching,* Washington, D. C., 1964, NEA.

National Eductional Association: *Schools for the Sixties,* a Report of the Project on Instruction, New York, 1963, McGraw-Hill Book Company.

Oberteuffer, Delbert: *School Health Education,* ed. 3, New York, 1960, Harper and Brothers.

Turner, C. E.: *Planning for Health Education in Schools,* 1966, Published by UNESCO and WHO. Available in U.S.A. through UNESCO Publications Center, 317 East 34th Street, New York, N. Y.

World Health Organization: *Expert Committee on Health Education of the Public,* Technical Report Series No. 89, Geneva, 1954, 41 pp. (Copies may be ordered from Columbia University Press, International Documents Service, 2960 Broadway, New York 27, N. Y.)

World Health Organization: *PAHO/WHO Inter-Regional Conference on the Post-Graduate Preparation of Health Workers for Health Education,* Technical Report Series No. 278, Geneva, 1964.

World Health Organization: *Teacher Preparation for Health Education,* Geneva, 1960. Report of a Joint WHO/UNESCO Expert Committee, Technical Report Series No. 193, 19 pp.

Chapter 11

The development and scope
of today's school
health program

This chapter reflects the development of the school health movement, indicates achievement and current problems, and presents a framework for further consideration of school health and health education. Let us first examine the origin and growth of the modern school health program. When, why, and how did it develop? How has it been related to the development of public health and public education?

Man's fight for life and health

As society looks ahead, it can conceive the hope that some day almost every human being will be well, intelligent, physically vigorous, mentally alert, emotionally stable, socially reasonable, and ethically sound. At least, society must concern itself with progress toward that goal. We have much left to do but much has been done already.

In prehistoric times primitive man had a constant fight for life. He was without adequate shelter. His food supply was uncertain. He had only a club or a rock with which to defend himself against wild animals. He was defenseless against disease. Its nature was beyond his comprehension. He believed it was caused by evil spirits. His curative medicine consisted of sacrifice, while his preventive medicine was the use of charms and magic substances to keep the demons away. As was the case with the animals around him, few of his offspring reached adult life. There are still some primitive people, more than half of whose children die before reaching the age of adolescence.

As man gained command over fire, achieved supremacy over the other animals of the earth, conquered famine, and adjusted his mode of living to unfriendly climates, his death rate gradually declined. But until comparatively recent times population groups were decimated by frightful epidemics. For example, smallpox was brought to Mexico in 1520 by the Spaniards and killed half the native population. Plague swept over Europe in the fourteenth century, killing some twenty-five million persons, or

Table 1. Expectation of life at birth in the United States. Total population* and white persons by sex, 1900-02 to 1963

Calendar year	Expectation, in years			Calendar year	Expectation, in years			Calendar year	Expectation, in years		
		White				White				White	
	Total*	Male	Female		Total*	Male	Female		Total*	Male	Female
1963	69.9	67.5	74.4	1948	67.2	65.5	71.0	1933	63.3	62.7	66.3
1962	70.0	67.6	74.4	1947	66.8	65.2	70.5	1932	62.1	62.0	64.5
1961	70.2	67.8	74.5	1946	66.7	65.1	70.3	1931	61.1	60.8	64.7
1960	69.7	67.4	74.1	1945	65.9	64.4	69.5	1930	59.7	59.7	63.5
1959	69.9	67.6	74.2	1944	65.2	64.5	68.4	1929	57.1	57.2	60.3
1958	69.4	67.2	73.7	1943	63.3	63.2	65.7	1928	56.8	57.0	60.0
1957	69.3	67.1	73.5	1942	66.2	65.9	69.4	1927	60.4	60.5	63.9
1956	69.6	67.3	73.7	1941	64.8	64.4	68.5	1926	56.7	57.0	59.6
1955	69.5	67.3	73.6	1940	62.9	62.1	66.6	1925	59.0	59.3	62.4
1954	69.6	67.4	73.6	1939	63.7	63.3	66.6	1924	59.7	59.8	63.4
1953	68.8	66.8	72.9	1938	63.5	63.2	66.8	1923	57.2	57.1	59.6
1952	68.6	66.6	72.7	1937	60.0	59.3	63.8	1922	59.6	59.1	61.9
1951	68.4	66.5	72.4	1936	58.5	58.0	61.9	1919-21	56.4	56.3	58.5
1950	68.2	66.5	72.2	1935	61.7	61.0	65.0	1909-11	51.5	50.2	53.6
1949	68.0	66.2	71.9	1934	61.1	60.5	64.6	1900-02	49.2	48.2	51.1

*Includes nonwhite population.
Source: National Center for Health Statistics, *Vital Statistics of the United States, 1963,* Vol. II, Section 5.

one-fourth of the population. In North America the first recorded epidemic took place among the Indians of the present New England area in 1618, just two years before the arrival of the Pilgrims at Plymouth. We do not know what disease it was; but it was reported to have reduced the number of Indian warriors from 9,000 to a few hundred and to have killed 2,700 out of 3,000 persons in the Massachusetts tribe alone.

During the last century especially, man's progress toward better health and longer life has been spectacular. The earliest American "life table," prepared by Edward Wigglesworth in 1789, gave the expectation of life at birth as 28.15 years. The expectancy of life of a baby born today is over 70 years. The United Nations Demographic Yearbook of 1963 reported that the expectation of life for female babies has reached 75 years in Sweden and about 74 years in the United States, Denmark, Czechoslovakia, and New Zealand. That for male babies is about three years less.[1] Table 1 shows expectation of life in the United States since 1900.[2]

Only a century ago, the death rate in American cities was about 30

[1]UNESCO *Courier*, February, 1965.
[2]*Statistical Bulletin*, Metropolitan Life Insurance Company, March, 1965.

Expectation of life in United States,

comparison of years 1789, 1850, and 1959.

Proportion of deaths by age groups in total mortality

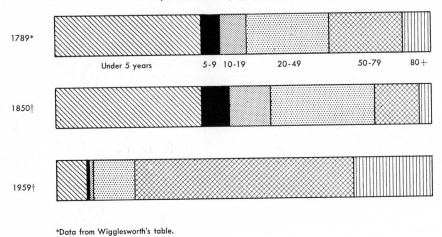

*Data from Wigglesworth's table.

†Basic data from United States Bureau of Census.

Fig. 3. You will see from this chart that over half of all deaths in 1850 occurred in children and youths under 20 years of age. One hundred nine years later, three quarters of all deaths occurred in people over 50 years of age.

deaths annually per 1,000 people. Today this rate is below 10 deaths per 1,000.

The changes in the ages at which deaths occurred in 1789, 1850, and 1959 are shown in the accompanying figure. You will notice that health was not as good in 1850 as it was among the more completely rural population of 1789; but you will see, also, that since 1850 the change has been tremendous. Note especially the proportions of the population which died at school age or at preschool age during these three different periods. Note also that in 1850 only about 17 per cent of the population reached the age of 50, while in 1959 about 70 per cent reached that age. The percentage of persons living beyond 80 was over five times as great in 1959 as it was in 1850.

Of the many factors which led to lower death rates during the last century, the most important one has been the reduction in infant and child deaths from communicable disease.

Scientists have estimated that the human species has been on earth for at least 300,000 years, perhaps for more than a million years. And yet the conquest of his microscopic enemies has taken place only in the last hundred years.

Imagine what it would have been like to teach in a typical, average-sized town in the 1850's, when tax-supported schools were new. Schoolhouses were primitive by modern standards. They were without modern sanitary conveniences. They had inadequate lighting, uncomfortable seats, and wood-burning stoves for heating.

Those schools felt only the obligation to teach the tool subjects of reading, writing, spelling, arthmetic, geography, and history. If a child was to learn something about music or agriculture or drawing or handwork, or other occupational subjects, he would do it outside of school. A very small percentage of students went to high school and the high schools were mainly devoted to preparing students for college.

Not only were public health activities absent from the schools; they were also absent from the community. There were no local health departments in the towns; nor were there any state departments of health. The Federal government had no public health program. About half of all deaths, and more than half the deaths of school age children, were from the various communicable diseases.

Civilization had not yet discovered that these diseases were produced by microscopic organisms. Terrible epidemics were still frequent. It was the general belief that disease bred in filth and that the cause of epidemics was some kind of poison which developed in the putrefactive process and which was air-borne for great distances. It was not realized that water could carry infection.

There was no immunization against disease, except in the case of smallpox. Jenner had discovered in 1796 that if some of the liquid from a cowpox sore was scratched into the skin it produced a local sore, and that having this cowpox sore protected the person from having smallpox. From this discovery vaccination procedures developed.

In the 1860's the work of Pasteur showed that microscopic organisms could cause disease; and the health sciences began to develop. The causative organism of one disease after another was discovered. By 1900 we knew the cause of many of the bacterial and protozoan diseases. In the 1890's we learned that the cause of tobacco mosaic disease and that of foot-and-mouth disease of cattle were too small to be seen under the ordinary microscope—so small in fact that they could pass through a porcelain filter. The conquest of the virus diseases began then.

The sanitation of our food and water supply, and the sanitary disposal of excreta, which developed rapidly after about 1890, brought an end to serious epidemics of intestinal disease.

Pasteur's dramatic experiment in which he protected animals from anthrax by vaccinating them with attenuated or weakened anthrax bacilli began the science of immunology. Through the development of vaccines, protective sera, and antitoxins we can now protect ourselves against a great many of the communicable diseases.

In the 1930's the sulfa drugs and other antibiotics came into use, and in the 1940's DDT and other new insecticides became available. These new tools in the hands of rapidly expanding medical science cut the death rate from many of the communicable diseases still further and very sharply.

We can see what has been happening to death rates in this country

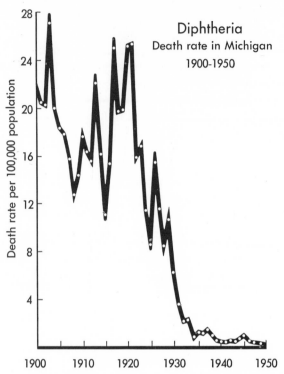

Fig. 4. Diphtheria and several other diseases were practically eliminated in the first half of the present century. (From Turner, C. E.: *Personal Community Health,* St. Louis, 1963, The C. V. Mosby Co.)

by examining the public health reports from one of the eastern cities whose data go back over a considerable period. We have no detailed statistics for the very early period, but Table 2 gives comparative figures on important death rates in Boston for 1865, 1905, and 1964.

Thus the discovery of the causes of the various infectious diseases and the development of sanitary science, immunology, and specific therapy have enabled man to go far toward conquering his microscopic enemies in less than a century.

Although the control and eradication of communicable diseases, especially those of childhood, represented the most striking development, there were many others of great importance. Significant progress has also been made against the noncommunicable diseases. Countless lives have been saved by advances in surgical skill and medical science. Specific curative agents have been discovered, such as insulin for diabetes and the "antianemia" substance for pernicious anemia. The discovery of vitamins in the first decade of this century has led to the conquest of a variety of deficiency diseases such as beriberi, scurvy, rickets, pellagra, and night blindness.

With a rising economic status housing has greatly improved. Diet is

Table 2. Comparative death rates in Boston

	1865	1905	1964
Deaths per 1,000 population	23.6	18.4	12.7
Births per 1,000 population	------------	26.8	19.9
Infant deaths per 1,000 live births	------------	136.5	25.5
Maternal deaths per 1,000	------------	6.7	0.0
Pulmonary tuberculosis death rates*	422.7	204.7	10.3
Diphtheria death rate*	69.7	22.1	0.0
Typhoid fever death rate*	65.0	19.6	0.0
Scarlet fever death rate*	26.0	7.4	0.0
Measles death rate*	7.8	9.0	0.1
Smallpox death rate*	59.8	0.2	0.0
Pneumonia death rate*	162.3	213.1	57.0
Cancer death rate*	29.6	105.0	222.6
Heart disease death rate*	65.0	181.0	559.0

*Per 100,000 population.

much better; so are working conditions. We are larger, as well as healthier, than were our ancestors. To cite a single set of data, Yale freshmen during the 1950's averaged almost a year younger than they did in the 1880's, but they averaged 2.6 inches taller and over 21 pounds heavier.

The development of organized public health

When any vast area of human knowledge is opened up, man quickly exploits its various regions. In the field of public health you know something of the work of sanitary engineers, sanitarians, bacteriologists, virologists, immunologists, laboratorians, vital statisticians, public health nurses, health educators, and health officers. Let us review briefly the development of public health programs, which are said to have begun in 1850 with the publication of the "Report of the Sanitary Commission of Massachusetts."

At the national level, the United States Public Health Service, which was so named in 1912, grew out of the Marine Hospital Service established in 1798. It is concerned with quarantine, communicable disease control, sanitary reports and statistics, scientific research, sanitation, mental health, industrial health, and many other problems. The United States Children's Bureau was established in 1912 and is particularly concerned with the health of mothers and children. The United States Office of Education is concerned with the physical and mental development of school children, as well as with general education. Since 1953 these activities have been located in the Department of Health, Education, and Welfare.

The Home Economics Division of the Department of Agriculture is promoting better health and nutrition, particularly among agricultural groups. Several other departments of the Federal government have some public health function.

Since 1885, each state has enacted a law creating a state board of health or its equivalent. These state departments of health usually have divisions of administration, public health education, sanitation, communicable diseases, vital statistics, maternal and child hygiene, public health nursing, laboratories, research and tuberculosis.

Many cities have public health departments which are older than the state health departments. The first county health department, however, was not established until 1911. There are now county or local health departments in the majority of our more than 3,000 counties.

The following outline lists, under eight major divisions, the typical activities of a city health department or a large county health department.

I. *Vital Statistics:* Records are kept of births, deaths, and communicable diseases. Maps and charts are made. The information collected is used by the health officer in planning his program and for the education of the public.

II. *Communicable Disease Control:* In controlling the various communicable diseases, the health department is concerned with isolation, quarantine, release of quarantined cases, home instruction, diagnostic aid to physicians, epidemiology, hospitalization, immunization, and the use of vaccines and other biological products. In the case of tuberculosis and the venereal diseases, clinics and hospitals may also be provided.

III. *Child Hygiene:* The department is concerned with providing well-baby clinics, nursing service, and supervision of institutional care for infants.

For the preschool child it is concerned with clinics, immunization, dental hygiene, mental hygiene, nutrition, correction of defects, and nursing.

If school health service is carried out by the health department, its activities in school hygiene involve sanitation, communicable disease control, examinations, follow-up, clinics, and cooperation with programs of health education and physical education.

IV. *Sanitation:* Activities here involve housing; vermin and insect control; milk supervision, including the setting of standards, as well as dairy inspection, pasteurization, and laboratory testing; the supervision of food handlers and food establishments; and the supervision of water supplies and sewage disposals.

V. *Laboratories:* The larger city health departments operate laboratories for the diagnosis of disease, and for testing the sanitary quality of water, milk, and other foods.

VI. *Health Education:* A major responsibility for the health education of the general public rests with the health department, and this program should be properly related to health education in the school.

VII. *Industrial Hygiene:* The health department tries to prevent industrial poisoning and the existence of harmful working conditions, and to promote health education in industry.

VIII. *Public Health Nursing:* This service by specially trained graduate nurses interprets to the home the medical, public health, and social procedures for the prevention of disease, the correction of defects, and the promotion of health.

We have become accustomed to these services for our protection and for the promotion of the public health. It is difficult for us to imagine how people got on without them a century ago or what would happen in the modern city if they should be taken away.

Public health has become a profession, or perhaps we should say an art and science, in which we find many kinds of professional workers. The professional association of public health workers, The American Public Health Association, was founded in 1872. Various sections were formed within this Association to accommodate the different types of public health workers. The sections are health officers, laboratory, statistics, engineering and sanitation, occupational health, medical care, mental health, radiological, food and nutrition, maternal and child health, public health education, public health nursing, epidemiology, school health, and dental health. Professional associations which have developed in the special field of school health are the American School Health Association and the American Association for Health, Physical Education, and Recreation, a department of the National Education Association.

There are many *nongovernmental* activities in the field of health. Public health is promoted by the medical, dental, and allied professions. In addition, the present century has seen the development of a great number of voluntary health organizations. Most of them are concerned with a specific disease or health problem such as tuberculosis, cancer, heart disease, blindness, or safety. They have become an important force for better national health. You are probably familiar with the local or state branches of some of these organizations. They are of special interest to teachers because many of them provide source material for health teaching. They will be discussed from that point of view in Chapter 15, together with governmental and commercial agencies.

Health programs enter the schools

As public health has been developing, the school has broadened its whole perspective and health has become a major concern. The school has recognized its fundamental obligation to protect the health of the child and to teach him how to protect and promote his own health. What have been the developments in school health?

A lengthy discussion of European developments in school health would be out of place, but we should realize that many school health activities had their beginnings abroad.

As early as 1833 the French government passed a law making school authorities responsible for the sanitary condition of school buildings and for the health of children. Later decrees (1842) required that physicians regularly inspect all public schools. Between 1868 and 1873 physicians were placed on the staffs of public schools in Sweden (1868), Germany (1869), Russia (1871), and Austria (1873). In 1874 Brussels, Belgium, developed the first medical inspection system, which consisted of regular trimonthly inspections of all schools by a physician. School dentists and oculists also began their work there.

Health education. Horace Mann suggested as early as 1842 that health should be taught in schools, but the idea was not well received. Although an occasional course in hygiene was introduced from time to time, relatively little was done prior to 1880. The stimulus then came from the Temperance Movement. Between 1880 and 1890 every state in the Union passed a law requiring instruction concerning the effects of alcohol and narcotics. In 40 states these laws specified that the instruction should be part of a broader program of instruction in physiology and hygiene. The resulting programs of instruction in hygiene were useful, although they dealt too little with health practices.

The modern program of school health education began about 1915. It has put emphasis on healthful living, at the same time supplying the health facts which are needed. It has recognized that healthful school living and the child's contact with school health services supply many of his most valuable health learning experiences. It has expanded incidental and correlated health teaching in other subjects, along with direct health instruction.

Much of the credit for the initiation, promotion, and development of this new program should be given to the Child Health Organization of America, the National Tuberculosis Association, and the National Education Association. These, together with various governmental agencies, colleges, and universities, pioneered the new program. In 1915 the National Tuberculosis Association introduced the "Modern Health Crusade" as a device for promoting the health of school children. It was based upon promotion toward "knighthood" on the basis of having followed certain health habits. The Child Health Organization of America (1918-1922), under the presidency of Dr. L. Emmett Holt and the active direction of Miss Sally Lucas Jean, did much to awaken the nation to the need for a more functional health education program.

Since 1920, developments in school health education have been rapid and numerous. Significant research and demonstration programs were developed early in several parts of the country. Malden, Massachusetts, with the cooperation of the Department of Biology and Public Health at the Massachusetts Institute of Technology, began such a program in 1921. Health education was an important part of child health demonstrations like the one in Mansfield, Ohio (1922-1925), supported by the American Red Cross; the one in Fargo, North Dakota (1923-1927), supported by the Commonwealth Fund; and the one in Cattaraugus County, New York (1931-1938), financed by the Milband Memorial Fund. These programs showed that habits could be changed and health improved through health education.

In 1924 the Joint Committee on Health Problems in Education of the National Education Association and the American Medical Association (established in 1911) issued its first report, *Health Education.* This book was a significant stimulus to the development of health education activities in the schools of the country.

Significant graded courses of study began to appear, like that of Cleveland, Ohio, in 1927. New, modern, and interesting textbooks came on the market. The American School Health Association (organized in 1927) and the American Association for Health, Physical Education, and Recreation (formed by a merger of the Division of Physical Education and the Division of School Hygiene of the National Education Association) have provided growing opportunities for the professional consideration of school health education. The American Public Health Association has a School Health Section and a Public Health Education Section, in both of which health education receives consideration. A professional Society of Public Health Educators was organized in 1950.

Many teacher colleges and schools of education give undergraduate majors and undergraduate minors in health education, and a considerable number give graduate degrees in this field. Most of the schools of public health accredited by the American Public Health Association offer a specialized program for the preparation of public health educators.

The first suggested educational qualifications for school health educators were set up by the American Public Health Association in 1938. Since then the American Association for Health, Physical Education, and Recreation has issued several reports in this area. In 1957 a special committee of the American Public Health Association issued the third report from that organization dealing with "Educational Qualifications and Functions of Public Health Educators."

Gradually there has developed the modern concept of a school health education program which is behavior centered, supported by the necessary information, developed and operated cooperatively by the whole school health team, adapted to individual needs, based upon the best educational and motivational methods, reinforced by available source materials, and related to community health problems and activities.

Physical education. According to Sargent the first step in the direction of physical education was the introduction of physical training in the schools of Northampton, Massachusetts, in 1825. The following year, Follen introduced gymnastics into the Boston schools, but there were no gymnasia or special facilities and the program did not receive public support. Although Beck, Follen, Lieber, Lewis, and others had done some work in private schools and colleges, the formal introduction of physical education into the public schools of the United States was an outcome of the activity of the *Turnvereine* (German-American gymnastic societies). These clubs were formed, beginning in 1848, by various groups of Germans who had recently arrived in the United States. By 1861 there were in existence 157 societies in 27 states, with a membership of 10,000. They undertook political, social, and religious reforms, conducted classes for people of all ages, including boys and girls of school age, and established Normal Schools of Gymnastics in some of the principal cities.

In 1885 Kansas City, Missouri, appointed the *first director of physical education.* This year saw the first professional association of physical educators. Between 1886 and 1896 there was a rapid adoption of physical education as a subject of instruction in the public schools of cities, especially in the Middle West.

In 1892 Ohio passed the first state law requiring *physical education* in the public schools of cities of the first and second class.

In 1899 North Dakota was the first state to pass a law making *physical education a required subject in all common schools.*

In 1903 a *department of physical training* was begun in the New York City schools. This provided organized physical training during recess periods.

The professionalization of physical education began with the formation of a professional association in 1885. As previously indicated the present American Association for Health, Physical Education, and Recreation grew out of this American Physical Education Association, which had become a part of the National Education Association in 1937. Courses for the professional preparation of physical educators at both the undergraduate and the graduate level increased rapidly. The public interest in sports has been a stimulus to the development of a program of physical education which has contributed to health and character as well as to athletic skills. The increasing urbanization of our population has resulted in an increasing number of children with inadequate physical activity in their daily programs and therefore a greater need for planned and directed physical education.

The program itself has expanded to include the learning of motor skills, the recreational use of games and sports, rhythmic activities, instruction in body mechanics, and modified activities for the physically handicapped. Intramural and interschool competition has developed in a variety of sports. Camping, hiking, outing, swimming, lifesaving, folk dancing, and a variety of other activities have found a place in the program.

Sanitation. Chapin, writing in "A Half Century of Public Health," published by the American Public Health Association in 1921, is authority for the statement that boards of education had recognized and accepted responsibility for maintaining proper sanitation in school buildings by about 1870.

That was at the beginning of the modern program of public health and communicable disease control but before the development of the modern science of sanitation and the sanitary engineering profession. In the next three decades sanitation became extremely important as our knowledge of water purification, food control, and waste disposal expanded to the point where we sharply reduced the amount of intestinal disease.

Our control over sanitation has continued to improve and our knowledge of lighting, heating, and ventilation has greatly expanded. School seating has improved. Modern gymnasia, school shops, and home economics classrooms now provide ideal places in which to play and work. It is still possible to improve our school sanitation further; but, compared with those of the past, modern school buildings seem excellent. A relatively recent problem which many cities have had to face is that of air pollution.

School health services. In 1894, following a series of epidemics among school children, Dr. Samuel Durgin, Health Commissioner of Boston, established the first regular system of *medical inspection* of the schools in the United States. Other cities (Chicago, 1895; New York, 1897; Philadelphia, 1898) soon undertook this work.

For some years the work of the physician in the school was mainly confined to the control of communicable diseases; but gradually the school health services became a team operation involving physicians, nurses, teachers, and others. The scope of these activities gradually expanded.

In 1899 the first law requiring that teachers in public schools *test the eyesight* of children was passed by the State of Connecticut.

In 1902 Miss Lillian Wald, known for her visiting nursing work on the East Side, presented to the Health Commissioner of New York City data which she had collected concerning children who, although excluded from school because of some physical defect or contagious condition, were not receiving supervision. On the basis of these data the Visiting Nursing Association was permitted to place a nurse in the public schools for a period of one month. Later in the same year, as a result of this successful experiment, 25 *school nurses* were appointed in New York City.

In 1903 the first *school dentist* was appointed in Reading, Pennsylvania.

In 1904 the State of Vermont began a system of *compulsory ear, eye, and throat examinations.*

In 1905 New York City schools began *examining each child for physical defects.*

In 1906 Massachusetts passed a *law requiring medical inspection in the public schools.* By 1910 medical inspection was required in 337 cities in the United States, and 1,194 doctors, 371 nurses, and 48 dentists were employed by school systems.

In 1914 ten *dental hygienists* were introduced into the schools of Bridgeport, Connecticut, by Dr. Alfred Fones, who is considered the father of this movement.

Home economics, nutrition, and school feeding. In 1887, in Boston, the School Committee took over the control of one of the two school kitchens that had been established privately in 1885 for experimental teaching. This was the earliest public school activity in *home economics.* It was established through the initiative of Mrs. Ellen H. Richards, then instructor in sanitary chemistry at the Massachusetts Institute of Technology and a distinguished pioneer in the home economics field.

Although some training in the art and science of home management had previously been given in the schools of the United States, the *organized home economics movement* began at the time of the first Lake Placid Conference on Home Economics, held in 1899. During this same year Mrs. Ellen H. Richards assisted in outlining the household science questions which the New York State regents had, in 1896, decided to offer in their college entrance examinations.

In 1910, in New York City, occurred the first formal installation of *lunches* in schools in the United States. The worth of this activity had been proved, through two years of experimental work in two large schools of the city, by a school-lunch committee composed of physicians and social workers who were trying to find out whether a three-cent lunch might be made self-supporting.

With an increased recognition of the importance of nutrition, further attention has been given to lunches which children bring from home, to the expansion of the cafeteria program, and, more recently, to the broad program of supplemental feeding and school feeding for a large part of our school population.

International developments

Health education, both in the school and in the community, is receiving increasing attention internationally. In 1949 the World Health Organization established a section on Health Education of the Public. In 1951 The International Union for Health Education, a nongovernmental organization, was established at a meeting in Paris. It has official relations with the World Health Organization and promotes both school health education and public health education.

The United Nations Educational, Scientific and Cultural Organization (UNESCO) has also been interested in health education. In 1959 it joined with the World Health Organization in establishing a joint WHO/UNESCO Expert Committee on Teacher Preparation for Health Education. The first report of the Committee was published in 1960. These two specialized organizations of the United Nations have just published a book for the use of curriculum committees, entitled *Planning for Health Education in Schools.*

In 1959 the World Confederation of Organizations of the Teaching Profession established a branch or Council on Health, Physical Education and Recreation.

Today's public health problems

We have seen the tremendous health progress which has taken place. However, many old problems persist, and new ones appear. Let us look at some of the more important health problems now confronting us.

Communicable disease. The intimate contact of school children provides an excellent opportunity for the spread of many communicable diseases. Although our conquest of communicable disease has made spectacular progress, it is far from complete. The common cold is still a major cause of illness and school absence. Vaccines in ever-increasing numbers have conquered some of the childhood diseases, but others still cause epidemics. The occasional neglect of sanitation permits the spread of intestinal disease. Even smallpox, poliomyelitis, and diphtheria, which should have been completely eradicated, produce sporadic epidemics because immunization has been neglected. Veneral disease, which decreased sharply with the development of antibiotics, is now on the increase, especially among the younger age groups.

It is obviously a responsibility of the school system and the health department to protect children against the spread of communicable disease. It is also an obligation of the school to teach children the facts which will enable them to protect themselves, to protect their families at a later time, and as citizens to support communicable disease programs for the protection of the community. We shall devote a special chapter to the important problem of communicable disease control.

The control of environment. Without the sanitary control of water and food supplies and without the sanitary supervision of waste disposal, modern community living would be impossible. Our comfort and our health are also affected directly by the heating, ventilation, and lighting of our buildings. Problems of environmental control exist at our schools in connection with water supply, the serving of food, waste disposal, seating, classroom and gymnasium construction, play grounds, pools, and the provisions for suitable recreation facilities. In many cities air pollution has become serious. The maintenance of a healthful school environment is an obligation of school administration and a means of strengthening important health learning in this area through the power of example.

Push-button living. In modern life the machine has replaced much of the muscular effort of earlier days. This is true at home and at work. Even walking has largely disappeared from the lives of many people. Watching television too often replaces play. Our culture is confronted with the danger of too little bodily activity for vigorous health and wholesome living. The child who lives in a city apartment is without the opportunities of the farm boy or girl in this direction. The school program of physical education is at least a partial answer to this problem and deserves special consideration. Today's schools are giving increased attention to programs for the maintenance of physical fitness.

Emotional stress and mental health. The complexities of modern living develop emotional stress of many kinds. Freedom means opportunity, and opportunity means competition. We are in a changing world where scientific knowledge doubles every ten years, and where customs are undergoing rapid change. National, social, and economic security are often uncertain. There is too much excitement and too little rest for many persons. Psychosomatic medicine has revealed many bodily ailments arising from emotional stress. Mental disease is a major health problem. We must give special consideration to the school program for mental health.

The stability of the family. The family is the basic institution of our culture. Its integrity is vital to our civilization. We live more hours within the family than outside. The mental and physical health of children depends largely on the hygiene of family living. The school cannot do less than make its maximum contribution to familial hygiene.

Accidents. Child accidents both at home and at school are all too high. The automobile, added to the other hazards of modern living, has made accidents the leading cause of death among children and youth. We must make life at school as safe as possible and provide a planned program of safety education.

Our growing and aging population. The population explosion is bringing new health problems. Man has been on earth some hundreds of thousands of years. The world population did not reach one billion until after the year 1800. Now it is over three billion. By the end of this century it will be over six billion if the present rate of increase continues. If fertility rates remain the same and mortality continues at the rate of decline of the 1950s, Africa and Southeast Asia will have an estimated three times as many inhabitants as they had in 1960.[3] There is an increasing percentage of older persons in the population. Cities are increasing in size and in number. As steps are undertaken to reduce the rate of the population increase, new problems in education will appear. In any case, we must educate for community living in large population groups and for the health problems involved.

Securing medical care. Modern scientific medicine has a previously unheard-of capacity for the cure and prevention of disease. Medicine and dentistry have many specialties. Nursing, laboratory diagnosis, and other ancillary services facilitate the success of modern medicine.

The life or health of a member of the family often depends upon the wise use of scientific medical service. The health of the school child may depend upon the effectiveness of the school health service. At the same time, modern society is given to health fads; it still tolerates quackery, superstition, and magic. It is constantly confronted with misleading health advertising.

Through its health services the school detects departures from normal health in vision, hearing, nutrition, and many other areas. It moves the student toward scientific medical care. By example, school health service is itself educational. Through health education the school helps children to avoid departures from health, to understand them if they do occur, to secure the greatest possible correction, and to adjust to residual difficulties. You are familiar with current legislative proposals and public discussions in relation to health insurance and the activities of government in the field of medical care.

Nutrition. Securing adequate nutrition is a major health problem, but not because our foods are insufficient in quantity or variety. This country produces an excess of foods. Obesity is a major problem. Foods and beverages are advertised on the basis of low calorie content.

The simple, natural foods of the previous century have largely been supplanted by a variety of foods and beverages which are pleasing to the taste but often lacking in dietary essentials. Dietary fads and reducing

---

[3]World Health, November, 1965.

fads thrive upon inadequate public knowledge and faulty practices in the matter of nutrition. The school must be concerned with promotion of sound dietary habits.

Harmful substances. For many years, health education has taught the dangers of alcohol and narcotics. Recent discoveries have shown the health dangers of cigarette smoking. Modern science is producing a long list of harmful substances. During the first months of this decade, some 5,000 babies were born in Germany and Great Britain with deformed or missing arms and legs because their mothers had taken sleeping pills containing thalidomide. The United States was spared a similar tragedy only because the Federal Food and Drug Administration had felt that the information at hand did not warrant the approval of the drug for sale. Various pesticides which are toxic to man are used in agriculture. The toxic effects of atomic radiation are well known. The scientific age in which we live has many advantages but it also has dangers which health education must help people to understand.

The health and health problems of the teacher

Clearly, today's public health problems demand a broad, carefully planned, and well-executed program of health education if the graduates of our schools are to be prepared for healthful living. The basis of this program lies in the educational relationships between teachers and pupils. What are the health problems which the teacher meets in maintaining his own health and in meeting his obligations to pupils and colleagues?

The personal health of the teacher is a major factor in his own happiness and achievement as well as in his effectiveness in the promotion of pupil health. Teaching is an honorable, esteemed, and rewarding profession but not an easy one. It brings appreciation from pupils, parents, and community and, after all, friendship forms the framework about which our daily living is built. The progress of the pupil is to the teacher what the recovery of the patient is to the physician. The service which the educator renders is a satisfying one; but it is more demanding and exhausting than it is thought to be by those who have not taught. Teaching has its own problems of occupational hygiene.

The teacher's day in the classroom can produce a high degree of nervous fatigue. He must continually adjust his thinking to what is going on in the mind of the pupil. This continual adjustment of thought and the necessity of keeping many activities under way at the same time is highly fatiguing. Group leadership for several hours a day with its high degree of stimulation and the required continuous mental alertness cannot be other than an exhausting experience.

Moreover, teaching carries a complicated set of relationships—to parents, to supervisors, to administrators, and to school organization and policies. Social and professional relations are complex. Too often the teacher, who must spend the full day working with children, lacks the adult social contacts which are needed outside of school hours. The teacher needs to give special attention to exercise, enjoyable adult recreation, stimulating social contacts, and the maintenance of optimal health.

Fortunately, properly prepared teachers today enter the profession in good health, because the process of selection has admitted only those who can work effectively without danger to their own health or the health of children. *Qualifications for admission to a teachers college* commonly include:

1. Sufficiently good health, vision, and hearing to permit satisfactory discharge of duties assigned to the teaching positions to which the student aspires. This requirement should be lenient enough to permit approval of students with such defects as slight heart damage followed by a symptom-free period of several years, moderate skeletal defects, or allergies which will not interfere with full discharge of duties. Obviously the duties of the teacher of physical education require a physical capacity greater than that of the classroom teacher.

2. Good physical appearance and personality, and normal speech. Standards for these qualifications are difficult to measure, but they should be sufficiently firm to eliminate students with grossly disfiguring disabilities, unclean personal appearance, unsocial attitudes, and serious speech defects.

3. Mental stability within the ranges considered to be normal by a psychiatrist or a guidance clinic.

4. Freedom from tuberculosis or other chronic communicable disease.

5. Freedom from serious or disabling defects such as neglected dental caries and muscular dystrophy, multiple sclerosis, or disabling arthritis.

The teacher training institutions have a most important responsibility for the selection of teachers who are themselves emotionally mature and who have the understanding and ability to deal with emotionally disturbed children. Furthermore, the teacher education curriculum must provide the student teacher with an adequate grounding in child growth and development, mental health, and human relations.

In the college for teacher education the modern program for the development and maintenance of healthful living includes several factors.

The health service of the teachers college is concerned with:

1. Evaluation of the physical and mental health of students.
2. Advice and direction in the correction of remediable defects and faulty health habits.
3. Provision for medical care for illness and injuries occurring while the student is enrolled in the college and for needed immunizations.
4. Participation in health education.
5. Promotion of normal mental health.
6. Student counseling.
7. Campus sanitation.

Healthful daily living for teachers in training is provided through the maintenance of suitable housing, the provision of adequate food and nutrition, a program of physical education, suitable social and recreational activities, appropriate health instruction, and a properly organized work schedule.

The health and health relationships of the teacher in service are influenced by many factors.

Because the occasional applicant for a teaching position may have allowed his health to deteriorate, most school systems, like other employers, require a physical examination before appointments are made, in order to make sure that the health of the teaching staff is basically sound.

Conditions of employment also facilitate the maintenance of health. In all good school systems the teacher-pupil load is not excessive; administrative regulations are clear and consistently enforced; a relationship of trust and respect exists between teachers and administrators; periodic physical examinations provide health protection; and a degree of security is provided by legal tenure and provisions for retirement.

School administrators share with the community responsibility for providing *living conditions* for teachers which will be desirable from the standpoint of health, comfort, and social living. They discourage the community from making too many *out-of-school demands* on the teacher while they encourage him to participate in some community activities of his own choosing. At the same time, the personal life of a teacher should be protected from community interference and dictation.

Administrators and supervisors advocate a *salary scale* that will provide comfortable living quarters and make it possible for the teacher to study, travel, and meet his personal and social obligations.

Because salaries are low in most cases, the teacher feels that he cannot afford to remain away from his work with loss of pay. Consequently, if there is no *sick leave* with pay given by the school board, he will very often work when he is ill, endangering his own health and, in many cases, the health of the pupils. A common practice is to allow ten days of sick leave without loss of pay annually, with the privilege of accumulating sick leave up to thirty or more days. Modern school systems have a definite sick leave policy.

Some teachers have too many *school assignments.* Extra duties are assigned to them, such as dramatics, choral work, and club work. Most of these activities are very much worthwhile and should be carried on in the school. However, they should not be the responsibility of only a few teachers.

Teachers are urged to take advantage of *group health and accident insurance* and a hospitalization plan.

In-service study requirements are not so extensive as to impair the health of the teacher.

Many of these conditions affecting the health of teachers and other school employes are primarily matters of administrative concern and responsibility. However, the individual still has the major responsibility for his health. He alone controls his extra-school schedule. It is his responsibility to plan relaxation, physical activity, and his own social and religious life. To a considerable extent, also, the staff can work cooperatively with the school administration in improving the healthfulness of the school program. The wise teacher appreciates the community which he enters, looks for what is good in it, becomes a part of it, and enjoys it. He gets some recreation every day and longer periods of recreation at frequent intervals. He gets enough physical activity daily to relieve nervous tension and make him ready for a good night's sleep. He comes to school rested and refreshed, with his work well planned. He is careful not to get bossy or habit-bound; but cultivates broad interests in music, art, recreation, and social activities.

It is of the greatest importance to the pupil that his teacher possess sound physical and emotional health. The good teacher adds to a love of children and youth a realization of each child's essential worth and dignity. He brings to his job a thorough understanding of children and a high degree of technical skill in working with them. He has a deep understanding of the fact that all behavior is caused behavior. Because of this he is never hostile in dealing with the pupil with overaggressive or deviant behavior. He is able to be objective yet sympathetic in seeking for causes and finding solutions to the behavior problems of pupils.

Children imitate their teachers in manners, mannerisms, attitudes, and behavior. They are alert to the grooming of the teacher. They learn politeness and courtesy from him. His real attitudes toward exercise, games, sportsmanship, health practices, choice of foods, and public health regulations are more important to pupils than what textbooks say the proper attitudes should be. If he is given to self-medication, to dietary fads, to boasting about how little sleep he needs, and to the candy habit, his pupils are more likely to do what he does than what he says they should do.

In health education, the teacher has close relationships with many colleagues in school administration and in health services. He realizes that the health education of the pupil comes from *all* the child's experiences in the field of health and not merely from factual instruction. He has, therefore, not only the problem of understanding the child, but also of understanding the health activities carried on in the school, the cooperative relationships of the teaching staff to the health specialists, and the relationships of the school health program to the health education of his pupils which takes place in the home and community.

The framework of school health and health education

The health protection and health education of the school child takes place through the following program of health instruction and health supervision:

Healthful school living. (1) *environmental sanitation* to guarantee a safe water supply, good plumbing, suitable drinking water facilities, sewage and refuse disposal, adequate ventilation, heating and lighting, sufficient hand-washing facilities, appropriate seating, safety supervision, ample, well-equipped playgrounds, and building maintenance; (2) *a hygienically organized school day,* which considers from the health standpoint such items as the length of the school day, the length of the class period and periods of unbroken study, play periods, the sequence of subjects, the amount of homework, the number of pupils per room, the alternation of different types of work, the nature and conduct of examinations, discipline and punishment, extracurricular activities, and the selection of proper textbooks and source materials, and which utilizes relaxation, the weighing and measuring of pupils, daily observation of individual pupils, and the school lunch to contribute to health; (3) *the maintenance of a healthful emotional environment* through sound teacher-pupil and intergroup relationships, recognition of individual differences, and curriculum adaptation.

Health services. These include examinations and procedures necessary to determine the health status of each child; the follow-up of children to get defects corrected; the maintenance of health guidance for all children according to their special needs; the selection and referral to special classes of those children whose health would be injured in the regular program; the technical supervision of those classes; some supervision of teacher health; emergency care; and the control of communicable diseases.

Health instruction. This includes (1) *direct health teaching* in time specifically allotted to health; (2) *correlated instruction* where health material is presented in connection with science, social studies, or other subjects; (3) *integrated health instruction* where health learnings occur as part of a broad "unit" or "project" or "problem-solving approach" organized around a central objective and involving also knowledge, action, or skills outside the field of health.

School, home, and community relations. These include the contact of the teacher and school personnel with parents, parent observation of and participation in school health activities, and school relationships with health education and health activities carried on by agencies in the community.

References

American Association of School Administrators: *Health in Schools,* Washington, D. C., 1951, the Association.

Anderson, C. L., and Langton, C. V.: *Health Principles and Practice,* ed. 4, St. Louis, 1964, The C. V. Mosby Company.

Blesh, T. E.: "Seventy-One Year Survey of Age, Height, Weight, on Entering Freshmen at Yale University," *The Physical Educator,* March, 1956.

Byrd, O. E.: *School Health Administration,* Philadelphia, 1964, W. B. Saunders Company.

Grout, Ruth E.: *Health Teaching in Schools,* ed. 4, Philadelphia, 1963, W. B. Saunders Company.

Haag, J. H.: *School Health Program,* ed. 2, New York, 1965, Holt, Rinehart and Winston.

Hunt, Caroline L.: *The Life of Ellen H. Richards,* New York, 1912, Whitcomb and Barrows.

Nemir, A.: *The School Health Program,* ed. 2, Philadelphia, 1965, W. B. Saunders Company.

Oberteuffer, Delbert, and Ulrich, Celeste: *Physical Education,* ed. 3, New York and Evanston, Ill., 1962, Harper and Row.

Ravenel, M. P. (editor): *A Half Century of Public Health,* New York, 1921, American Public Health Association.

Sargent, D. A.: "Physical Training," *Papers of the American Public Health Association,* 9:116, 1883.

Shattuck, Lemuel: *Report of the Sanitary Commission of Massachusetts, 1850,* facsimile edition, Cambridge, Mass., 1950, Harvard University Press.

Turner, C. E.: *Planning for Health Education in Schools,* 1966, published by UNESCO and WHO. Available in U.S.A. through UNESCO Publications Center, 317 East 34th Street, New York, N. Y.

Winslow, C. E. A., Smillie, W. G., Doull, J. A., Gordon, J. E., and Top, F. H.: *The History of American Epidemiology,* St. Louis, 1952, The C. V. Mosby Company.

World Health Organization: *Joint WHO/UNESCO Expert Committee Report on Teacher Preparation for Health Education,* 1960. Available from Columbia University Press, International Documents Service, 2960 Broadway, New York, N. Y. Price 25 cents.

Chapter iii

The well child

The teacher is in closer contact with the child than anyone else except the parent. His professional training and his experience with many children have made him more skillful than most parents in detecting changes in the child's health status. In schools without the services of health specialists, as was the case of the beginning of public education, the teacher was the only school person to detect departures from normal health. In the home it is the parent who calls the doctor. In the school the teacher calls to the attention of the nurse or physician the child who is not well.

The teacher works with children. He guides them through learning experiences. The better he understands them, the more enjoyable his work becomes. The health of the child influences behavior and the quality of school work to such an extent that the good teacher must be concerned with child health as well as with the learning processes.

Teachers never assume medical responsibility; they never make diagnoses or prescribe treatment. But the teacher can tell when there is something wrong with the child. He is alert to the early symptoms of acute illness as well as to signs which may indicate that some underlying health problem could be developing. His skill comes from his knowledge of child hygiene, from studying the growth and development of children, from the opportunity to work with physicians and nurses in the health examinations of the children, from teacher-nurse and teacher-physician conferences about individual children, and from experience in working with the same children day after day. In matters of health the teacher needs to know the physiological differences between children and adults, the nature and extent of individual differences between children, the signs of health, the physiologic changes at different age levels, the ways in which the quality of health is evaluated, and simple tests or screening procedures for finding out when something is wrong.

Children contrasted with adults

There are many differences between children and adults besides differences in size and in body proportions, such as the child's relatively longer arms and legs. Circulation is more rapid in a child. It enables him to be

Fig. 5. A well child.

comfortable at temperatures which seem too low to the adult, in spite of the fact that the child's heat loss per unit of body weight is greater than that of the adult, due to the fact that the body surface of the child is relatively greater. The child requires more food for his weight than does the adult. He consumes more oxygen and burns more fuel, relatively. He needs protein for growth, as well as for repair.

The child has fewer red blood cells per unit volume of blood. Thus anemia may develop somewhat more easily.

The heart beats faster. It is smaller in proportion to the arteries and muscles which it serves.

The child is more susceptible to infectious disease because he is still in the process of acquiring his immunities. Middle ear infections occur more easily in children because the Eustachian tube is short and straight, making it easier for infectious organisms to enter from the nose and throat.

The eye socket is shallow in young children but it gradually becomes deeper. This may cause the eyeball to elongate, producing nearsightedness. As children enter the period of rapid growth and in early adult life, nearsightedness frequently progresses more rapidly.

The stomach is more tubular in shape. Tonsils and adenoids and other lymphatic tissue have a tendency to enlargement.

The different parts of the body grow at different rates. By the age of 10 only the brain and the eyes have reached their full size. The heart is less than one-half its final size. During adolesence the heart develops more slowly than the arteries. Although it is now considered that the normal heart is not likely to be damaged by strenuous physical activity, adolescents during periods of very rapid growth should have their activity programs adjusted to their physical reserves. The maturing process of the brain continues past middle life. The lungs and digestive system keep pace with the general growth of the individual.

Individual differences

Well children vary sharply from each other. There are some general signs of health, to be sure, but children are not as like as a room full of the same make of new automobiles. Red cheeks, which are normal for James, may be a danger signal in Henry. The teacher as well as the health specialist is aware of these individual differences, and the teacher is able to notice changes from day to day.

Differences in the skin produce differences in coloring and complexion. Variations in features may suggest a degree of fatigue or of cheerfulness which does not actually exist.

Sharp differences exist in the emotional reactions of children, in their degrees of excitability, in their levels of nervous tension, and in their social adaptations.

There are differences in the vitality and endurance of children. Some children are so robust that they can break various health rules for some time without showing any ill effects. Other children, with a less fortunate constitutional endowment, need to adhere quite strictly to a hygienic schedule if they are to carry their school work in buoyant health and good spirits. Lack of sleep, going without breakfast, or some other unhygienic practice is quickly reflected in their health status.

Children vary in size and in their rate of growth, which may be affected by heredity, hygiene, the activity of the endocrine glands, food intake, climate, activity, rest, physical environment, and other factors. The well child grows reasonably continuously but at varying rates at different ages.

There is considerable seasonal variation in the rate of gain in weight in the temperate climates, but not so much variation in the rate of gain in height. Weight increases more rapidly in the late summer and fall and seems to be due to changes in diet, activity, habits of living, and (in the weighing of school children) weight of clothing. There does not appear to be a comparable seasonal rhythm in growth in height.

In general, children are more plump from 1 to 4, from 8 to 10, and from 16 to 19, being more lean and lank from 5 to 7 and from 11 to 15. These changes do not take place abruptly, or to the same extent in all children. One period merges into the other and the changes take place in different degrees and at different ages in different children.

Children vary in skeletal build. Some are stocky with heavy bones and with large vertebrae which keep the back straight. Others have a slender skeleton with the joints of a contortionist and long slender vertebrae which make a drooping posture far too easy. We say that John is stocky or that Bill is slender or that Henry is of medium build. We easily recognize the wide differences in both size and bodily proportions at different ages; but, at the same time, we realize that there are all gradations between the big, heavy, stocky child and the small, thin, slender child.

One way of describing differences in body build was proposed by Dr. W. H. Sheldon[1] in the early 1940's. He used the three primary growth layers of the embryo as the basis of his terminology and described three "components" or "vectors" each in terms of the germ layer (endoderm, mesoderm, or ectoderm) which seemed to have furnished the distinguishing characteristics. In his terminology, *endomorphy* is represented by massive digestive organs, which dominate the body economy, and by thin, soft muscles and smooth body contour. *Mesomorphy* is seen in the solidly built person with large, firm, strong muscles and great interest in vigorous activity. *Ectomorphy* is reflected in the slender, linear body with small bones and muscles, and with long arms, legs, and thorax. Very briefly we

---

[1]Sheldon, W. H., Stevens, S. S., and Tucker, W. B.: *The Varieties of Human Physique,* New York, 1942, Harper & Brothers.

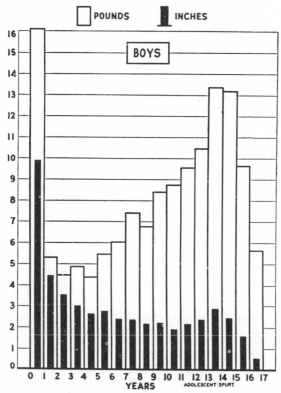

Fig. 6A. A growth chart for boys. (Courtesy Metropolitan Life Insurance Company.)

may describe endomorphy as softness of mass and reduced peripheries, mesomorphy as muscle and bone development, and ectomorphy as linearity.

Sheldon recognized that persons cannot be readily distributed into three distinct classes but that each individual has these three components of physique in a different degree. Therefore, instead of trying to classify a child into a specific body type, as an endomorph, mesomorph, or ectomorph, he classifies him in terms of the degree to which he exhibits each of these three sets of characteristics. He uses a seven-point rating scale. For example, a very slender child showing extreme ectomorphy might be recorded as Endomorphy 1, Mesomorphy 1, and Ectomorphy 7, or 1-1-7. A child representing the mid-point in all three characteristics would be recorded as 4-4-4. In some situations it may be desirable to group individuals on the basis of similarities in physique. In this case it is possible to arrange groupings according to that vector which appears to be best represented in the individual. Examples of dominant endomorphy, dominant mesomorphy, and dominant ectomorphy are given in Fig. 7.

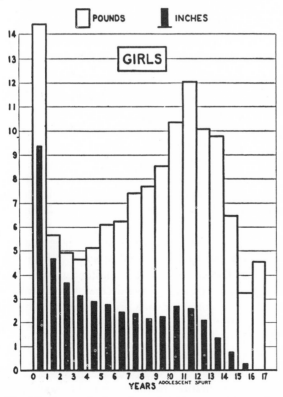

Fig. 6B. A growth chart for girls. (Courtesy Metropolitan Life Insurance Company.)

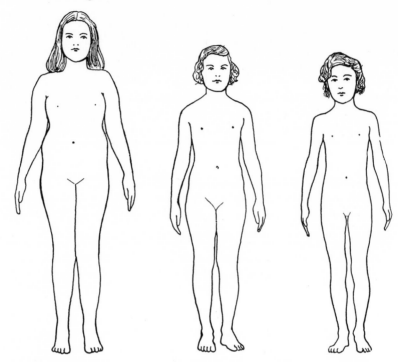

Fig. 7. Physique differences in 10-year-old girls. From left to right, dominant endo-morph (6-3-3), dominant mesomorph (4-5-2), and dominant ectomorph (2-2-6). The line drawings are traced from somatotype photographs. (Courtesy Dr. Stanley M. Garn.)

Height and weight records which show a childs relationship to other children of his body build give a better picture of his growth progress than a chart or record which compares his height and weight with all children of his age. Figures 8a and b show cross-section charts upon which the growth of boys and girls may be recorded at different ages. These charts indicate the usual pattern of growth for three types of physique. Each chart carries printed directions for weighing and for measuring. They are issued by the Joint Committee on Health Problems in Education and are available from the American Medical Association or the National Education Association.

The graphic recording of serial measurements on height and weight charts will reveal whether a child has deviated at some point from a pattern he has been following. Deviation from a consistent growth curve may often be noted as a result of illness. However a consistent growth pattern cannot always be taken as absolute evidence of good health. The teacher's day-to-day observation of the pupil's classroom behavior, his emotional reactions, and his physical stamina may be more reliable indications of the pupil's health status and need for professional evaluation.

We must understand the signs of health, but we must also understand the individual child. It will be helpful to the student in training if he can be assigned one or two children for case study. A thorough acquaintance

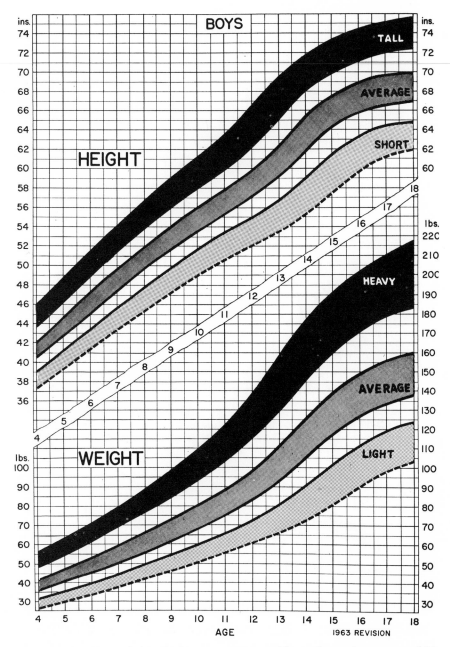

Fig. 8A. Growth record chart for boys 4 to 18 years old. Duplicate charts are available from the American Medical Association and the National Education Association. (Courtesy Joint Committee on Health Problems in Education.)

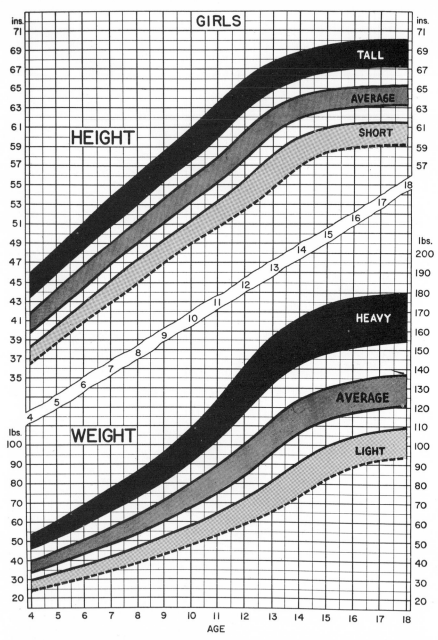

Fig. 8B. Growth record chart for girls 4 to 18 years old. Duplicate charts are available from the American Medical Association and the National Education Association. (Courtesy Joint Committee on Health Problems in Education.)

Fig. 9. Today's teacher understands the health and developmental status of her pupils.

with one child and success in helping him to solve his health problems is the best possible approach to health work with a class. The teacher then thinks of his pupils as individuals demanding individual consideration, but capable of receiving some aspects of health training as a group. He is not misled by the belief that his main function is to operate upon an impersonal "audience" with a variety of group instructional methods.

Signs of health

We recognize that the physically vigorous child enjoys a general sense of bodily comfort, buoyancy, and well-being. He is not conscious of his body or its functions. He grows at a reasonably steady pace, making a satisfactory gain in weight from month to month. He possesses a habitually wholesome appetite, a good digestion, a clean, red tongue, and a sweet breath. He is energetic, alert, happy, and active. He enjoys and needs physical activity. He does not become unduly fatigued by a reasonable amount of physical exercise, and responds to the invigorating effect of regular periods of rest and sleep. He is in general at ease and free from continuing tension. He adapts himself satisfactorily to new situations or to changes in environmental conditions.

His eyes are bright, clear, and free from inflammation. There are no dark rings under them. His hair is lustrous, not dull and dry. The coloring of the child is usually a mark of health. In some well children the skin may be clear and smooth but pink cheeks may be lacking. The well child's muscles are firm and well developed, not flabby. The legs are straight, not bowed, and the joints are of normal size. In standing, the head is well back, the chin in, the abdomen flat, the back straight, the knees slightly flexed, and the toes pointed straight ahead. The feet have strong arches and a straight line from the heel to the tip of the great toe. The chest is broad and the shoulders are not rounded forward.

The teeth are well formed and even, clean, free from cavities, and with good occlusion. The gums are pink, firm, and healthy. The lips will be of good color, and pink color will show through the fingernails. The subcutaneous tissue has a detectable fat deposit.

There are tests for the evaluation of positive health in terms of muscular strength, muscle tone, endurance, the rate of recovery from fatigue, the efficiency of the circulatory and the respiratory systems, the amount of subcutaneous tissue, the absence of nervous tension, the capacity for concentration, and the signs of good nutrition. These tests are used by physicians, physical educators, and other specialists, with the necessary consideration of age and individual status, and under carefully controlled conditions. Probably these tests are not used enough. Unfortunately too many persons think of health as implying only a mediocre quality of bodily function. However, it should be noted that muscle testing alone does not provide a valid basis for estimating physical fitness or good health.

We are likewise able to recognize certain signs of mental health, including: (1) an intelligence developed to a sufficient degree to meet the demands of everyday life; (2) interest and curiosity about affairs and things in the world about one; (3) the ability to concentrate attention; (4) a capacity for facing realities and for overcoming difficulties; (5) self-confidence, so that one expects and achieves a reasonable amount of success; (6) emotional responses that are useful rather than detrimental, positive rather than negative (predominance of such traits as courage, cheerfulness, and happiness rather than of fear, shyness, and timidity); (7) the capacity for self-expression in such objective interests as games or hobbies; (8) ability to cooperate and to enjoy normal social relationships; and (9) a sympathetic appreciation and understanding of others.

The child with mental health is emotionally stable, self-controlled under ordinary circumstances, self-reliant, confident, courageous, sincere, adaptable, and congenial. He feels secure in his ability to achieve a reasonable degree of success and in his relations with others. He recovers quickly from the inevitable emotional upsets of school life and does not harbor deep and continuing grudges and hates. He has many interests and a sense of humor. He is not given to excessive daydreaming. He likes both adults and other children.

Characteristics and needs of children at different stages of growth and development

In understanding children and in planning for their education in health, we need to keep in mind the successive stages of development which the child passes through. The physical, mental, and social traits develop in definite sequence; but the rapidity of development and the timing of specific changes vary in different children. Each child matures in his own way. There are also differences in the rate of development in different ethnic groups and at different latitudes.

It is by firsthand observation of the individual child that we determine his stage of development and his educational needs. It may be helpful to have at hand, however, a somewhat tabular statement of the general characteristics of school age children by three-year periods. There are appreciable changes in any three-year period, and in any class some children will have reached a greater degree of maturity than others. It is not possible to predict what changes will take place in a particular year of age or in a specific grade. For these reasons, it seems suitable to present the characteristics and needs of school age children by three-year age groups.

The following topical arrangement states the more important characteristics of children of different age groups and desirable experiences to meet their developmental needs.

Children six, seven, and eight years of age (grades 1, 2, and 3)

Physical traits

Physical growth is slow and steady.
At the beginning of this period front teeth are likely to be missing.
Deciduous teeth are being replaced, and interest in teeth is increasing.
Eyes are still developing.
Many six-year-olds are still farsighted, and muscles of accomodation fatigue easily.
Eye accidents are frequent.
Brain reaches full weight by end of this period.
The youngster tires easily and recovers quickly.
The child may not recognize it, when he is tired.
Breathing begins to be less diaphragmatic and more costal.
Sleep requirements are about 11 hours for six-year-olds and 10 hours for eight-year-olds.
Posture is likely to be poor, especially in tall children.
Movement tends to involve the whole body.
Children are clumsy with their hands but enjoy cutting, pasting, painting, drawing, and handling simple tools.
At age six, childhood diseases and infections are prevalent; but they gradually become less common.
Breakfast habits may be poor.
Habits of elimination are improving.
The Eustachian tube is short, wide, and straight, and middle ear infections occur.

Mental traits

Children like riddles and slapstick jokes.
They are interested in specific information but not in generalizations.
They enjoy simple tasks within their capacities.
They like repetition.
Attention span is short.
Memory is strengthening.
Questions about sex are frequent.
Dramatic play and make-believe comic books and animal stories are enjoyed.

Imagination is active.
Children love pets.
They like to produce well-made objects.
This is sometimes called the "eraser age."

Social emotional traits

Children are more self-centered than group-centered.
Being fair is very important.
Children want to feel that they have done right, and wrongdoing leaves them unhappy and worried.
They are boisterous, energetic, and daring.
Praise is important to them.
Interest in competition awakens.
The sense of responsibility is growing.
Gradually these children begin to accept blame and to apologize.
Children are interested in growing.
Cleanliness is not important to them.
Boys and girls are interested in the same things.

Health needs and desirable developmental experiences

These children need activities for the large muscles and practice in improving posture.
Vigorous games and outdoor play with running, chasing, hunting, throwing, catching, and climbing are desirable, as are singing games and rhythms.
Boys and girls play together.
Daytime rest is helpful.
Guidance in establishing handedness is needed.
The children profit by dramatic play and opportunity for creativity, such as finger painting or clay modeling.
Habits of cleanliness may need improvement.
Work periods should be short and ample time given for any task.
There is need for opportunity to develop leadership through various social situations.
Opportunities to agree or disagree in a desirable manner are needed.
Children need safety precautions.
These children need expanding opportunities for oral self-expression.
Regular meals and good eating habits should be encouraged.
Some children may need to learn to like new food.
Understanding and friendship on the part of the teacher are of great importance.

Children nine, ten, and eleven years of age (grades 4, 5, and 6)

Physical traits

The children tend to be physically active, working and playing to the peak of capacity.
Slouching posture is frequent.
They lack judgment in limiting their activities in order to prevent overfatigue.
Blood vessels increase in size, but heart remains small.
Proficiency in physical skill is increasing.
Girls grow more rapidly than boys.
Motor coordination and eye-hand coordination are increasing.
Different parts of the body may begin to show uneven growth.
Functions of the eye are becoming well established, and it adjusts for both near and far vision more readily.
Brain has stopped increasing in size.

Mental traits

Attention is given to subjects of interest for longer periods of time.

There is increased interest in constructive projects.

Interest in books about adventure, science, nature, and home life is increasing.

Interest is increasing in exploring and experimenting, and in how things are made and how they work (including the human body).

Memory reaches its height.

Ability to budget time is increasing.

Ability to plan and work with a group is improved.

Social emotional traits

The children are still self-assertive and apparently selfish, but tendency to co-operate in games appears for the first time.

The children are interested in the group and in team spirit.

They enjoy competition and matching skills with others.

They desire status in the gang or club and are willing to assume more responsibility.

Some antagonisms to the opposite sex may appear.

Emotions are becoming more stable.

Special friends are likely to be chosen among the child's own sex.

The sexes have different recreational interests.

Increased independence appears when away from the family group.

Hero worship appears.

Children are anxious to be chosen and to do well.

Health needs and desirable developmental experiences

A balanced program of big-muscle activities and quiet activities.

More formal games of great physical activity involving chasing, hunting, and throwing; these are such games as prisoner's base, three-deep, and tag games, calling for individual speed and skill, but not great endurance.

Opportunities to learn and practice good health habits.

Some separate play for boys and girls.

Activities that involve cooperative or team play and give individual satisfaction.

Sufficiently long periods of time to complete group projects.

Opportunities for creative expression.

Guidance in setting personal goals and evaluating achievements.

Opportunities to discuss social and personal problems, to make decisions, and to be independent.

Learning for life-long memory.

Safety precautions.

Opportunities to learn and use social skills.

Acceptance by the group.

Access to a wealth of biographical and other reading materials.

Protection against the danger of becoming overfatigued.

Guidance in problem-solving and critical thinking.

An emotional climate conducive to the discussion of personal problems.

Opportunities for success and achievement.

Opportunities to collect, identify, and classify objects.

Attention to body mechanics.

Youth twelve, thirteen, and fourteen years of age (grades 7, 8, and 9)

Physical development

This is the age of puberty, characterized by rapid acceleration of bodily growth.

Heart and lungs are developing rapidly.

Appetites are often enormous and dietary excesses are common.
Difficulties with elimination may appear.
At age twelve the eyes reach maximum growth and acuity.
Arms and legs are out of proportion to the trunk.
Awkwardness occurs.
Hearing acuity nears its height at end of this period.
Bones and ligaments are not yet strong enough to withstand heavy pressure.
Girls are maturing more rapidly than boys.
Postural defects are more obvious.
Endurance is small, and the child is easily fatigued.
Girls are more precise in their movements than boys.

Mental development

Pupils enjoy working on concrete problems.
Ability to apply scientific problem-solving approaches is increasing.
Wider variations in abilities and capacities appear.
Attention span continues to increase.
Charts, maps, and diagrams are increasingly useful.
Reading rates approach the adult level.
Desire for creative expression is growing.
Interest in problems of human relationships is increasing.

Emotional social development

Daydreaming is common.
Emotions are somewhat unstable.
Confusion and timidity may appear in social situations.
There may be rapid changes in mood.
Frustration may grow out of conflict with parents or peers.
Hostility to adults may appear.
Interest in team play and competitive games is increasing.
Positive reactions to ideals are strong if they are properly presented.
Fears and anger are common.
The approval of the peer group is becoming more important and that of adults
less important.
There is a desire to conform in language, dress, and manner.
Hero worship is general.
Friends are mostly of the same sex.
Interest in personal appearance is increasing.
Interest in the opposite sex is beginning.
There is increased interest in team play and competitive games.

Health needs and desirable developmental experiences

Competitive games involving quickness and skill and only moderate fatigue or
emotional stress are desirable, such as relay races, swimming, rowing, bicycling,
touch football, softball, field hockey for girls, tennis, and volleyball.
Group sports needs supervision to avoid activities beyond the strength of the child.
Eyes, ears, and teeth may require attention.
Most children need nine hours of sleep.
Difficulties with elimination may need attention.
Sound group guidance is important.
Practice is needed in selecting an adequate diet, in leading and in following, and
in improving body mechanics and grooming.

Youth fifteen, sixteen, and seventeen years of age (grades 10, 11, and 12)

Physical development

Physical coordination becomes adequate.
Heart is becoming larger.
Growth is nearing completion.
Trunk increases in proportion to length of legs.
Skeletal growth is complete at ages seventeen to nineteen for girls and at ages eighteen to twenty for boys.
Strength increases rapidly.
Graceful and controlled movement is possible.
Posture is improving for most students.
Acne is a common emotional and health problem.
Appetites are heavy.

Mental development

There is expanding interest in the exact and behavioral sciences.
Students possess increased capacity in organizing their own activities.

Social emotional development

Emotional problems increase.
These students tend to be idealistic, inconsistent, sensitive, and insecure.
They resent restraints and orders.
They need approval.
There is increased interest in the opposite sex and in grooming.
The peer group is a dominant force.
Boys enjoy sports, while girls are more interested in social organizations.
Accident rate is very high.
There is a feeling of growing independence from parental rule.
There is often a critical attitude toward parents.
Marriage is not infrequent.

Health needs and desirable developmental experiences

Regular and vigorous physical exercise is necessary.
Competitive sports of all kinds, including baseball, football, basketball, tennis, golf, volleyball, swimming, softball, and field and track, are desirable.
Individual guidance and approval are required.
Help is needed in developing self-discipline, orderliness, self-reliance, self-esteem, self-confidence, adaptability, and a sound philosophy of life.
Good coeducational activities, such as social dancing, volleyball, tennis, and badminton, provide wholesome recreation.
Hiking and camping are desirable.
Safety education including driver education is needed.
Family life education is important.

Growth as a sign of health

There is a relationship between health and growth. We weigh children every month or frequently in order that they may watch their growth and maintain their interest in those hygienic practices that promote growth. At the same time cessation of growth for an appreciable period can be used as an indication of lack of health or of unhygienic living.

We have made studies[2] to determine to what extent intermittency occurs among elementary school children and the extent to which intermittency in growth is associated with unhygienic living, physical defects, and illness. They show that, for screening purposes, intermittency in growth should be defined as *failure to gain in weight for each of three successive months*. It is recommended that schools should weigh children every month of the school year except June, and give special attention to children with such a cessation of growth.

About 10 per cent of the elementary school children will be selected by this procedure—more being found in the spring than in the fall because of the seasonal fluctuation in growth. A four months' intermittency would give us too few children, only about 4 per cent. A shorter period of intermittency would select too many children. Practically all elementary school children (98.4 per cent of the 4,200 children studied) fail to show a gain on at least one monthly weighing during the school year. A little over one-half of the elementary school children fail to gain for two successive months.

The omission of the June weighing is advocated, because June is a short school month, because it is at the season of poorest growth, and because the termination of the school year makes it impossible to follow up individual children.

This screening process picks up a few children who are purposely trying to lose weight. It is desirable to learn who these children are, to make sure that they are reducing under the supervision of a physician or a clinic, or that they are not following injurious procedures in order to lose weight.

For other children who fail to grow for three months in succession an investigation into recent illness, unhygienic habits, and the presence of physical defects is recommended.

One of our studies[3] compared 95 children having intermittent growth with 100 children who had been growing regularly. Among the children showing intermittency there were approximately three times as many pupils (33:12) having two or more unhygienic habits, about twice as many (27:14) having serious physical defects, and about twice as many who had been ill recently. The number of children defective in two or all three of these respects was over four times as great (34:8) among the poor growers. Another series of case studies was made of a different group of children showing intermittent growth.[4] These studies included an examination by

[2]Turner, C. E., Lytle, E., and Winnemore, C.: "Intermittency in Growth as an Index of Health Status," *American Journal of Public Health*, vol. 22, no. 5, May, 1932. Also, Turner, C. E., and Nordström, Alfred: "Extent of Seasonal Variations of Intermittency in Growth," *American Journal of Public Health*, vol. 28, no. 4, April, 1938.

[3]Turner, C. E., Lytle, E., and Winnemore, C.: "Intermittency in Growth as an Index of Health Status," *American Journal of Public Health*, vol. 22, no. 5, May, 1932.

[4]Turner, C. E., McKenzie, W. L., Marston, V., and Christie, P.: "A Study of the Health of Children Showing Intermittency in Growth," *Journal of School Health*, October, 1940.

a pediatrician, an investigation into recent illness, and a study of the personal hygiene of the child. Causes of failure to grow in each case were neither difficult to find nor impossible to remedy.

It seems clear that these supposedly well children are in much greater need of individual attention than the average child. The use of this screening process with a satisfactory follow-up seems definitely worthwhile. It is especially worthwhile since it is desirable to weigh and measure children for educational reasons—i.e., in order that watching his growth may be used as an incentive for the child to improve his health practices.

It should be pointed out that the temporary cessation of growth does not necessarily mean that growth will be permanently retarded or that the final size will necessarily be reduced.[5] Neither does temporary cessation of physical growth or even slow physical growth necessarily indicate slow mental growth. Correlations between size or physical maturity and intelligence test scores are low. This is in spite of the fact that many gifted children are above average in size, strength, and beauty; and some mentally deficient children are below average in these respects. It is not true that mental development takes place at the expense of physical development.[6]

Observing danger signs

Teachers also recognize the well child by the absence of danger signals which suggest that something is wrong or that the child, although not "sick," is note entirely well. In the following chapters, we shall consider specific physical defects and illnesses in some detail. The conditions and actions listed here are danger signals which teachers commonly observe and record in working with supposedly well children.

Eyes

Blinks frequently	Styes or crusted lids
Rubs eyes	Eyes inflamed
Eyes water	Squints at book or chalkboard
Holds book near face	Eyes are crossed

Ears

Picks at ears	Frequent earaches
Discharge from ears	Fails to hear questions

Nose and mouth

Difficulty in nose breathing	Nasal discharge
Frequent colds	Sore throat

Behavior

Restless	Shy
Listless	Bites nails
Twitching movements	Emotional disturbances

---

[5]Hardy, Marcha C.: "Frequent Illness in Childhood, Physical Growth and Final Size," *American Journal of Physical Anthropology*, vol. 23, January, 1938.

[6]Terman, L. M., and Burks, B. S.: *The Gifted Child*, ed. 2, Worcester, Mass., 1933, Clark University Press.

Behavior, cont'd.

Quarrelsome
Uncooperative
Nervous

Speech defects
Visits toilet frequently

General condition

Reading difficulty
Tires easily
Poor posture
Does not appear well

Very fat
Very thin
Poor muscular coordination
Poor school work

Health habits

Poor sleep habits

Poor food habits

Absences for illness

Colds

Digestive upsets

Teacher observations provide information which will be helpful to the physician. They are not in themselves diagnoses. Many of these signs, particularly those that suggest the early stages of a communicable disease, are noted in the daily observation carried out by most teachers each morning. Others, like fatigue, may be more obvious later in the day. Others, like food habits, frequent headaches, or stomach-ache, can be learned only by skilled and friendly questioning. Still others can be observed at any time or whenever particular conditions arise.

The acquisition of skill in observing departures from normal health is important to the teacher. Diagnosis and treatment cannot aid the child who needs attention until someone "calls the doctor." At home it is usually the mother who does it. At school it is most often the teacher who takes the first step. These are the two people who are with the child several hours day by day. Both accept this obligation toward the child.

In the onset of a communicable disease, easily observed symptoms may appear quickly either at home or at school; and the alert parent or teacher sees immediately that something is wrong. In other situations, such as a gradually developing hearing loss or a gradual lowering of the nutritional status, for example, the teacher has a better chance than the parent to become aware of the condition. To be sure, the mother is closer to the individual child than the teacher; but perhaps she is too close to notice very gradual change. The teacher on the other hand sees many children of that age and observes the individual child in comparison with others.

Noting departures from normal health is of course quite different from knowing what is wrong and correcting the condition. The automobile owner goes to the garage and says to the repairman, "There is a strange noise under the hood. Something is wrong; but I do not know what it is." The automobile mechanic who knows every detail of the engine may know immediately what is wrong. If not, he knows how to find out. In the much more complicated problems of the human mechanism, the physician is the expert who can determine and correct the condition. Anyone can hear the beat of the heart. It is the physician, with his detailed knowledge of anatomy, physiology, and pathology, who, with the aid of the stethoscope and electrocardiogram, can tell what is wrong and what should be done.

The teacher knows his pupils individually and comparatively. When there appears to be a condition which needs attention, he does something about it. He may turn to the school nurse, who will know the urgency of the problem and who can bring it to the attention of the school physician and the family. If there is no school health service, the teacher may discuss with the parents his anxiety over the apparent condition of the child.

As teachers study the personality, attitudes, and behavior of the pupil, they realize that there is often a physical basis for a particular characteristic. In place of the primitive concept that children are very much alike except that some are "good" while others are "bad," they proceed upon the modern, scientific concept that children are widely different individuals, each being the result of his heredity plus his physiological and psychological experiences. Thus, in the classroom and on the playground, the alert teacher looks for physical and psychological causes of inattention, irritability, unsocial behavior, and other undesirable reactions.

References

Almey, Millie Corinne: *Child Development,* New York, 1955, Henry Holt and Company.

Bayer, Leona M., and Bayley, Nancy: *Growth Diagnosis,* Chicago, 1959, University of Chicago Press.

Blair, A. W., and Burton, W. H.: *Growth and Development of the Preadolescent,* New York, 1951, Appleton-Century-Crofts.

Breckenridge, Marian E., and Vincent, E. Lee: *Child Development, Physical and Psychologic Growth Through the School Years,* ed. 4, Philadelphia, 1960, W. B. Saunders Company.

Children's Bureau: *Your Child From Six to Twelve,* publication no. 324, and *Guiding the Adolescent,* publication no. 225, Washington, D. C., Department of Health, Education, and Welfare.

Gesell, A., Ilg, Frances L., and Ames, L. B.: *Youth—The Years From Ten to Sixteen,* New York, 1956, Harper & Brothers.

Hurlock, Elizabeth B.: *Child Growth and Development,* ed. 2, New York, 1956, McGraw-Hill Book Company, Inc.

Joint Committee on Health Problems in Education: *Health Appraisals of School Children,* ed. 3, Washington, D. C., 1961, National Education Association.

Lindgren, H. C.: *Mental Health in Education,* New York, 1954, Henry Holt and Company.

Meredith, H. V.: "A Physical Growth Record for Use in Elementary and High Schools," *American Journal of Public Health,* 39:878, 1949.

Metropolitan Life Insurance Company: *What Teachers See,* New York, 1948, Metropolitan Life Insurance Company, 33 pp.

Mussen, P. H., Conger, J. J., and Kagan, J.: *Child Development and Personality,* ed. 2, New York, 1963, Harper & Row.

National Education Association and the American Medical Association: *Health Appraisal of School Children,* Washington, D. C., 1957, National Education Association.

President's Council on Youth Fitness: *Youth Physical Fitness—Suggested Elements of a School-Centered Program, Parts I and II,* Washington, D. C., 1961, United States Government Printing Office.

Reeves, Katherine: *Children—Their Wants and Needs,* New York, 1960, Education Publishing Corporation.

Sheldon, W. H., Stevens, S. S., and Tucker, W. B.: *The Varieties of Human Physique,* New York, 1940, Harper & Brothers.

Strang, Ruth: *Introduction to Child Study,* ed. 3, New York, 1953, The Macmillan Company.

Stuart, H. C., and Prugh, D. G.: *Healthy Child,* Cambridge, Mass., 1960, Harvard University Press.

Tuddenham, R. D.: *Physical Growth of California Boys and Girls From Birth to 18 Years,* Berkeley, 1954, University of California Press.

Watson, L. H., and Lowrey, G. H.: *Growth and Development of Children,* Chicago, 1951, The Year Book Publishers, Inc.

Wetzel, N. C.: "Assessing the Physical Condition of Children," *Journal of Pediatrics,* January, February, and March, 1953.

Wheatley, G. M., and Hallock, Grace T.: *Health Observation of School Children,* ed. 3, New York, 1965, McGraw-Hill Book Company, Inc.

White, V.: *Studying the Individual Pupil,* New York, 1957, Harper & Brothers.

Chapter iv

Defects of vision and hearing

Because of their effect upon the health of the child and their interference with his school work, defects of vision and hearing are given careful attention by school authorities.

Defects of vision[1]

Defective vision is of special concern to all who have any responsibility for the education of children. Most states have laws which provide for testing the vision of each pupil enrolled in school and for the notification of parents when a visual defect is found or suspected. Teachers, physicians, nurses, and administrators share responsibility for the appraisal of the eye health of school age children. Modern parent education programs stress the importance of a preschool eye examination by an eye physician, preferably before the child reaches the age of four, because serious eye defects such as marked astigmatism, hyperopia, and strabismus may be present in the very young child and should be treated before he enters school.

Teachers should be aware of the effects which visual defects have on the health and personality of the child and the adjustments which can be made in the interests of his health and educational progress.

What are the visual defects which the teacher should assist in detecting?

Myopia (nearsightedness) is caused by an abnormally long eyeball which places the retina far back, so that rays of light focus in front of it. When an object is held nearer the eyes, the image moves back onto the retina so that vision becomes possible. This visual limitation leads the child toward study rather than activity, inasmuch as reading is easy, but activities involving distant vision are difficult. Poor posture with forward head and round shoulders frequently results. Suitable outdoor activities should be encouraged to assure normal physical development. Myopia may be corrected by the use of properly fitted concave lenses.

Hyperopia (farsightedness) occurs when the eyeball is too short from

---

[1]Special publications on vision problems and the education of the partially sighted child may be secured from the National Society for the Prevention of Blindness, 16 East 40th St., New York, N. Y. 10016.

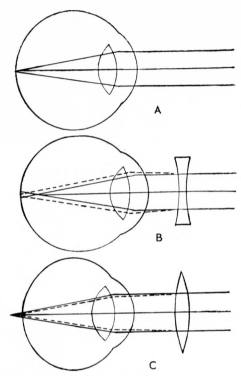

Fig. 10. A, The normal or emmetropic eye is of the proper depth, and the image forms upon the retina. **B,** The short-sighted or myopic eyeball is too long, and a concave lens is needed to make the image fall on the retina. **C,** The long-sighted or hyperopic eyeball is too short, and a convex lens is needed to make the image fall on the retina. (From Bard: *Medical Physiology,* St. Louis, 1961, The C. V. Mosby Co.)

front to back and the image is formed behind the retina. This is the most frequent eye defect of childhood. The ciliary muscle must constantly be brought into action in order to round the lens and bring the image forward onto the retina. This results in eyestrain. Activities involving distant vision are easy, but reading is difficult. Hyperopia tends to diminish as children get older. Slight or moderate degrees of hyperopia do not call for correction with glasses unless there are also symptoms of visual discomfort or eye fatigue, such as nervous irritability, headaches, inflamed lids, or aversion to reading and other forms of close work.

Astigmatism is due to irregular curvature of the cornea or the lens. In this condition some of the rays of light come to a focus on the retina, whereas others may come together in front of or behind the retina, so that the image that is formed is blurred or distorted. Vision in certain planes is distinct, while in others it is not.

Eyestrain usually accompanies astigmatism, and a large percentage of functional headaches are caused by it. Many symptomatic conditions, including dizziness, rapid heart, indigestion, lack of emotional control, and pains in the various parts of the body, are ascribed to astigmatism. Chil-

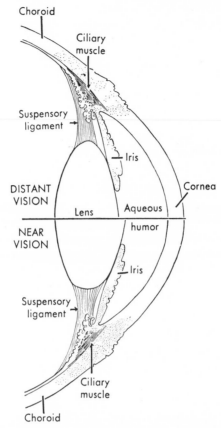

Fig. 11. Diagram illustrating the changes taking place during accommodation in the eye. (From Turner: *Personal Community Health,* St. Louis, 1963, The C. V. Mosby Co.)

dren suffering from it may develop lateral curvature of the spine from the tilting of the head and shoulders, in an effort to secure a clear image. The use of properly fitted glasses is the only method of relieving this condition. By the use of this corrective measure early in life, the degree of astigmatism may be reduced. Correction should be undertaken in the first grade if not secured earlier. Astigmatism frequently occurs along with hyperopia or myopia.

Strabismus (cross-eye or squint) is the result of a lack of balance of the eye muscles, which causes a deviation of one of the eyes from its proper direction. A personality difficulty may result if the afflicted child is ridiculed by his playmates. The treatment may be in the nature of glasses, of exercise, or of an operation, and should never be undertaken except in the hands of a competent eye physician. The prospect of ultimate success is better if the treatment is given during the preschool period, preferably as early as 3 years of age or even earlier. This is because the brain disregards the image formed by the squinting eye and the sight of that eye is soon lost.

Impaired binocular coordination, varying in degree, occurs in some children who do not have strabismus. Among the conditions causing lack of coordination are:

1. One eye muscle stronger than its opposing muscle.
2. Faulty attachment of the muscles to the eyeball.
3. Inequality in the refraction of the eyes.
4. Undeveloped fusion sense.

The practical significance of severe ocular muscle imbalance is that it makes it difficult for the child to maintain fusion and causes severe eyestrain when the individual is engaged in reading or other types of close work.

Color blindness (color-vision defect) occurs, according to a recent study by Thuline,[2] in about 6.2 per cent of boys and 0.55 per cent of girls. The condition is hereditary and sex-linked, being transmitted from an affected man through his unaffected daughter to a grandson. A few boys are completely color-blind, but more commonly the boy is only partially color-blind, being unable to distinguish red from green, for example. Although this hereditary defect does not interfere with reading ability, the school ought to detect it in order to warn the child against vocations where color perception is necessary.

Much of the art work in kindergarten and first grade requires color discrimination and the color-vision defective child finds himself at a disadvantage, the cause of which is often unrecognized either by the teacher or parent. Knowledge of this condition has important implications for other areas of instruction, such as science, safety, and driver education. Early recognition of the condition may help the child adjust to his problem with less emotional disturbance. Many eye physicians give color-vision tests in the preschool examination, in which case re-examination is unnecessary.

For testing color discrimination, sets of pseudoisochromatic plates put together in book form are recommended.[3] Hardy-Rand-Ritter plates and Ishihara plates are satisfactory for use in schools, and both are available in book form.[4]

Unless tests for color discrimination are given under daylight or correct illumination, the results are not reliable. The Source C. Macbeth Easel Lamp is the only available lamp giving proper illumination. This may be purchased from the Macbeth Daylight Corporation, Newburgh, New York, or the American Optical Company, Southbridge, Massachusetts.

---

[2]Thuline, H. C.: "Color-Vision Defects In American School Children" *Journal of the American Medical Association* **188**(6):514–518, May 11, 1964.

[3]National Society for the Prevention of Blindness, Inc., 16 East 40th Street, New York, N. Y., 10016.

[4]Hardy-Rand-Ritter Test can be purchased from the American Optical Company, Southbridge, Massachusetts, and the Ishihara Test from the Takamine Overseas Corporation, 10 East 40th Street, New York, N. Y.

Detecting visual abnormalities

The teacher easily detects the child whose eye disease or visual defect is indicated by frequent headaches; styes; red, swollen, inflamed, or crusted lids; reddened conjunctiva; watery eyes; or discharges. A child may complain of dizziness, nausea, blurred vision, or sensitiveness to light, any one of which may be related to eye conditions. The National Society for the Prevention of Blindness lists the following behaviors which may indicate visual disturbances[5]:

1. Rubs eyes frequently
2. Attempts to brush away blur
3. Is irritable or cries when attempting close work
4. Is inattentive in chalkboard, wall-chart, or map lessons
5. When looking at distant objects:
   a. holds body tense
   b. screws up face
   c. thrusts head forward
6. When reading:
   a. blinks continually
   b. holds book too far from face
   c. holds book too close to face
   d. makes frequent change in distance at which book is held
   e. is inattentive during lesson
   f. stops after brief period
   g. shuts or covers one eye
   h. tilts head to one side
   i. tends to reverse words or syllables
   j. tends to look cross-eyed
   k. tends to lose place on page
   l. confuses the following, in reading or spelling: o's and a's; e's and c's; n's and m's; h's, n's, and r's; f's and t's

Tests of visual acuity

Loss of visual acuity is most commonly detected by the use of the Snellen test in a screening of all pupils near the beginning of each school year. The Joint Committee on Health Problems in Education of the National Education Association and the American Medical Association gives the following *suggestions regarding screening tests for vision.*[6]

Preparation for administering the Snellen test

The Snellen chart must meet standard specifications concerning the size and spacing of letters or symbols. Checking these standards is a technical task which can be avoided by purchasing charts from reliable sources.[7] Two types of charts are com-

---

[5]*A Guide for Eye Inspection and Testing Visual Acuity*, National Society for the Prevention of Blindness, 16 East 40th St., New York, N. Y. 10016 (price 5¢).

[6]*School Health Services*, 1964, National Education Association, Washington, D. C., or the American Medical Association, 535 N. Dearborn St., Chicago 10, Ill.

[7]Equipment may be obtained from the National Society for the Prevention of Blindness, 16 East 40th Street, New York, N. Y. 10016, or the American Medical Association, 535 N. Dearborn St., Chicago, Ill. A Snellen chart with built-in illumination may be obtained from Goodlite Company, 7426 Madison Street, Forest Park, Illinois.

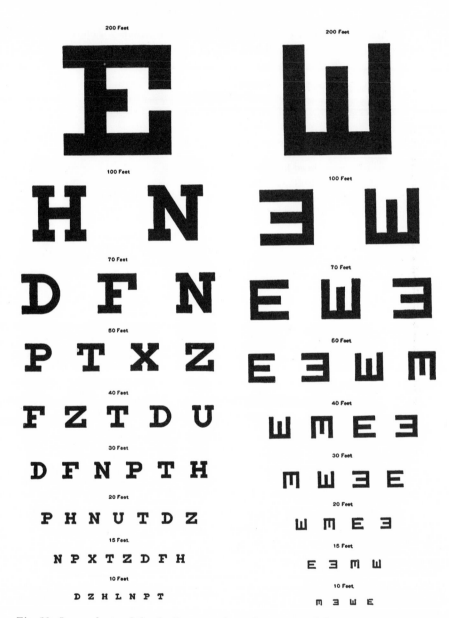

Fig. 12. Large charts of the Snellen type shown here are used for testing visual acuity. The E chart is especially useful for little children and illiterates. The child indicates which way the letter points. The charts from which the above reproductions were made were supplied by the National Society for the Prevention of Blindness.

monly used, one with letters and the other with the symbol E in various positions. The latter may be used with children from about 3 years of age and up; the former with children old enough to read letters easily.

For use in covering parts of the chart not being used, two pieces of cardboard are needed. One 9″ × 11½″ is used to cover the upper half of the chart, leaving the 50-, 40-, 30-, and 20-foot lines exposed. A smaller card, 9″ × 3¼″, can be clipped on the chart to cover the section below the 20-foot line.

One window card, 11″ × 14″, with centered square hole 1¾″ × 1¾″ should be used to show a single letter through the hole as the test proceeds. The 1¾″ × 1¾″ hole permits this to be done for the 20/20 to 20/70 foot lines. The card should be held vertically for the 70 foot line; horizontally for the others. Results are more reliable when the child sees only one letter at a time.

When the symbol E chart is to be used with small children, the teacher, or other tester, should have two large E's mounted on either side of the cardboard, with the shafts pointing in the same direction. These are used to familiarize children with the various positions of the E and make it possible for the tester to check to see exactly how the child sees the symbol.

With equipment in readiness, attention should be given to other arrangements. Illumination on the chart should be 10 to 30 foot-candles, evenly diffused over the chart and with no glare. Amount of illumination may be checked through use of a light meter.[8] General illumination should be not less than one-fifth of the chart illumination, and there should be no bright light in the child's field of vision. In order to gain the child's complete confidence and cooperation, the test must be given in a quiet room and with a reasonable degree of privacy. The tester should be friendly and patient.

The chart should be hung with the 20-foot line at average eye height and a line marked 20 feet away. Children may stand or sit when being tested. If standing, their heels should touch the 20-foot line; if seated, the back legs of the chair should touch the line.

The testing procedure

For valid results children must be at ease and encouraged to do the best they can. Children being tested for the first time with the E chart need to be taught how to indicate the direction of the shafts of this symbol in its different positions.

Both eyes should be open during the test. The eye not being tested should be covered with a small card or folded paper resting obliquely across the nose. For reasons of sanitation and aesthetics each child should have his own individual card or paper.

A standardized routine avoids confusion and facilitates recording. The following procedures are recommended: (a) If a child wears glasses, test him with his glasses. (b) Test the right eye first, then the left. (c) Begin with the 30-foot line and follow with the 20-foot line. (Some testers prefer to begin with the 40-foot line.) It is not necessary to test below the 20-foot line. If a child is suspected of having low vision, or if he fails the 30-foot line, start with the 20-foot line. (d) Keep unused parts of the chart covered, using the window card to expose single letters. This improves concentration and prevents memorization. (e) Move promptly and rhythmically from one symbol to another at a speed with which the child can keep pace. (f) Consider that a child sees a line satisfactorily if he reads correctly three out of four symbols. (g) Record results immediately in fraction form, the numerator representing distance from the chart (20 feet) and the denominator representing the lowest line read accurately.

While testing, note if the child strains to see. Evidence of this includes tilting the head, watering of the eyes, excessive blinking, thrusting the head forward, frown-

---

[8]A light meter may be purchased. Frequently one may be obtained from the local health department or light company.

ing or scowling, squinting, or closing one or both eyes. Observations of this nature should be recorded and the child referred for examination.

With the test completed and results recorded, the next step is the selection of pupils for whom an eye examination is to be recommended. All children who have exhibited signs or symptoms of eye disease or defect should be referred; testing is not required. Children failing the screening test should be retested before recommendations are made for referral. When this is done, parents should be urged to secure eye examinations for children who are in the following categories: (a) those who consistently exhibit symptoms of visual disturbance, regardless of the results of the Snellen test or other tests, (b) older children (8 years and older) who have a visual acuity of 20/30 or less in either eye, with or without symptoms, and (c) younger children (7 years of age or less) who have a visual acuity of 20/40 or less in either eye, with or without symptoms.

The Snellen test is a "screening" procedure and in no sense an eye examination. We find, for example, that the 30-foot line on the chart has the smallest letters that John can read, whereas a child with normal vision could read smaller letters on the 20-foot line. We record Johns vision as 20/30 to indicate that fact. It does not mean that his vision is twenty-thirtieths of normal.

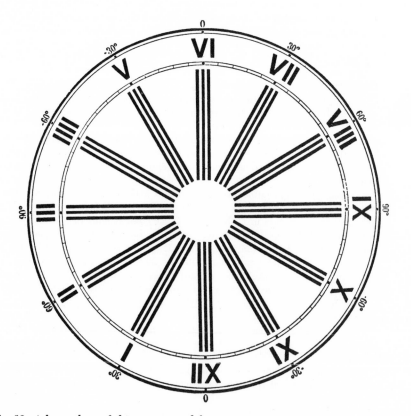

Fig. 13. A large chart of this type is used for testing astigmatism.

The Snellen test does not indicate the presence and seriousness of astigmatism. This shows up clearly, however, in the uneven appearance of the radiating lines on a clock-type chart. The child with astigmatism may be able to read the smaller letters on the Snellen Chart and yet have a refractive error so severe that continued reading is extremely uncomfortable.

A child has remarkable powers of visual accommodation. Because of this, he may receive a 20/20 rating on the Chart test and yet have defects leading to inflamed lids, headaches, and burning eyes. A special examination in which the accommodation is paralyzed by the use of drops, or in which some other special procedure is followed, may be necessary to find the real facts concerning the childs visual ability.

The Snellen test does not check the coordination and efficiency of the two eyes working together at the normal reading distance. What additional tests, if any, should be used in a school vision screening program is a matter of considerable controversy. The National Society for the Prevention of Blindness recommends, as the basic minimum procedure, only an annual test for distance visual acuity using the Snellen chart, combined with teacher observation for symptoms that may be related to eye problems.[9] However, the convex lens test for farsightedness and certain tests for muscle imbalance are included in the vision screening programs of some communities.

In the convex lens test the pupil is asked to read the 20-foot line of a Snellen chart with suitable convex lenses in front of the eyes and with both eyes open. He *fails* the test if he *can* do this, because it is possible only with farsighted eyes. A type of lens known as the Maddox rod is used in the muscle balance test. An evaluation of these tests as screening procedures was made in a study carried out in the St. Louis schools by the National Society for the Prevention of Blindness, in cooperation with other agencies.[10] Authorities differ as to the value of these two screening procedures.[11]

One of the more commonly used vision screening devices, which includes the convex lens test, the Maddox rod test for muscle imbalance, and built-in illumination for the Snellen chart, is the Massachusetts Vision Test,[12] which was developed under the Massachusetts Department of

---

[9]"Vision Screening in Schools," The National Society for the Prevention of Blindness, Inc., 16 East 40th Street, New York, N. Y. 10016.

[10]Crane, Marian M., M.D., et al.: "Study of Procedures Used for Screening Elementary School Children for Visual Defects," *American Journal of Public Health* **42**: 1430–39, November, 1952.

[11]A pamphlet entitled "Identification of School Children Requiring Eye Care" is available upon request from the National Medical Foundation for Eye Care, 1100 Seventeenth Street N.W., Washington, D. C.

[12]The Massachusetts Vision Test Equipment may be obtained from the American Optical Company (Southbridge, Massachusetts) and Welch-Allyn Company (Skaneateles Falls, New York).

Health. Another somewhat similar device is the Atlantic City Vision Test, which was developed for use in the Atlantic City school system.[13] Various other screening devices are on the market. Whether these instruments should be used in schools as screening devices will need to be determined locally with professional guidance, keeping in mind the cost of equipment, operating time of personnel, and the tendency to overreferral for minor deviations not requiring treatment.

Obtaining care for the eyes

There are three kinds of persons who render services in the care of the eyes. An *oculist* or *ophthalmologist* holds the degree of M.D., and his practice includes the treatment of eye diseases. Many ophthalmologists are Diplomats of the American Board of Ophthalmology, which requires postgraduate training of as much as four years. The *optometrist* is licensed by the state as a specialist in vision and, if he has graduated since 1955, is required to have five years of training in a school or college of optometry approved by the American Optometric Association in order to be eligible for a state examination. He tests vision and fits glasses. Patients with eye disease are referred to a general practitioner or an ophthalmologist. The *optician* fills prescriptions for glasses much as the pharmacist fills prescriptions for drugs. He is not licensed to examine eyes or vision. He grinds lenses, sets them into frames, and adjusts the frames to the wearer.

In referring children for eye examination the teacher or school nurse should explain that only a thorough examination by an eye physician can determine whether glasses are needed or not. If glasses are recommended, the teacher's encouragement is often needed to persuade parents to secure glasses for the child. It may be necessary to combat the groundless superstition that wearing glasses in childhood weakens the eyes. When glasses have been secured, the teacher needs to see that the child wears them regularly. The myopic child may need supervision to avoid overuse of the eyes. The maintenance of good lighting in the schoolroom and the best possible seating of children with visual difficulties are also teacher responsibilities. In doing these things, the teacher is making health education direct, personal, and applied.

Children whose vision is worse than 20/70 (the child cannot see at 20 feet what the normal person can see at 70 feet) have difficulty in the regular classroom and should be assigned to a special class. Usually borderline cases are more carefully retested by the ophthalmologist or school physician.

Visual defects and other causes of reading disability

A visual defect is only one of the causes of reading disability. For several decades the general public, as well as educators, has shown growing concern over the high percentage of children (10 to 15 per cent) with

---

[13]The Atlantic City Vision Test Equipment may be purchased from Freund Brothers, Atlantic City, New Jersey.

normal intelligence who have reading disability. In a society where employment and social and economic success have depended increasingly on higher and higher levels of education, any major obstacle to learning is a matter of deep concern to all involved in the educational process. Since reading is so basic to learning, any failure or unusual difficulty which a pupil has in this field becomes a matter of great anxiety to parents, teachers, and to the pupil himself. Frequently, the teacher and/or the system of reading instruction has been held to blame and made the scapegoat for the apparent increase in the number of pupils having reading disability. How much of this increase is actual or how much is related to the intensified program of compulsory education is a moot question.

The causes of reading difficulty are multiple, and may be related to brain damage, defects of cortical function, limited intelligence, visual or hearing defects, endocrine disorders, problems of maturation, lack of reading readiness, emotional disturbances due to parental pressures, feelings of failure, sibling rivalry, and other factors. Park[14] as the Dyslexia Memorial Institute has made intensive studies of reading disability and cautions against assigning to it a single causative factor.

The condition is found four times as frequently in boys as in girls. In some instances, the disability has been found in successive generations of the child's ancestors. In Park's study, 27 per cent of the children had hypothyroidism and 4 per cent hyperthyroidism. Fourteen per cent gave a history of abscessed ears. Whereas ocular functions were inferior in dyslexia (reading difficulty) cases, actually only 19 per cent of Park's cases required glasses. With due attention to the physical and emotional factors involved and an instructional program of remedial reading, it is estimated that 85 per cent of the cases of dyslexia are correctible.

According to Anderson,[15]

It is imperative that every child with a reading disability be given an examination which will screen for the following:

  (a) Defects of vision: acuity, astigmatism, fusion, etc.
  (b) Defects of hearing.
  (c) Defects of cortical function, mixed dominance, visual agnosia (inability to recognize), auditory agnosia.
  (d) Defects of emotional adjustment or intellectual capacity.

In cases where screening procedures indicate that further evaluation is necessary, the child should be referred for pediatric, ophthalmological, audiological, otological, and neurological consultation. The examination of a child with reading disability cannot be considered adequate until all these factors have been thoroughly screened and, if necessary, further investigated.

---

[14]Park, George E., M.D.: "Medical Aspects of Reading Failures in Intelligent Children." Reprinted from the *Sight-Saving Review*, vol. 29, no. 4, 1959. Publication 255. The National Society for the Prevention of Blindness, 16 East 40th Street, New York, N. Y., 10016.

[15]Anderson, Ursula M., M.D., D.P.H.: "Reading Disability—What Should The School Physician Look for in Determining Its Causation," *The Journal of School Health*, vol. 35, no. 4, April, 1965.

Blind and partially-sighted children

The educational requirements of blind and partially-seeing children differ considerably. The blind child must be taught essentially through his "fingertips" and through senses other than his eyes. The partially-sighted child is "visually oriented" and can be taught through the medium of sight. It is important to provide an education which will meet the needs of these two groups and enable them to adjust in the social and economic world of the seeing.

1. *Blind children.* Generally speaking, a blind person is one who has a sufficient visual handicap to require reliance on the other senses for the ordinary activities of life. More specifically, a blind person is one who, following competent medical eye care, has no more than 20/200 vision (Snellen chart) in the better eye, or one who has better than 20/200 vision but an equivalent handicap due to limitation of side or field vision to a diameter of 20° or less.

Blind children are found through:
a. Referral by family
b. School census
c. Eye physicians, physicians, and other health personnel in the community
d. Interested persons in the community.

Fig. 14. A woman's hand guiding the hand of a pupil who is learning to read Braille.

Special educational methods and devices are necessary. The substitution of embossed type (Braille) for reading is desirable, as well as special arithmetical apparatus, embossed or bas-relief maps, and other tactual devices. "Talking books" on long playing records are used.

2. *Partially-sighted children.* The problem of educating partially-sighted children is twofold. It must meet the needs of those who, because of progressive eye difficulties, should not use the ordinary school equipment and of those who, because of low vision, cannot do so. Broadly speaking, a child is considered "partially sighted" whose vision ranges between 20/70 and 20/200 in his better eye after all medical and optical help has been given.

Where numbers of partially-sighted children make it feasible, sight-saving class facilities should be provided for grade, junior, and senior high school students.

The following standards describe a *sight-saving classroom*:

a. The methods of instruction should be suited to the needs of the pupil. Essentially, the sight-saving room is a homeroom in which lessons are prepared and reading done. The pupils go to their regular classrooms when feasible to recite and to participate in other activities that do not cause a strain on the eyes.

b. The teacher should have taken a course for the preparation of teachers of partially-seeing children which includes educational and medical lectures, observations, and some participation in a well-equipped and well-conducted demonstration class and in eye clinics.

c. The classroom must be equipped with sufficient indirect light to place 30 foot-candles on each pupil's desk, without shadows and without glare. Translucent window shades should be attached to the center of the window instead of at the top. They should cover the glass only when necessary to keep out direct sunlight. All furniture, walls, and floors should have a dull finish in order to avoid glare. Desks should be movable and should have tilt-tops to hold books at a proper reading angle. The chalkboard should be of nonglare variety. Of course, these minimum standards for sight-saving classrooms are maintained, ideally, in the regular classroom for all children.

d. Books should be printed in large type on nonglare paper. So-called "clear-type" texts are recommended. Maps should be drawn to a large scale, free from detail. Typewriters equipped with "jumbo" size type should be used both by the teacher and by the pupils. Paper should not have a glossy finish.

e. The maximum class size should be twelve or fifteen pupils, depending upon the number of grades in the room. The larger the number of grades represented the fewer is the number of pupils who can be taught adequately.

The partially-sighted child in the small urban or rural community will need *individual attention*:

a. If not already done, refer the child for a complete eye examination and, with parents' permission, request report from eye physician regarding both findings and recommendations to make certain that vision cannot be improved to the point where the child will not need special help.

b. Discuss the child's eye condition with parents and interpret the use of a "sight-saving" program so that their cooperation can be secured.

c. Plan program for child which will minimize the strain of seeing and enable him to compete on a more even level with other children in his grade. This implies the use of sight-saving equipment, which includes use of the eyes under the best conditions: good lighting, proper seating, good posture, rest periods, "clear-type" books, oral work, yellow chalk, "sight-saving" paper, adaptation of the work of the class to the child's needs in terms of his eye condition.

d. Interpret the situation to the child so that his cooperation may be secured.

Children with a double handicap, i.e., a handicap other than blindness or partial sight, such as, for example, deafness or a serious orthopedic defect, are educated in a facility set up to meet the needs of that defect which is the greater handicap to him. For example, a deaf child who is also partially sighted should be referred to the school for the deaf and given sight-saving equipment.

Defects of hearing

The early recognition of even a slight degree of impaired hearing is extremely important for the child's psychosocial development, emotional stability, language development, communicative skills, and learning capacity. About 4 to 5 per cent of school children have some measurable hearing impairment. The child will not tell us he cannot hear well. He has no basis of comparison to show him that he hears less well than other children.

Types of hearing impairment

Hearing impairment may be either congenital or acquired, and may vary from profound to mild in degree. There are two main types of hearing impairment: (a) conductive, in which the difficulty is in either the middle or outer ear, and (b) sensorineural, involving the inner ear and/or the auditory nerve. Sometimes both types of impairment are present. An occasional case of conductive hearing impairment is due to the accumulation and impaction of ear wax, which can be removed by a physician without difficulty. It is not unusual for children to stuff small objects, such as peas and beans, in their ears, and this possibility should be kept in mind.

Middle ear disease. The great majority of cases of conductive deafness in school age children are due to middle ear disease. The middle ear contains three tiny ear bones, known as ossicles, namely, the hammer, anvil, and stirrup, which connect the ear drum with an opening in the bony wall of the inner ear. This ossicular chain, attached by means of tiny ligaments, must be freely movable in order to transmit vibrations efficiently from the eardrum to the inner ear. In middle ear infections, when fluid accumulates in the middle ear cavity or adhesions develop on the ossicles, the transmission of vibrations to the inner ear is impeded and hearing impairment results.

Any symptom of middle ear disease, such as earache, a feeling of "fullness" in the ears, or any reduction of hearing acuity, should always receive prompt medical attention. When treatment is delayed or inadequate the eardrum may rupture spontaneously from pressure of the infectious material in the middle ear. In some cases the perforation in the eardrum is so large that it will not heal, resulting in some permanent hearing loss and the danger of repeated infections through the outer ear. Fortunately, with early treatment and prompt use of modern drugs, the infection can usually be controlled without rupture of the eardrum or surgical incision. Another gain from the use of modern drugs has been the virtual disappearance of mastoiditis as a dangerous complication of the middle ear disease.

Middle ear infection not uncommonly results from improper noseblowing forcing infectious material through the Eustachian tube into the middle ear. Children should be taught to blow the nose not too forcibly and with both nostrils open.

Middle ear disease may also develop from chronic blocking of the Eustachian tube due to excessive adenoid growth or swollen tissues. When air cannot reach the middle ear, negative pressure develops which may force exudation of serum from the tissues lining the Eustachian tube and the middle ear. Unless this fluid is evacuated surgically, it tends to thicken and become glue-like, impairing the efficiency of the sound-conducting mechanism with consequent hearing loss.

Diseases of the inner ear. Otosclerosis, which causes progressive loss of hearing, is a disease of the bony capsule of the inner ear. In this condition, a spongy type of bone develops around the oval window of the inner ear where the stirrup bone is attached, impairing its ability to transmit vibrations from the eardrum and the other ossicles to the inner ear. It seldom becomes manifest until the late teens or early twenties. Audiometric screening in the eleventh or twelfth grade has been helpful in identifying possible cases for otological referral and early diagnosis.

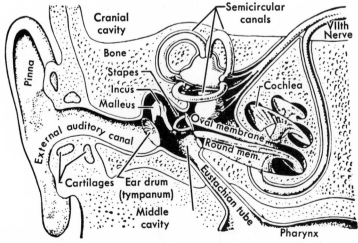

Fig. 15. Diagram of the ear. (From Storer and Usinger: *General Zoology*, ed. 4, New York, 1965, McGraw-Hill Book Co. Used by permission.)

Sensorineural hearing impairment is relatively uncommon in school children. It may be hereditary or due to viral disease incurred by the mother during the early weeks of pregnancy. It also may be acquired at any time after birth, due to meningitis, a skull fracture through the inner ear, or certain viral diseases, especially measles and mumps. Sensorineural hearing loss may range from mild to complete. In many congenital cases, the loss is profound to the point of complete deafness.

Detecting hearing defects

The alert teacher may note various indications that the child has a hearing difficulty, such as the following:

1. He may appear to be inattentive when casually spoken to.
2. He may constantly ask to have questions repeated.
3. He may watch the teachers face closely or with an anxious expression, in an effort to understand him. He develops a peculiar listening posture.
4. He may have difficulty in copying dictation.
5. His responses are irrelevant or he may fail to answer easy questions.
6. He may interrupt without realizing he is doing it.
7. His voice may sound flat or unnatural. He may articulate certain sounds poorly and talk in too loud or too low a tone of voice.
8. He may appear to be bored or withdrawn, sullen or hopeless.

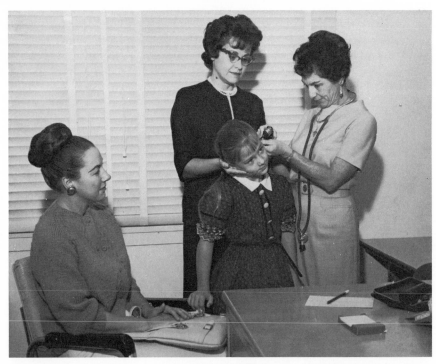

Fig. 16. The observation of a slight hearing difficulty by the mother and teacher is followed by an examination of the ears. (Courtesy Los Angeles City Schools.)

9. He may be easily frustrated over difficulties he does not understand, or be defiant in the face of reasonable instructions or requests.
10. His school achievement may be below his potential ability.
11. He may have frequent colds, earaches, or a discharging ear.

The signs of possible hearing difficulty are often wrongly interpreted, and the child may be thought to be mentally retarded or emotionally unstable, thus compounding the problem and causing serious damage to the personality and educational progress of the child. When any of the above manifestations suggestive of hearing impairment are observed, it is of primary importance that the cause of the condition be discovered and proper medical and educational procedures initiated. It has been estimated that, out of every ten children found to have impaired hearing in an adequate screening examination, two will have permanent impairment not amenable to reversal or sufficient functional recovery by medical and surgical procedures; eight will have hearing losses that can be reversed or greatly relieved by minimal medical care if the cases are found early and treated adequately.[16]

Who should be tested?

Ideally all pupils should be given a hearing test annually. If such a program is found to be too costly, priority should be given to testing pupils in kindergarten and in the first three grades, and all referred pupils. Referred pupils include all those suspected of hearing problems either by parents or teachers because of any of the conditions mentioned above, and pupils new to the school or discovered by a previous test to have hearing impairment. The discovery of hearing impairment at the earliest possible time in the school life of the child is extremely important because of the frequency of hearing defects in the young child, the favorable response to treatment at an early age, and the serious interference with the learning process which hearing loss causes, especially if the teacher is unaware of the child's problem. Pupils should be tested at least once in both junior and senior high school with an interval of not more than two or three years.

In recent years progress has been made in establishing classes for preschool children with hearing loss. Children as young as two or three years of age have been fitted with hearing aids and given a head start in their training. Early recognition and speech training during the preschool years have greatly advanced the speech and language capacity of these children, so that by school age they are socially, psychologically, and developmentally better able to take full advantage of their educational opportunities.

Who shall test hearing

The person who tests hearing must be well trained in the techniques of audiometry. In California, satisfactory completion of courses in audiology and audiometry at a recognized university or college is required for

[16]Hardy, W. G.: "Team Work in Prevention of Hearing Impairment in Children," *Public Health Nursing*, **43:5:**278-282, May, 1951.

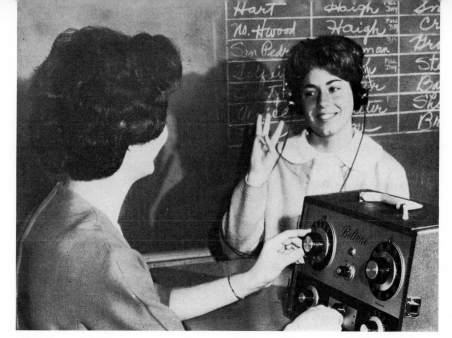

Fig. 17. Individual, pure tone audiometry. The audiometrist is presenting a number of "beeps" and asking the pupil how many she hears. (Courtesy Los Angeles City Schools.)

certification by the State Board of Public Health.[17] In most districts qualified supervisors of health, usually school nurses who have taken this special training, are required to carry out the hearing testing program in addition to their other duties. In districts where school audiometrists are available, their employment has been found to be highly satisfactory and economically advantageous.

Audiometric testing in schools

Screening procedures. In many parts of the United States, hearing testing of school children is required by state law. The routine use of the audiometer is our greatest single aid in detecting hearing deficiencies. The pure-tone audiometer, because of its accuracy and adaptability to children of all ages, is preferred for use in schools. In the hands of a skilled operator using the individual sweep-check method as a screening device, nearly as many children can be screened in a given time as can be screened with group methods.

The sweep-check method, using a pure-tone audiometer, is one in which the child is expected to respond to a predetermined intensity level of 10 or 15 decibels at several selected frequencies, for example, 500, 1,000, 2,000, and 4,000 cycles per second. The testing environment should be quiet. Failure of the child to respond to any one of these screening frequencies at an intensity level of 15 decibels indicates that additional tests are required.[18]

---

[17]California Administrative Code, Title 17 (Public Health), section 2950.

[18]"Hearing Testing of School Children and Guide for Hearing Conservation Programs," California State Department of Public Health, 2151 Berkeley Way, Berkeley 4, California.

The group pure-tone test was first devised by Dr. P. W. Johnson of Massachusetts and is known as the Massachusetts Group Screening Test. It enables school systems equipped with the multiple headphones and attachments of the old phonograph group-testing audiometer to utilize this equipment for group pure-tone testing by having it connected to a pure-tone instrument.

The instrument at this time must be recalibrated and corrected to take the load of additional headphones. As with the individual pure-tone instrument, the testee indicates whether he hears the burst of tones at each frequency. Instead of signaling the operator that he hears the sound, he records "yes" or "no" on the test form. Although some of the disadvantages of the phonograph group method still are present, it is possible with this hybrid instrument to test as many as 80 children in an hour and still retain the advantages of the pure-tone instrument by detecting loss in the higher frequencies. This method is not suitable for use below the fourth grade.

Tests for referral purposes. Pupils who fail one or more frequencies in either ear in the screening tests are given *threshold tests.* Pure-tone air conduction threshold tests are designed to determine the level of hearing sensitivity for medical referral purposes. Measurements are generally recorded for the frequencies of 250 through 6,000 cycles per second. The generally accepted criteria for medical referral established many years ago by the Committee on Conservation of Hearing of the Academy of Ophthalmology and Otolaryngology are: hearing losses of 20 decibels or more at any two frequencies in either ear, or a loss of 30 decibels or more at any single frequency in either ear.

Follow-up procedures

Children with hearing loss are referred for an examination by an otologist to learn whether the difficulty lies in the accumulation of earwax, in the more common involvement of the middle ear, in diseases of the nose and throat, or in sensorineural hearing impairment. The earlier medical treatment is started, the greater the hope of curing or alleviating the condition. Periodic re-examination should be scheduled to determine whether the hearing loss tends to be progressive.

Classroom adjustments

A child with slight or moderate hearing loss (10 to 30 decibels) in the better ear, or with hearing loss in only one ear, may well be seated at the front of the room and allowed to shift seats in order best to follow any change in the class routine. During seat recitations he should be allowed to turn and face the class so that he can see the face of the reciter. When reports are given, the report should be given from the front of the room, facing the class.

The teacher can greatly assist the hard-of-hearing child if he observes some simple precautions such as (1) not standing with his back to the window while talking (shadow and glare make it difficult to see his lips),

(2) not speaking while writing on the chalkboard, (3) keeping hands and book away from the face while speaking, (4) standing still while speaking and standing in a place where light falls on his face, (5) always conducting class recitations and discussions from the front of the room, and (6) making sure that he has the child's attention before starting to give an assignment.

The teacher should stress clear enunciation by all pupils and practice it himself. A loud voice and exaggerated lip movements should be avoided. Children who are hard of hearing should be encouraged to develop any musical ability which they may have and to participate in group extracurricular activities. They may require special help in spelling, reading, and speech because of their failure to hear well.

In some school systems children with hearing loss have been roughly classified in three groups: those with less than 30 decibel loss in the better ear as measured by a pure-tone audiometer; those with 30 to 50 decibel loss; and those with 50 to 70 decibel loss. Children in the first group, with relatively slight impairment of hearing, do very well without speech reading if the teacher follows the simple precautions outlined above. However, children with less than 30 decibel loss should receive speech-reading instruction if the ear condition tends to be progressive.

Children with 30 to 50 decibel loss should have speech-reading instruction one period daily in addition to the regular classroom work. They should be provided with a carefully selected hearing aid and given adequate instruction in its use.

Children in the third group, with 50 to 70 decibel loss, after all necessary medical care has been given, may do well with speech-reading instruction in a regular class if satisfactorily fitted with an individual hearing aid. If not helped by a hearing aid, or if their adjustment to the regular classroom is unsatisfactory, this group will need placement in a special class for speech training, speech reading, and language instruction. It may be possible for them eventually to enter the regular class for the major part of the day. In any event they should be made to feel an integral part of the school life. Usually these special classes are provided in schools for the deaf and hard of hearing, where children with a hearing loss of 70 decibels or more, who have been deaf from birth or from illness in early infancy, receive auditory training and instruction in speech from specially trained teachers of the deaf.

Deaf children

Totally deaf children are recognized early by their absence of speech and failure to respond to sound stimuli. They should attend a school where special methods are used for education of the totally deaf, beginning at age 3 if possible and not later than age 5. They should *not* be retained in regular schools.

References

American Speech and Hearing Association: "Identification Audiometry," *Journal of Speech and Hearing Disorders,* Monograph Supplement No. 9, Washington, D. C., September, 1961, the Association.

California State Department of Education, Sacramento: *A Guide for Vision Screening in California Public Schools,* 1964 edition.

Children's Bureau, United States Department of Health, Education, and Welfare: *Screening School Children for Visual Defects,* publication no. 345, Washington, D. C., United States Department of Health, Education, and Welfare.

Davis, Hallowell, and Silverman, S. Richards (editors): *Hearing and Deafness,* New York, 1960, Holt, Rinehart and Winston.

Hathaway, Winifred: *Education and Health of the Partially Seeing Child,* ed. 3, New York, 1954, Columbia University Press.

Joint Committee on Health Problems in Education of the National Education Association and the American Medical Association: *School Health Services,* Washington and Chicago, 1953, NEA and AMA.

Massachusetts Department of Public Health: *The Massachusetts Vision Test,* Auburn, New York, The Welch-Allyn Company.

Metropolitan Life Insurance Company: *What Teachers See,* New York, 1948, Metropolitan Life Insurance Company, 33 pp.

National Medical Foundation for Eye Care: *Identification of School Children Requiring Eye Care,* 250 West 5th Street, New York 19, N. Y.

National Society for the Prevention of Blindness, 16 East 40th Street, New York, N. Y. 10016, publishes materials on visual defects and testing for visual acuity.

Newby, Hayes, A.: *Audiology—Principles and Practice,* New York, 1958, Appleton-Century-Crofts.

Streng, Alice: *Hearing Therapy for School Children,* ed. 2, New York, 1958, Grune and Stratton Company.

Vail, Derrick: *The Truth About Your Eyes,* New York, 1959, Farrar, Straus & Cudahy, Inc.

Wheatley, G. M., and Hallock, Grace T.: *Health Observation of School Children,* ed. 3, New York, 1965, McGraw-Hill Book Company, Inc.

Chapter V

Departures from normal health

Teachers do not need the medical knowledge upon which diagnosis and treatment are based. They neither diagnose nor recommend treatment. They do call to the attention of physician or nurse children who seem to have something wrong and need further examination. They are concerned with helping the child to adjust his daily living to whatever physical limitation he may have.

The teacher wishes to know the nature of the common departures from health, their relative frequency, the more obvious signs which suggest their presence, and how they affect the child as a pupil. We shall consider these points in this chapter. The chapter on school health services will show the procedures by which the school health team, under medical leadership, cares for the health of pupils.

Communicable diseases, although of greatly reduced importance as a cause of death, still pose a constant threat to classroom groups of school age children. Tuberculosis and other serious diseases still occur. Common cold, measles, mumps, and other ailments, including skin diseases, can disrupt a school program. They sometimes lead to serious complications or sequelae. A separate chapter is devoted to their consideration.

Many departures from health have their effect upon classroom procedures. The individual child may need a modified study or activity program. Special facilities may have to be provided for him. His academic progress may have been interrupted by frequent short absences or by an absence so long that instruction has been given to him at home or in the hospital. Where there is a serious departure from normal health or a mental hygiene problem, some adjustment of the class to the pupils condition may be necessary.

Table 3 shows the relative frequency of the more common departures from health and health practices as reflected in medical appraisals of nearly 15,000 school children in the schools of Denver, Colorado, in the school year 1963-64.

Studies have shown wide variation in the percentages of pupils which different school systems report as having various physical defects. Such data are not directly comparable because the definitions and standards for determining the defects were different.

Let us consider here the more common departures from health, exclusive of the communicable diseases.

Low nutritional status

A nutritional defect may be mild or severe. It may be the result of a single dietary fault or the diet may be defective in many ways. Rickets, scurvy, pellagra, and beriberi are deficiency diseases. They are clear-cut in the more advanced stages, but in the earlier stages or in the milder cases the nature of the nutritional disturbance is not obvious.

The diet may be deficient in calories, proteins, fats, or liquids, as well as in vitamins. Schools must be on the watch for generally poor nutrition and, having discovered it, get help from the specialist in finding the exact cause and remedying the condition.

The diagnosis of malnutrition is not easy. It has been necessary to abandon the belief, once widely held, that all children appreciably below average weight for their height and age are malnourished. It has been shown that the precision of the underweight determination is low and that a child's percentage-of-normal weight fluctuates widely because of the determination.[1] The correlation between height and weight is not high. The height-weight ratio is primarily determined by the child's skeletal build.[2]

Various soft-tissue indices have been suggested by which, through a series of measurements, it is possible to determine where the child stands among his skeletal peers in respect to the amount of muscle tissue and subcutaneous fat. Such objective measurements are helpful, but it cannot be said that we have, at present, a satisfactory and generally accepted objective index of malnutrition.

The best diagnosis we have of malnutrition is still the judgment of the physician. This is a subjective judgment and there may not always be agreement between different physicians.[3] In forming his opinion, the

---

[1]Turner, C. E.: "Precision and Reliability of Underweight Measurement," *American Journal of Public Health* 19:969–977, September, 1929.

[2]Franzen, Raymond: *Physical Measures of Growth and Nutrition*, School Health Research Monograph, New York, 1929, American Child Health Association.

[3]Mayhew Derryberry, when Senior Public Health Statistician of the United States Public Health Service, in a study of "Reliability of Medical Judgments on Malnutrition" (Reprint no. 1909, from *Public Health Reports*, vol. 53, no. 7, February 18, 1938), stated: "In routine examinations, physicians differ widely in their estimates of the nutritional status of the same children. The differences in judgments are so great that estimates based on a single examination are of little value in determining the relative amount of malnutrition among any group of children at any one time or changes in the amount from one time to another. Neither are these nutritional estimates reliable bases for determining which children of a group are malnourished.

"It is therefore suggested that practical nutritional programs be focused on correcting the faulty food habits of children rather than expending energy on routine examinations to determine nutritional status. It is also proposed that research workers concentrate on the construction of valid methods of determining nutritional status rather than on making surveys which are of doubtful significance because of the inaccuracies of the estimates upon which their findings are based."

Table 3. Common conditions and defects found on medical appraisals in Denver, Colorado schools

	Number	Percent
Poor health habits*	3,468	23.6
Heart murmur (innocent)	2,277	15.5
Ears	1,101	7.5
Throat	986	6.7
Skin	909	6.1
Eyes	663	4.5
Orthopedic	636	4.3
Nutrition	533	3.6
General poor health†	388	2.6
Genitourinary and hernia	383	2.6
Heart murmur (organic‡)	165	1.1

Courtesy Denver Public Schools.

*Health habits are considered poor when they definitely hinder the best growth and functioning of an individual. Faulty diet, no breakfast, inadequate sleep, overstimulation, and neglected personal hygiene are conditions considered to be poor health habits.

†General poor health tabulates those with frequent colds, earaches, stomach trouble, and so forth.

‡Murmurs are recorded as organic and are referred for further diagnostic attention whenever the school examining physicians believe or are suspicious that the murmurs are typical of organic disease. It is thought preferable to overrefer rather than miss early cases of organic heart disease.

doctor considers the quality and quantity of soft tissue. He also looks for poor and drooping posture, for flabby muscles, for rough and dry skin, dull lusterless eyes, and poor color. In the more severe cases, many of these symptoms are so obvious as to impress themselves upon the alert parent or teacher.

A summary of signs of malnutrition may be helpful.

1. How does the child look?
   a. Skin pale or sallow
   b. Mucous membranes pale, indicating anemia
   c. Hair dry and dull looking
   d. Dark circles under eyes (fatigue or poor diet)
   e. Unusually thin, spindly arms and legs; flat chest
   f. Muscles stringy or flabby
   g. Fatigue slouch
   h. Expression pinched, anxious
   i. Teeth decayed; gums spongy
2. How does the child feel?
   a. Easily tired
   b. Nervous, irritable
   c. Concentration poor
3. How does he act?
   a. Restless and overactive or apathetic
   b. Fidgety, nervous, unstable
   c. Finicky appetite

    d. Sleeps poorly
    e. Dislikes too many articles of diet
    f. Wants too much candy
    g. Susceptible to colds, sore throat, skin infections
    h. Does poor work in school

The following list of causes of poor nutrition is based upon on analysis originally prepared by Professor Lydia J. Roberts.

I. Faulty Diet
    1. Diet insufficient in amount
        a. Inadequate breakfasts due to poor appetite, hurry, no breakfast prepared, or dietary fad
        b. Inadequate lunch due to hurry or inadequate lunches at school or at home
        c. Insufficient food intake
            1. Not enough provided for any meals
            2. Poor appetite for all meals, due to physical defects, lack of outdoor play, overfatigue, inadequate or unpalatable food
    2. Poorly balanced diet
        a. Too little milk
        b. Too few vegetables and fruits
        c. Too much candy and sweets
        d. Use of coffee or tea
    3. Bad food habits with hurried or irregular meals and between-meal lunches
II. Faulty hygiene
    1. Too little sleep
        a. Going to bed too late because of TV, movies, homework, or parties
        b. Up too early to work, to get to school, or to conform to adult hours
        c. Unable to sleep because of noise, fatigue, or excitement
    2. Overexercise and fatigue
    3. Too little fresh air and sunshine
III. Defects or disease

There are two phases of the nutrition program: (1) the conduct of general health education in such a way as to maintain the best possible nutritional standards among *all* children, and (2) the necessary intensive work with the individual malnourished child. The classroom teacher is vitally concerned with both of these activities. In increasing degree, teachers are realizing the importance of the subject of nutrition for the maintenance of their own health, and for understanding and assisting the pupil. The professional leadership and cooperation of the physician, the nutritionist, the school nurse, and the nutrition clinic are extremely important with the more severe cases of malnutrition.

Dental defects

While practically all school children need dental care, the number of children with serious dental defects has been greatly reduced from that of a generation ago. The public has realized that tooth decay can be reduced through prompt filling of small cavities, oral cleanliness, fluoridation of public water supplies, and suitable diet, especially that of the expectant mother and young child.

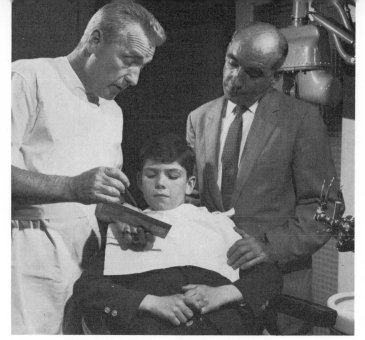

(A. Devaney)

Fig. 18. The pupil and the parent need to know of dental defects.

Dental research would warrant the conclusion that, for most individuals, dental caries is due to the action of bacteria on carbohydrate food particles, particularly sugar, producing acids which are capable of eating into and dissolving the enamel and dentin structure of the tooth. Those who suffer from dental decay should, in addition to consuming a well-balanced diet, restrict to a minimum refined sugars in the form of cookies, candy, cake, pastry, and soft drinks. As far as possible the natural craving for sweets should be satisfied by the natural sugars found in fruits. School cafeterias can assist in the dental health education program by avoiding the sale of candy, soft drinks, and rich sweet desserts. Moreover, it helps to avoid decay if the teeth are cleansed immediately after eating. If a toothbrush is not available, rinsing the mouth thoroughly with lukewarm water after eating is helpful. When rinsing the mouth with water after eating at school pupils should be instructed to swallow the water, otherwise a sanitary problem may be created.

Oral cleanliness has greatly improved and the schools have, in increasing degree, attempted to secure dental care for all children at least once a year. (Dental treatment twice a year, or at the interval suggested by the dentist, is to be preferred, but as a practical administrative procedure for the public school, annual dental attention is perhaps a satisfactory standard.) These developments have greatly improved dental health in the present generation of children and young people.

The teacher realizes that the effects of extensive tooth decay may go beyond the pain incident to toothache. They may interfere with the proper chewing of food and hence with digestion and nutrition. If an abscess develops at the root of a tooth, it may become a source of infection capable of ultimately producing disease of the heart, kidneys, joints, or other parts of the body. Irregularities in the spacing and position of the teeth (malocclusion) may cause early dental diseases as well as difficulty of speech and embarrassment to the child. Assistance in securing correction for these more serious defects will be of vital help to the individual pupil. It is particularly important that orthodontic treatment should be started early if the position or alignment of the teeth needs to be changed. Such correction is much more difficult after the early teen years. Consideration should be given also, to the prevention and treatment of gingivitis in childhood. There is considerable evidence that neglect of this condition results in periodontitis in later years, with degeneration of the periodontal membrane, formation of pus pockets, and loosening of teeth. Infectious gingivitis is due to poor oral hygiene and the growth of bacteria between the teeth and under the gum margin. The condition is aggravated by calcium deposits and uneven teeth. Dental prophylaxis at regular intervals and proper tooth-brushing are the most effective means of prevention and treatment.

Teachers can be very effective in securing regular dental treatment through education to that end. If we can get all school children to a dentist or a dental clinic for the necessary corrective work at least once a year, there is little point in having dentists examine the teeth of children at school and chart the findings. In Los Angeles, California, school dentists serving as resource personnel in health education have been very effective in deepening interest in the dental health education program through in-service education of the classroom teacher. Methods used have included classroom demonstrations of dental health education teaching techniques, using models, charts, film strips, and other audiovisual aids and teaching materials. In this program there is strong emphasis on proper nutrition, avoidance of excessive carbohydrates, especially candy and other sweets, and correct oral hygiene, as well as regular dental care.

In an experiment in Malden, Massachusetts, we found that the teachers and the private dentists can work together with excellent results. The first dental survey showed that 30 per cent of the children had received dental care within the year. At that time we began the practice of encouraging children to secure dental attention each year. The schools provided certificates that the dentist could sign indicating that all necessary dental work had been completed. These certificates were brought back to the classroom, and an honor roll for teeth was made that included all children possessing such a certificate.

Four years later, 60 per cent of our elementary school children were securing such certificates. During the same year a report by the State of Massachusetts, on a campaign embracing 178 towns and 265,626 children, stated that 18 per cent of the children had all dental work completed and that approximately one-half of these certificates came from private dentists and the other half from dental clinics. In Malden only 25 per cent of the certificates came from dental clinics. Still later the percentage of children having necessary dental work completed rose to nearly 81 per cent. These changes were accomplished by health education, not by increasing free dental service.

The Astoria Demonstration Study in New York also tested these possibilities. In her report Nyswander[4] says:

> As Turner[5] and Morris[6] have stated, almost the entire problem of dental health of the school child is one of education—the type of education which is not a thing apart but is integrated with classroom instruction concerning all phases of health. Turner's work in Malden, based on this premise, had during a ten-year-period brought such excellent results that an adaptation of his procedures was formulated for the eight experimental schools in Astoria. . . .
>
> Experience indicated that the dental health of school children in Astoria would not be improved by better case-finding techniques in the school. What is needed is education in the values of dental service in order to secure earlier detection of caries and treatment.[7] In two experiments emphasis was placed on this aspect of dental care; in the first, the dental hygienist assumed the responsibility for instructing children and parents; in the second, the classroom teachers took over the task. In both experiments the private dentists gave most of the treatment services.
>
> Both procedures brought comparable results, but it is evident that the dental hygienist who conducts such a program for an entire school would be sorely taxed for time if she gave, in addition to her examinations, prophylactic treatments or assistance to the dentist in the clinic. Furthermore, it is out of keeping with sound theory in health education to emphasize one program to the exclusion of other efforts to provide for the child's welfare. The child cannot be helped to assume responsibility for his health through campaigns carried out by specialists. Sound attitudes can be developed only through unified teaching and through one source of instruction—the teacher.

The promotion of dental health education is often complicated by a shortage of dental services for children unable to afford private care. The classroom teacher and the dental hygienist are confronted by the fact that, in many instances, they are educating children to seek dental services which are unavailable. Most urgent therefore is the need for education of all children in those measures of nutrition and oral hygiene which will at least diminish the constant stream of persons needing dental attention.

One of the most favorable developments in the prevention of dental caries is in the adjustment of the fluoride level of drinking water, which is now accepted public procedure in many cities. Drinking water containing sodium fluoride in a proportion of one part to a million when used from birth on will prevent approximately 60 per cent of dental caries. Children who are older when they commence drinking fluoridated water

---

[4]Nyswander, Dorothy B.: *Solving School Health Problems,* New York, 1942, The Commonwealth Fund, pp. 211 and 220.

[5]Turner, C. E., Marshall, F. G., and Ross, A. R.: "Dental Health Education in Malden, Massachusetts," *Journal of the American Dental Association and The Dental Cosmos* 24:1189-1191, July, 1937.

[6]Morris, Emory W.: "The Utilization of Community Resources in the Health Program," *Journal of the American Dental Association* 26:493-505, March, 1939.

[7]Similar conclusions are reported by Walker, W. F., and Randolph, C. R.: *School Health Services,* New York, 1941, The Commonwealth Fund, p. 50.

receive somewhat less protection. A 2 per cent sodium fluoride solution is sometimes applied to the teeth by the dentist to help prevent dental decay.

We may list the common dental defects and difficulties as follows:

1. Cavities in the teeth
2. Malocclusion
   a. Crowded arches
   b. Protruding teeth
   c. Spaces between teeth
   d. Poor articulation (bite)
   e. Mouth breathing (may cause malocclusion)
   f. Pressure habits (resting chin or face on hand, finger sucking, lip or tongue sucking may cause malocclusion)
3. Broken teeth (should be seen by dentist immediately, no matter how slight the external appearance of the fracture)
4. Sore or inflamed gums
5. Offensive breath (may indicate an infection of the membranes of the mouth and throat, if gums are severely inflamed)
6. Dead or abscessed teeth

Defects of speech[8]

Speech defects include stuttering, lisping, baby talk, nasality, unpleasant accent, substitution of one sound for another, and harsh or monotonous voice. These various conditions have a variety of causes, including partial deafness, structural difficulties in the organs of speech, or the hearing of defective speech in the home.

Retarded speech development occurs in about five out of every 1000 children. The causes of this condition include subnormality, prolonged physical illness during early infancy, overly attentive parents, and, at the other extreme, emotional deprivation. A thorough diagnostic study should be made in each case before commencing treatment.

Many of the less important speech defects, including the milder cases of stuttering and lisping, may be corrected by the classroom teacher. The more serious or more unusual cases should receive the attention of a specially trained speech correctionist. The correct handling of these cases is directly related to the mental hygiene of the child.

The stutterer is usually the unstable, anxious, nervous type of child. With this nervous predisposition, some shock, injury, or fright may have been the actual exciting cause. Parental anxiety over the child's early speech problems, accompanied by pressure, ridicule, or censure, accentuates the difficulty. The friendly sympathy of the teacher reflects itself in minimizing the seriousness of the defect and in directing the pupil's attention away from actual speech production when he talks. The teacher should give the pupil plenty of time to organize and vocalize what he has to say when reciting. Helping the stutterer to pronounce the word is the wrong procedure.

The majority of young children who stutter will easily recover without

---

[8]Literature on speech correction problems can be secured from The Speech Correction Fund, 11 South LaSalle St., Chicago, Ill.

special treatment, if they can be helped to build up good general health and assume an unemotional attitude toward the defect. Undoubtedly some of the good results obtained by the speech correctionist are due more to the loving attentions which the child receives than to the techniques of treatment, important as these may be.

Lisping (imperfect letter sound) may be caused by malformation of the speech organs, but more commonly it is either a habit continued from early childhood or a procedure assumed as a means of getting attention.

Harelip or cleft palate requires surgical treatment in infancy. Children with speech defects due to cerebral palsy should commence treatment by an expert speech correctionist during the preschool period.

Defects of the nose and throat

Sinus infections, enlarged and diseased tonsils and adenoids, nasal obstruction due to deviated septum, polyps, and chronic inflammations are conditions of the nose and throat that commonly need attention. Chronically infected and hypertrophied adenoids may cause nasal obstruction and mouth breathing. This is particularly unforunate when the condition begins in infancy, since thoracic deformity may develop and the facial contour be changed because of the high and narrow palate. The voice takes on a nasal quality and the face an expression of dullness. The open mouth contributes to this unfortunate appearance.

Children with this condition have great difficulty in breathing when lying on the back, with the result that sleep is disturbed. In class they are usually listless and inattentive, frequently giving the impression of mental retardation. Many have persistent nasal discharge, which also occurs in chronic rhinitis and in the presence of nasal polyps.

Mention has already been made of the frequency of hearing impairment due to hypertrophied adenoid tissue obstructing the Eustachian tube and due to the extension of nose and throat infections into the middle ear. The teacher will recognize the handicap these children are working under and report their observations to parents and to school health personnel. After correction, the improvement in the child's behavior, school performance, and appetite is often dramatic.

In recent years the effectiveness of antibiotics and chemotherapy has markedly reduced the necessity for tonsil and adenoid removal. Frequent common colds, repeated attacks of tonsillitis, and uncomplicated chronic rhinitis are no longer considered adequate reasons for tonsillectomy by most physicians. Rarely is simple tonsillar enlargement sufficient reason for removal. In view of the fact that tonsils and adenoids serve as a valuable defense mechanism against infection, adenotonsillectomies are being restricted to those cases where there is strong evidence that the health of the child is being impaired in spite of adequate medical treatment.

Rheumatic fever

Rheumatic fever, although still a major cause of heart disease in children, is declining in incidence and severity. This decline may be due to the widespread use of antibiotics and chemotherapy in the treatment of streptococcic sore throats. Prophylactic treatment of children who have had rheumatic fever with such medicines as penicillin and the sulfa drugs may also be a factor in the reduction of this disease. In diagnosed cases the prophylactic treatment is usually continued until at least eighteen years of age.

The degree of heart damage which a child receives from rheumatic fever depends in a very large measure on early recognition, prompt treatment, and careful health supervision. In the early stages rheumatic fever may be difficult to recognize because the first symptoms are frequently mild or obscure and may be present in malnutrition and various infections. A rheumatic attack may begin with the signs and symptoms listed here. Children with the following symptoms should be referred for examination by a physician:

Failure to gain weight	Low persistent fever
Poor appetite	Frequent complaints of pain in the arms,
Pallor	legs, joints, or abdomen
Repeated nosebleeds	Undue lassitude and fatigue
Rapid heart action	Nervous jerky movements

Not all children who have had rheumatic fever are left with heart disease. They may have healed valve lesions.

There is evidence that rheumatic fever develops in connection with a hemolytic streptococcic sore throat or upper respiratory infection. It is extremely important, therefore, in the prevention of rheumatic fever, to exclude from school children with sore throats, so that they may receive early and adequate treatment, and avoid passing on the infection to other children.

Children with severely crippled (rheumatic) hearts may be:

Undersized
Pale
With deformed chest
With very rapid pulse at rest
Slightly short of breath at rest
Very short of breath on exertion
Easily fatigued

At the present time most surveys indicate that there is a higher incidence of heart disease due to congenital defects than to rheumatic fever. A child with congenital heart disease may appear normal if the lesion is slight. Other children with more serious congenital heart disease may be:

Pale
Undernourished
With deformed chest
With blue lips
With clubbed fingers
Short of breath on exertion
Faint after exertion or excitement

The lack of development that often goes with heart disease may be indistinguishable from that accompanying malnutrition, except by the physician.

Cardiac defects. Approximately 1 per cent of school children have heart defects. There has been a tendency on the part of school personnel to regard all heart cases with considerable anxiety and in many instances to impose unnecessary restrictions. It is important to realize that heart conditions vary all the way from quite mild to severe. Accurate diagnosis, therefore, by a competent physician is essential so that, in planning the school activities of the child, arrangements can be made for a program which is as nearly normal as possible. Most of these children do well when left in the regular classroom. Written instructions from the physician should indicate the degree and type of physical activity permitted. One or another of the following groupings is usually stipulated:

a. No restrictions
b. Regular physical education but no competitive athletics
c. Adapted physical education (games and activities to be specified by the physician)
d. Rest period (in severe cases)

While it is extremely important to discover the child with heart disease, great caution should be exercised to avoid developing cardiac neurotics. When heart disease is merely suspected, no intimation should be given the child. By the same token a child who has been left in a state of uncertainty with regard to a heart condition should have the benefit of a diagnosis by a cardiologist if possible. Delabeling a child who has lived under the shadow of an incorrect or unwarranted cardiac diagnosis is one of the finest services which can be rendered.

The teacher has a major role in helping the child with heart disease to carry out effectively and cheerfully the program advised by the physician. Avoidance of oversolicitousness is important. The fear, so common among teachers, that children with heart disease are likely to die suddenly from overactivity is quite unfounded. Some children with severe heart disease do well in a school for the handicapped, with frequent rest periods and classes on one floor. Children with such serious heart defects that walking is undesirable are withdrawn from school and assigned home teachers.

The importance of discovering children with congenital heart disease at an early age has been greatly increased by the various modern surgical procedures, which in many cases will restore the cardiac cripple to normal health.

The undervitalized child

The child who lacks vitality should be the concern of the teacher whether his depleted state is the result of poor nutrition, lack of rest, too fatiguing a daily program, poor heredity, anemia, chronic infection, or poor general hygiene. The school physician or nurse should be consulted

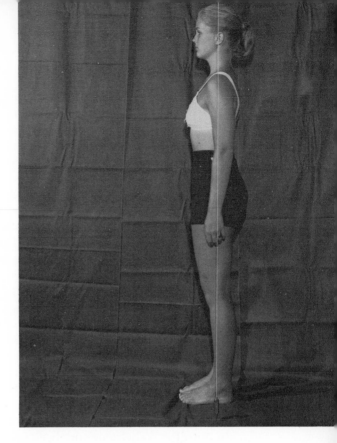

Fig. 19. Excellent static posture is shown by the plumb line. (Courtesy Los Angeles City Schools.)

in order that measures may be initiated to find the cause and secure its removal. This condition is usually of long standing and cannot be corrected overnight. Extra consideration from the teacher may be very important. The child needs extra rest, which may involve a shortened school day with rest instead of play at recess. A well-balanced lunch and a better program of food and rest at home may be needed.

Defects of posture

Common postural defects are the following:

1. Round shoulders, with protruding shoulder blades, depressed chest, and protruding abdomen
2. Scoliosis, or lateral curvature of spinal column
3. Forward-tilting head
4. Lordosis, or forward curvature of the spinal column in the lumbar region or lower back
5. Flat back (not common in school children)
6. Improper balance
7. Pronated ankles
8. Flat feet
9. Fatigue slouch
10. Knock knees
11. Pigeon-toed walk

If we are to understand the child with poor posture, we must recognize that this condition may be due to one or more of several widely different causes.

One common cause of poor posture is malnutrition. The child's muscles are weak. He needs better food, more rest, and greater muscular strength. Fatigue may underlie his poor posture. Because of poor hygiene or recent illness the child does not have sufficient strength to carry the day's program without becoming overtired; this fatigue shows itself in his slumped position. In other cases the difficulty is structural and often congenital.

The obese child is likely to develop poor posture because of the excessive weight which the body framework has to carry. The child with some visual or hearing defect may carry his head forward or tip it to one side. Improperly adjusted clothes or high heels and wrong habits in using play materials or carrying burdens are sometimes responsible for the poor mechanical use of the body.

In most cases posture is the result of some underlying difficulty which we should find and correct. Poor posture is not an independent health problem which can be corrected by telling the child to stand and sit erect. This does not mean that posture training is never of value. Without being given an interest in good posture and some help in attaining it, few children will develop the best mechanical use of the body.

Even when the underlying cause is removed, the child is likely to need some help in posture improvement. If the poor posture is of long standing, certain muscles may need strengthening and others may need stretching to bring the body framework back to proper position. Some postural faults are due to poor habits of sitting or standing and walking. Here corrective exercises, as well as habit changes, are usually needed.

The teacher realizes that poor posture in itself may have unfortunate results in reducing lung capacity, in increasing fatigue, in developing nervous tension, or in causing the dropping down of abdominal organs, thus producing digestive difficulties. Correction, therefore, is highly important. Although posture training and instruction in good body mechanics may be undertaken by the average well-trained physical education instructor, severe defects of posture require correction by specially prepared teachers under professional supervision. All normal children need physical activity and the development of good body mechanics.

Departures from mental and emotional health

From infancy, life is a problem of adjustment between the desires of the individual and that which is best for the group or for society. These adjustments are difficult to make. No child has perfect behavior from the standpoint of the teacher, but the average child, through succeeding adjustments, develops gradually a more mature point of view. We should remember that the behavior that may be most convenient for the teacher may not necessarily be best for the child. The pupil who never demands or requires the attention of the teacher is not necessarily making the best adjustment to life. The problem child is one who falls far short of a reasonable adjustment of his behavior to the social environment.

There are two opposite ways by which the individual evades the re-

Table 4. Behavior problems conceived as evasions of social requirements

Evasion by withdrawal		Requirements imposed on individual behavior by	Evasion by attack	
Fearfulness		*Family*	Temper tantrums	
Sulkiness			Disobedience	
Dreaminess		*Neighborhood*	Overactivity	
Shyness			Aggressiveness	
Dependency on adults			Defiance to authority	
Cowardliness		*Companions*	Fighting	
Unsocialness			Delinquency	
Dependency on routine		*Church*	Rejection of routine	
Pedantry			Pursuing own methods of work	
Solitariness		*School*	Wanting to direct	
Fear of criticism			Breaking conventions	
Suspiciousness			Antagonistic attitudes	
Inability to carry responsibility		*Traditions*	Exploitation of own authority	
Inefficiency			Contentiousness	
Social inadequacy		*Customs*	Egocentricity	
Regressive escapes	*Productive activity*	*Law*	*Constructive attacks*	*Destructive attacks*
Neurotic	Invention		Competitive	"Psycho-
complaints	Research	*Industry*	sports	pathic"
Economic	Science		Exploration	tendencies
dependency	Literature		Industrial	"I won't
Alcoholism	Art		exploits	work"
Drug addiction			Social and	Crime
Functional			political	
insanity			reforms	
Suicide				

quirements imposed upon him by society. Table 4, originally developed by E. K. Wickman and presented here by permission of the Commonwealth Fund, lists behavior problems arising from the child's attempt to evade social requirements by either withdrawal or attack.

Psychosomatic or mind-body realtionships are clearly recognized. Bodily impairment may lead to poor mental health. Conversely, poor mental health may be a cause of stomach ulcers, sleeplessness, loss of appetite, headaches, and other physical difficulties.

Adolescence is a period of special emotional stress. Growth is rapid. Acne is common. Secondary sex characteristics appear. Interest in the other sex increases. The child is beginning to find his place in the adult world and to make more of his own decisions. New problems and behavior patterns appear in the field of mental health. He needs to be accepted by his group, his family and his teachers.

In the more common problems involving, to a limited degree, lack of self-control, emotional instability, disobedience, apparent indifference, deceitfulness, or laziness, the teacher will seek to understand and remove the underlying cause. For the more difficult problems of the children their teacher will seek the assistance of the physician, the psychologist, psychiatrist, or child guidance clinic. Chapter 6 presents a more detailed discussion of the teacher's contribution to the emotional and mental health of his pupils.

The teacher who has acquainted himself with the facts of mental hygiene can, with the assistance of the health service staff and by wise guidance of his pupils, do much to forestall mental maladjustment and delinquency. He will watch for the following:

1. Personality traits suggestive of need for attention
   a. Shyness and lack of self-confidence
   b. Daydreaming (excessive)
   c. Withdrawal from group activities
   d. Fears, timidity, and excessive modesty
   e. Excessive self-assertion and pugnacity
   f. Crying and whining
   g. Temper tantrums
   h. Obstinacy and negativism
   i. Suspiciousness and "picked-on" complex
2. Asocial and antisocial behavior requiring study
   a. Lying
   b. Stealing
   c. Destructiveness
   d. Truancy and running away
   e. Cruelty
   f. Excessive or morbid interest in sex
3. Undesirable habits
   a. Speech defects—stuttering, lisping, etc.
   b. Nail-biting, thumbsucking, etc.
   c. Tics and habit spasms
   d. Enuresis and self-wetting
   e. Feeding and eating problems

It is estimated that at least 12 per cent of school children are maladjusted to such a degree that professional psychological and psychiatric help is urgently needed. The earlier these conditions are recognized, causes determined, and preventive or corrective measures begun, the more probable is a satisfactory adjustment. The well-staffed school system will have available counselors, visiting teachers, psychologists, psychiatric social workers, and child psychiatrists to whom these maladjusted children can be referred for special study and assistance. It is highly desirable that every community should have the benefit of child guidance facilities.

Mentally retarded children. Moderate mental retardation is found in children with I.Q.'s between 50 and 70—with some leeway, plus or minus. The school seeks to give these children a program adapted to their mental capacities and, so far as possible, to guard against personality difficulties arising from their frustrations in academic work. Special guidance is

Fig. 20. Orthopedic defects do not prevent student activity.

needed to help them achieve an adult life satisfying to themselves and acceptable to the community.

Children with an I.Q. below 50 are classed as severely mentally retarded. School systems have established special classes for selected children from this group with favorable results. These children do not profit from regular school education. It is often necessary, however, for someone on the school staff or the staff of a community agency to advise the parents regarding the best procedure. This is especially true when, as is usually the case, it is for the best interest of the child and the family that he should receive institutional care.

Orthopedic defects

Cerebral palsy, congenital defects due to improperly developed bones, poliomyelitis, and traumatic injuries, such as amputated limbs and crushed joints, are the usual causes of orthopedic handicaps.

Crippled children are to be accepted as members of the group and belong in the regular classroom unless the risk of accidental injury is too great, or unless they require the educational facilities and services of a special room or school, including bus transportation, occupational and physical therapy, and speech correction.

Most crippled children make a good emotional adjustment to the situation. The classroom teacher helps them to be accepted by the class as full members of the group and to participate in the play activities as well as in the work. He works cooperatively with the school physician, nurse, and other health and educational specialists in developing the child's greatest potential. Specially trained teachers of the handicapped are adept at organizing recreational and educational programs adapted to the positive assets and abilities of these children. An atmosphere of optimism and cheerfulness is a goal which these schools achieve to an amazing degree.

Education is now being provided for the child hospitalized over a considerable period because of some crippling condition. The physician decides when such education is desirable. The teacher works with the doctor, nurse, and physical therapist.

Endocrine disorders

Children with poorly functioning endocrine glands often become socially maladjusted. They need expert diagnosis and treatment. Space forbids a discussion of these conditions. Some of their common signs may be listed.

1. Underactive thyroid gland (hypothyroidism)
   a. Rough, dry, and cold skin, ashy pallor of lips and cheeks
   b. Dry brittle hair
   c. Slow pulse
   d. Marked overweight with even distribution of weight (25% of cases)
   e. Marked underweight (75% of cases)
   f. Fatigability, sleepiness
   g. Mental reactions slow
   h. Poor muscle tone
   i. Distended abdomen
   j. Constipation
   k. Menstrual irregularities in girls
2. Overfunctioning thyroid (hyperthyroidism), rare in children, occurs more frequently in girls
   a. Enlargement of thyroid gland
   b. Rapid heart rate
   c. Nervousness, distractability, irritability
   d. Tremor of fingers (occasionally)
   e. Sweating
   f. Protrusion of eyeballs (exophthalmos) occasionally
3. Underactive pituitary gland (hypopituitary dwarfism). May be due to absent or inadequate secretion of the growth hormone, hereditary factors, or tumors involving the pituitary gland
   a. Marked growth retardation
   b. Sexual maturation retarded
   c. Voice and body hair remain childlike
   d. Emotional disturbance prominent due to small size and infantilism
4. Sexual infantilism (Fröhlich's syndrome), occasionally confused with simple obesity
   a. Obesity, especially around the hips and breasts
   b. Hands and feet plump but not large, fingers tapering
   c. Delayed puberty
   d. Retarded development of secondary sex characteristics
   e. High-pitched voice
   f. Increased tendency to inactivity and to sleep
   g. Behavior problems
5. Overproduction of the growth hormone of the pituitary gland (hyperpituitarism) results in
   a. Gigantism, which is rare (not to be confused with hereditary tall stature)
      (1) Increased length of long bones
      (2) Moderate enlargement of flat bones, especially of the jaw
      (3) In most cases abnormal growth starts at puberty
   b. Precocious puberty (pseudopuberty) may show early development of sec-

ondary sex characteristics. In true precocious puberty there is also early development of secondary sex characteristics

   c. Incomplete (partial) precocious development, rather rare. Development of breasts and of pubic and body hair, sometimes axillary hair as well

6. Gonadal (sex gland) deficiency in adolescence (rare)
   a. Pupil may be fat, especially at hips
   b. Tall and slender with wide hips
   c. Sexually underdeveloped
   d. In girls, menstrual irregularities
   e. May have high-pitched voice
   f. Personality defects
   g. Problems of adjustment
7. Pancreas
   a. Overfunction—Hypoglycemia
   b. Underfunction, as in diabetes
      (1) Excessive thirst
      (2) Excessive urination
      (3) May show irritability
      (4) Frequent infections
      (5) Slow healing of lesions
      (6) Coma or insulin reaction may occur
8. Other endocrine disorders occasionally occur, but are not of practical importance from the standpoint of the teacher
   a. Adrenal gland abnormalities
   b. Thymus gland (persistence beyond normal age)

Diabetes. Diabetes is an endocrine disorder which deserves special mention because of the number of diabetic children found in the public school. The child is usually following the program laid out by his physician. He does not need daily attention from the school; but school people should understand the condition and the adjustments which may occasionally be necessary.

Sugar diabetes (diabetes mellitus) is caused by the failure of the islands of Langerhans in the pancreas to produce a proper amount of insulin to meet the varying body needs under different conditions. Insulin makes possible the metabolism of carbohydrates in the body. In mild cases where the pancreas produces nearly enough insulin, the condition may be controlled by a modification of the diet. If the disease is severe, insulin must be taken regularly. The amount needed is influenced by the severity of the disease, the amount of carbohydrates in the diet, and by the amount of exercise the individual takes. Exercise decreases the need for insulin by facilitating the burning of blood sugar.

Diabetic children are taught to limit the quantity of their food intake and to keep sugars and starches at a fixed minimum. They may bring part or all of their lunch from home in order to keep to their schedule. Due to improvements in insulin therapy and dosage regulation it is unnecessary for a child to have insulin injections at school. Oral insulin-sparing drugs, which have been found useful in adults, are ineffective in children. However, research is continuing in this area.

Two possible difficulties may arise—insulin shock when there is too much insulin in the body, and diabetic coma when there is too little.

If the diabetic child has received too much insulin, or too little food, or if he has had too much exercise, he may suffer from insulin shock. The blood sugar falls below normal. An "all gone" feeling develops, with numbness and tingling of the lips, hands, and feet. Trembling, cold perspiration, and prostration may follow. The body needs more sugar, and the eating of a lump of sugar or a piece of candy or an orange gives prompt relief. Diabetic children commonly carry lump sugar or candy for such an emergency.

The opposite condition, resulting from too little insulin in the body, leads toward diabetic coma. It is reflected in uncontrollable drowsiness, excessive thirst, nausea, vomiting, or abdominal pain. The child needs immediate medical attention for the administration of insulin.

The teacher needs to know of the diabetic child in his room and the child himself should carry an identification card with the name and address of his physician, as well as his own. Diabetes is so readily controlled today, however, that the diabetic child should be accepted by the teacher and the other children without undue concern.

Allergies

A considerable number of school children have allergies. The offending substance may be one of any number of foods, pollens, or dusts, including occasionally chalk dust, crayon, or other materials used at school. The physician detects the cause of the allergy by dietary studies of foods eaten or by skin tests with the various dusts or pollens.

Symptoms of allergy are varied and include hives, bronchial asthma, symptoms like those of a head cold, nausea, vomiting, or sick headaches. These symptoms may, of course, be due to other causes as well.

The child with a severe allergy should be under medical care, and the physician will prescribe any necessary modifications in the pupil's program or diet. The child with hay fever or asthma, for example, may have to limit his activity program, or be especially careful to avoid dusts. If the child is being given antihistaminic drugs, they may make him sleepy, less alert, and more subject to accidents. Modern immunizing procedures not only bring much relief to the child but frequently prevent complications which may be difficult to cure in later years.

Epilepsy

The school has been worried about the occasional epileptic child, largely because the convulsions are rather terrifying to those who have not seen them before. Actually the convulsion is self-limited and the chief immediate concern is to protect the child from injury by falling. First-aid procedures suggest lowering the child gently to the ground and placing a stick rolled in a handkerchief or a similar soft, firm object such as two tongue blades between the teeth, to prevent him from biting his tongue. The child requires rest and sleep after the convulsion is over.

Children with frequent or severe seizures are not likely to be in school, but milder cases are today commonly enrolled in regular classes. Present methods of diagnosis and treatment can completely prevent seizures in some cases and reduce them in others. The epileptic child has learned to recognize the sensations which precede a convulsion. He should be allowed to leave the classroom without asking permission, in order that he may go to a safe and quiet place before the seizure begins.

Most epileptic children do well on a program of regular physical activity, and little if any modification of the school program is required. The attending physician will prescribe needed limitations in the physical or academic program of the child, who may also need special attention against accident hazards.

There is a less serious form of epilepsy (petit mal) in which convulsions do not occur. The child has frequent temporary pauses in conversation, movement, or mental activity, with apparently complete absent-mindedness for a few seconds. The condition is not serious, and tends to disappear after adolescence.

Psychomotor epilepsy is a third type. It is characterized by trancelike states, hallucinations, and compulsive and violent behavior. This type does not commonly occur in children.

Problems arising from left-handedness

Left-handedness is a natural condition, not a departure from health. However, emotional and other problems, such as difficulties in speech, in reading, and in writing, arise when the school fails to accept it as such and tries to make a right-handed child out of a left-handed one. No one tries to make a "right-hander" out of a "southpaw" pitcher. The left-handed pupil requires special consideration in lighting, seating, laboratory equipment, and in learning to write.

References

American Heart Association, Inc., will send publications dealing with cardiac defects, 44 East 23rd Street, New York 10, N. Y.

American Dental Association, Council on Dental Health: *Dental Caries: Prevention and Control*, Chicago, 1960, the Association, 11 pp.

Anderson, C. L.: *School Health Practice*, ed. 3, St. Louis, 1964, The C. V. Mosby Company.

Bunting, Russell W.: *Oral Hygiene and Preventive Dentistry*, Philadelphia, 1950, Lea & Febiger.

Byrd, O. E.: *School Health Administration*, Philadelphia, 1964, W. B. Saunders Company.

Lippman, H. S.: *Treatment of the Child in Emotional Conflict*, ed. 2, New York, 1962, McGraw-Hill Book Company, Inc.

Martin, E. A.: *Nutrition in Action;* also, *Nutrition Education in Action*, (A Guide for Teachers), New York, 1963, Holt, Rinehart and Winston.

National Education Association and American Medical Association Joint Committee: *School Health Services*, ed. 2, Washington, D. C., and Chicago, 1964, NEA and AMA.

Nemir, A.: *The School Health Program*, ed. 2, Philadelphia, 1965, W. B. Saunders Company.

U. S. Department of Health, Education, and Welfare: *Health of Children of School*

Age, Children's Bureau Publication no. 427, 1964. Reprinted 1965, for sale by the U. S. Government Printing Office, Washington, D. C., 20402, 32 pp. Price 25 cents.

Wheatley, G. M., and Hallock, G. T.: *Health Observation of School Children,* ed. 3, New York, 1965, McGraw-Hill Book Company, Inc.

Chapter *vi*

Interpersonal relations and mental health

The element of healthful school living which is most directly in the hands of the teacher is the maintenance and promotion of mental health through his day-by-day interpersonal relations with his pupils.

Mental health is determined by the way a child feels about himself, by the way he feels toward others, and by the way he is able to face and adjust to day-by-day conditions of living. The teacher has an opportunity, second only to that of parents, to help children accept themselves, learn to get along happily and successfully with others, and make wholesome adjustments to living. He is concerned with helping all children attain mental health, so that they may develop into mature, responsible, well-adjusted adults.

The teacher has both a positive and a preventive role in mental health. He pays careful attention to the promotion of positive mental health by providing the kind of environment at school in which children may grow and develop normally. He makes possible the kind of learning experiences by which wholesome attitudes and behavior patterns are formed. He is concerned also with discovering and preventing the further development of minor disorders and with referring for psychiatric services those children with serious emotional disturbances.

Teacher-pupil relations

Educators in one state (Kansas) have indicated desirable teacher-pupil relationships in terms of the following advice[1] to the teacher.

1. *Have genuine interest in children.* Love children and show a real and intelligent affection for each of them. Understand the characteristics of children at various levels of development. Seek to know their individual interests, potentialities, and problems.

2. *Respect personality.* Teach the child, not the subject matter. Realize that each child is a different person. Have respect for the dignity of the individual, show respect for the child at all times in his thinking, actions, etc. A spirit of toleration should pervade the schoolroom. Intolerance on the part of either teacher or pupils often causes damaging stresses and strains.

---

[1]From "Health Education in Elementary and Secondary Schools," issued jointly by the State Department of Public Instruction and the State Board of Health of Kansas.

Fig. 21. Mental health.

3. *Strive to give each child a feeling of security, of belonging, and of being of value to his group.* The child must have a feeling of security and affection. The child's need for recognition and approval must be recognized. He must feel he is wanted in the group. The teacher should make it possible for every child to have the thrill and exhilaration of accomplishment. Teacher-pupil planning is essential. Help given when needed is important. The teacher should help the child to understand his limitations and potentialities and to take them into account in laying his plans. A distinction should be made between constructive planning and worry. The former is stimulating; the latter nerve-wrecking and destructive. The teacher should give the child opportunities to assume partial responsibility for his actions, as much as he can assume successfully. The teacher should not break the spirit of the child by demanding of him things he cannot do.

4. *Have a sense of humor, so children will be happy and live in an atmosphere of happiness.* Laugh with the children, not at them. The teacher should not indulge in sarcasm and sharp-tongued procedure. He should not maintain a "sour-puss" atmosphere but should strive to create an environment of happy industry.

5. *Be impartial in relations with all pupils.* An impersonal and objective attitude, as well as a constructive attitude toward offenses, should be shown. The teacher should give the child an opportunity to profit from his mistakes. The teacher should give social approval when approval is merited.

Characteristics of good mental health

The development and maintenance of the teacher's own mental health is important to him. Moreover, good mental health is contagious. An excellent statement of mental health in positive terms mentions the following characteristics:[2]

[2]Peck, Robert F., and Mitchell, James V., Jr.: *Mental Health*, Washington, D. C., 1962, Dept. of Classroom Teachers, Amer. Ed. Res. Assn. of the National Education Association, 33 pp., price 20 cents.

1. *Objective judgment:* the ability to look at all kinds of facts squarely and accurately, neither overlooking some nor exaggerating others. This ability is also called rationality, good sense, and even common sense.

2. *Autonomy:* the ability to deal with daily events in a self-starting, self-directing manner. Such terms as initiative, self-direction, and emotional independence are often used to convey this idea.

3. *Emotional maturity:* the ability to react to events with emotions which are appropriate in kind and in degree to the objective nature of the situation.

4. *Self-realizing drive:* the habit of working hard and purposefully to one's full capacity. People vary greatly in their physical, intellectual, and social potentialities, but it is possible to see in each case how far the given individual is putting his own particular potentialities to work to achieve personally worthwhile results. His powers, of course, are delimited by the stage of his development. They are shaped by the opportunities he has had as well as by his innate potentialities.

5. *Self-acceptance:* a positive, self-respecting attitude toward one's self. Conscious self-insight or self-understanding may not be absolutely essential to an attitude of self-acceptance, but either seems to enhance considerably the objectivity and the wisdom of a person's self-regard.

6. *Respect for others:* a positive, acceptant attitude toward other people.

It is often difficult to tell how well adjusted a child is; but there are some significant signs. Some specific indications are these: (1) the well-adjusted child knows how to play and work with others so successfully and satisfactorily that he is acceptable to them as a companion and co-worker; (2) he is able to accept himself and the conditions of his life with fairly persistent satisfaction; (3) he faces the problems that confront him day by day without evasive or compensatory reactions; (4) he absorbs or masters the inevitable conflicts, frustrations, disappointments, and temporary defeats without undue emotional turmoil; (5) he contributes in a spirit of cooperation and good will to the necessary activities of his group; (6) he has wide interests, attacks his work with zest, and gets satisfaction out of doing it. (See also page 48.)

The incidence of mental disorders

It has been reliably estimated that approximately one person in ten in the United States suffers from mental illness of varying degrees of severity. During World War II more than one-third of the rejections (men 18 to 37 years of age) were on neuropsychiatric grounds. More than half a million patients are now receiving psychiatric care in federal and state hospitals. This does not take into account those receiving psychiatric treatment in private hospitals. In 1963 new patients admitted to state and county mental hospital were 285,244 in number.[3]

In addition to those who are so seriously ill that they must be hospitalized, there are many persons in our population whose emotional and personality disorders undoubtedly underlie their social maladjustments. Some of these are found among juvenile delinquents, criminals, suicides, and chronic alcoholics. Many others, while apparently making a satisfactory

---

[3]National Institutes of Mental Health: "Mental Health Statistics, Current Reports," Bethesda, Maryland, January, 1964.

Fig. 22. The promotion of mental health is always a school consideration. It involves happy, interpersonal relationships.

social adjustment, are emotionally unstable, find it difficult to get along with others, and live in a state of anxiety and unhappiness.

Virtually all of these—the mentally ill, the socially inadequate, and the chronically unhappy—have been pupils in our schools. Many of them were manifesting danger signals, even in their early years. The schools have frequently failed to recognize these early signs of maladjustment and may have actually contributed to the further development of the condition.

A sensitive teacher with insight and understanding can detect maladjustments when they may be corrected most easily and inexpensively. A small cavity in a tooth may be filled with little pain and expense; if it is not discovered in its early stages, extensive damage may be done and repair becomes difficult. Likewise, a mild emotional disturbance may often be easily dealt with by the classroom teacher; if undetected in its early stages, it may become a fixed behavior pattern requiring long, expensive psychiatric treatment. If neglected, it may develop into mental illness requiring hospitalization, or into other serious social problems with ever-increasing cost to the individual and to society. Most important is the preventive care which keeps the problem from developing in the first place. This is the greatest challenge to the classroom teacher.

Mental health related to learning

The mental health of a child is closely related to the learning process. Fear, insecurity, and feelings of inadequacy are conducive to failure, while self-esteem and self-confidence facilitate learning. How a child learns is important. In fact, *how* he learns frequently determines *how much* he learns. Experimental and clinical evidence shows that children learn better and learn more under conditions fostering mental health. A happy, healthy child is in a condition to profit most from what the school has to offer.

The close relationship between physical health and mental health is sometimes overlooked. The tired, chronically fatigued, or malnourished child is a poor subject for education. He tends to be irritable and unreasonable, or lethargic and withdrawn. His attention span is short. Reading and language difficulties, which so often result in emotional problems, are not infrequently due to physical disabilities of vision, hearing, or even neurological disorders. The first step in considering the problem of a child with a learning difficulty or an emotional disturbance is a complete physical examination followed by appropriate health guidance.

The teacher seeks, through the influence and activities of the school, to develop courtesy, orderliness, friendliness, truthfulness, promptness, cheerfulness, unselfishness, emotional control, honesty, a sense of humor, the ability to meet disappointment bravely and to remain cool and good-natured under trying circumstances, the enjoyment of work, and the power to continue a task until it is successfuly completed.

The development of this last-mentioned characteristic, persistence, is particularly important. It would seem that no other mental characteristic is so valuable as native intelligence, and yet someone has said that success in life for people of normal mentality depends more commonly upon mental stamina than upon the basic quality of the mind. The gradual development of the power to attack a problem and persist until it is solved is perhaps one of the most important characteristics the school can help the child to acquire.

The teacher is concerned with developing such specific characteristics as: kindliness toward younger children and toward animals; the habit of cooperation at home and at school; fair play; a keen interest in games, hobbies, and the world about him; willingness to share his possessions, but respect for the property rights of other children; the ability to forget a grudge; group participation; and willingness to obey the rules of the group.

The background of behavior

Children come to school with attitudes and behavior patterns which have been determined by their previous experiences. Involved in molding each child's personality have been the kind of home and community in which he has lived, the family circle, the cultural background, religious beliefs, economic and social status, his physical condition, and his peer groups.

In our schools there are normal, cheerful, successful, lovable children and also no less lovable children who need a little more help. There are hurt and nervous children from homes broken by divorce and from homes in which there have been tension and unhappiness. There are lonely children whose parents feel that they are too busy or too tired to spend much time with them. There are children loaded with cares and demands beyond their years because of economic pressures. There are unsettled children constantly on the move and living in trailer camps. There are frustrated children who play in crowded city streets. Some are undisciplined, others are overcontrolled and overprotected. The twentieth century with its wars, atom bombs, air transportation, mass media of communication, and urbanization has brought new speed and tension into living. Its unsettled and overcrowded conditions, its anxieties, and its fears are often reflected in the lives of children. They are the products of their environment and experiences as well as their heredity.

Fundamental needs of the child

Just as a child has basic organic needs for living and growing, so does he also have fundamental needs for developing and maturing emotionally. Among the most significant of these are the needs for (1) love and affection, (2) security, (3) acceptance and belonging, (4) successful achievement, (5) recognition and status, (6) friends and companions, (7) varied and interesting outlets for his energies in work and play.

A child needs to feel first the certainty of his parents' love. There is no substitute for this. He needs to know that he is wanted and that there are people near him who care what happens to him. In school he wants to feel that the teacher and the other pupils like him. Knowing that he is loved and wanted enables him, in turn, to express love and affection for others.

Security comes from being loved and accepted; but mere loving by the teacher may not provide it. The child may have been disappointed by people and have developed defences against being loved. We must also help him develop security by building *adequacy* in the area of academic achievement and in the area of effective human relations.

Feelings of security strengthen the child's ability to meet the situations and problems with which he is confronted. Feelings of insecurity tend to generate fear, tension, and anxiety. A child develops feelings of one kind or the other, day by day, through the experiences he is having at home, at school, and at play. Through experiencing love, success, and belonging, at home and at school, he gradually develops an inner security that enables him to cope with new situations and problems. He needs to feel that he, himself, is accepted at home and at school, although what he does may not always be approved.

No child can stand to be ignored. He wants to be "in" the groups of which he is a part. He must find a place where he fits in. He needs recognition and position.

Both young and old have a desire to be recognized as worthy, to be respected and admired, and to have recognition for successful achievement. A child is happiest when he feels the approbation of the adults in his world and the approval of his peer group. Every child needs to experience a certain amount of success in areas which, to him, are important.

Feelings of competence build self-confidence. Success in his undertakings encourages the child to try new tasks; thus he gains strength from success. Failure often disheartens him and discourages effort. Every child needs to succeed at something. He needs to feel that he can do some or perhaps many things as well as most of his peers.

Man is essentially gregarious. The desire for companionship is a strong motivation to conduct. By the end of the primary period, a child usually has a "best friend." Group membership becomes important to him during the intermediate years. In the preadolescent and adolescent years, his desire for belonging and acceptance by a peer group often becomes the controlling influence in his life. He needs to learn how to get along with others.

A child needs activity. An infant needs opportunities to move about. The young child needs to learn about his world by seeing and doing things. He needs safe ways to let off steam, to reduce the pressures inside. As he gets older, games, sports, athletics, and creative activities, such as art, music, rhythms, and dramatics, offer wholesome outlets for his abundant energy. Each child should have a chance to find satisfaction in active play and creative work.

While the fundamental emotional needs are similar at all age levels, the ways in which they may be satisfied change with the maturity level of the individual. An infant first feels the warm, supporting love of his mother; this is gradually extended to include his family circle. As the child enters school, this need for acceptance and affection widens to encompass his teacher and classmates. In adolescence and young adulthood, as the desire to marry and establish a home emerges, the love of one person becomes of paramount importance. After marriage, the love of his mate and children help fill this need. As the child matures into manhood, however, the continuing love of those who have been important to him in his growth and development strengthens and supports his emotional stability.

Both overgratification and the deprivation or frustration of these fundamental needs create behavior problems. A child who receives too much recognition may become self-centered and egotistical. A child who is denied recognition may become discouraged and develop feelings of inferiority. A child who is adored and overprotected may become spoiled and have difficulty in getting along with other people, while a child who is deprived of love and affection may feel unwanted, lonely, defensive, and unhappy. A child who has all of his wants supplied by his family may not be able to cope with his world outside the home when his wants are not catered to. A migratory child who has few of the material things he desires may feel insecure and rejected.

The artistry as well as the science of teaching is reflected in the teacher's ability to understand children, to discover each child's emotional needs, and to help fulfill these needs in the right amounts at the right time. Thus a teacher helps a child to grow and to achieve emotional maturity.

Conditions contributing to mental health in the classroom

The teacher's attitude toward his work, the way he feels about children, and his professional competence are reflected in the atmosphere of his classroom. If he cares about children—the dirty, the poor, the dull, as well as their opposites—he will find ways for this concern to shine through. If he has the insight and understanding to see their potentialities, they will feel his interest. If he is emotionally secure so that his own problems are not projected on the children, he will be able to help them grow toward emotional maturity. Children know when a teacher is interested in them and when he has faith and trust in them. In living and working with children the teacher nurtures sound mental health in many different ways, some of which are quite indirect.

Of first importance is a warm, friendly classroom environment wherein children can learn and grow, "belong," and succeed. The teacher can make

Fig. 23. This aquarium helps to make the classroom a more interesting place.

his classroom a place of life and color with such things as an aquarium or terrarium, a pet, potted plants, flowers on his desk, gay bulletin boards, or a bright print. Something the children have made or brought to school, a mural, a collection of sea shells, or a cocoon to watch, lends interest to the room. A science corner, a reading table with brightly colored books, an informal arrangement of the furniture tend to make the classroom more homelike and the atmosphere more relaxed.

The teacher can help the children to feel his friendliness and interest in them in many small but important ways. The way he smiles each morning as he greets each one individually by name, the tone of his voice, and the way he occasionally pats a child on the back, puts his arm gently around his shoulders, or sits beside him builds friendship. The teacher can show his interest in pupils by finding something personal to say to each about a new dress, a new necktie, hair neatly combed, new shoes, a new baby brother, a pair of new glasses, a recent trip, or a special honor. He can show that he likes the things they like by going after school to see the new puppies or the new airplane model.

The teacher can show that he is interested in the personal life of the children by talking to them about things that interest them. He can indicate his interest in an absent pupil by sending him an attractive get-well card, by calling his home to inquire about him, or by having the class remember him in some way if his absence is extended. When the pupil returns, the teacher can welcome him back and tell him that he was missed.

The teacher can share himself with his pupils by telling them things that happen to him outside of school. He can tell about his hobbies, pets, and funny little experiences. As teacher and children laugh, play, and work together, they enjoy each other and become closer friends.

The shy, timid, or withdrawn child is the one who most needs the satisfying feeling of "belonging." This can be achieved in such ways as giving him important duties to perform for the teacher, helping him to join in games and parties, and drawing him into the planning and par-ticipation of various class activities. By helping him to acquire a skill that children appreciate, he may be brought into that magic circle of those who are liked and accepted. Friendship with a popular child may draw him in. The teacher may be able to cultivate such a relationship by seating him by a popular and friendly child, giving them jobs to do together, or seeing that they get on the same committee or team.

A stimulating and creative school program with the kind of activities in which children plan and work together will provide a sound basis for developing mental health. Children learn and work hard at jobs that have meaning to them. The demands should not be above the level of develop-mental tasks for which they are ready. By means of flexible standards and differential assignments each child can be led to experience success within his own limits.

Honest praise for real accomplishment makes a child feel good within himself and encourages efforts to be successful. Recognition of achievement gives a child a feeling of satisfaction for his efforts. Emphasis placed upon participation, for its own sake and for the fun derived from it, rather than upon winning helps a child develop worthwhile values. He needs, however, to learn desirable ways of competing, and to accept losing and disappointment. He cannot always have his way and always win. Losing is no disgrace if he has done his best.

There are times when it is wise to pass over many of the things boys and girls do, without correcting or nagging them. We can help them far more by trying to understand why they are acting as they do and setting right the cause of the undesirable behavior. A child needs to understand that everybody makes mistakes, and that we try to correct our mistakes, but that we must not worry too much about them. An understanding friend is a source of help in time of trouble, not one who criticizes and blames. Strang,[4] however, points out that:

> . . . most psychiatrists agree that there comes a time when the child must learn that certain behavior is not socially acceptable and that he cannot always have what he wants when he wants it. Some frustration is an inevitable part of life. Normal children need to learn to tolerate and handle a reasonable amount of inescapable frustration. In a culture demanding inhibitions, an individual who acts solely on his impulses often hurts himself and other people. Mild frustrations, obstacles on the paths to a goal, call forth learning. Mild frustrations which youngsters can surmount with reasonable effort are emotionally strengthening. However, serious frustrations which confront any individual with repeated failure are disintegrating.

A child must also learn to handle the various feelings inside him, such as fear, anger, and jealousy, in ways that will not hurt him or others. If these feelings are repressed and not allowed to come out, they build up until they are beyond control. They are likely to make the child act in socially unacceptable ways. Through the school program, opportunities can be provided to help children bring their troubled feelings to light and get rid of their tensions and worries through safe pathways of action. Stories or films about the way other children feel offer opportunities for them to tell about ways they feel. The open-end story, which presents a situation and stops when the problem has been stated, can be followed, by older pupils, with a discussion of what would have been the best solution. It can present a common type of problem in an impersonal way. Children can express their feelings through role playing, writing, and art work in safe and acceptable ways. Games, sports and athletics provide wholesome emotional outlets for pent-up energy and teach the principles of sportsmanship. When a child misbehaves, he needs to see that it is not himself but his behavior that is not acceptable.

Identifying the disturbed child

Behavior disturbances occur in children of all ages and from many causes. Normally they are transient and their occurrence need not be

---

[4]Strang, Ruth: "Many-Sided Aspects of Mental Health," *Mental Health in Modern Education*, Fifty-Fourth Yearbook of the National Society for the Study of Education, Part I, Chicago, 1955, University of Chicago Press, p. 36.

interpreted as indicative of deep-seated or permanent maladjustment. Many parents and teachers are unnecessarily alarmed over behavior in their children which is really quite normal for the child's stage of development. Symptomless children are very rare, perhaps nonexistent. As Rivlin[5] has pointed out:

He (the teacher) may either read far more significance into a child's action than is warranted or he may fail to recognize symptoms of serious impending difficulties.

If the teacher is to go to either of these two extremes, it is better for him to overlook some instances of maladjustment than to overestimate the seriousness of insignificant behavior problems or to attempt diagnosis and therapy he is not qualified to conduct. With emotional problems, as with physical ones, one must not underestimate the child's ability to cure himself. Just as the body can correct many of its own ills so can the child's emotional organization adjust itself to minor or temporary strains . . . In his legitimate concern for the present and the future adjustment of today's child population, the teacher must be careful not to exaggerate the importance of minor deviations from perfect adjustment.

Early detection of emotional disorders is of paramount importance. Frequently the parents, because of their close day-by-day contact and emotional attachment to the child, may not observe the gradual deterioration in his adjustment. Actually, they may be part of the difficulty. The teacher, therefore, may be the first to observe the child's deviation from normal behavior. The teacher notes, especially, children who exhibit extreme aggressiveness, antisocial behavior, shyness and withdrawal tendencies, or discrepancy between ability and school achievement.

Sudden changes in attitudes, behavior, or scholarship and marked deviation in behavior from that of other children or from his usual self should alert a teacher that a child is disturbed. Undesirable behavior and unhappy feelings are generally evidence of inner turmoil. School behavior is also a revealing index of adjustment to other situations as well.

Teachers need to have an understanding of the significance of the signs of undesirable behavior and the degree of seriousness of a child's problem. The attitudes and behavior which he is exhibiting are his way of adjusting to his life situation. The standards of behavior held by other adults in his environment may vary decidedly from the standards of behavior held by the teacher. Mores of families and communities vary greatly. Therefore, teacher judgments of the child must be related to his cultural and family background and to his total personality.

Fenton[6] has classified the behavior problems of children roughly under three levels of seriousness:

On the first level are the types of problems to which all children fall heir, problems so common that the average child manifests several of them. Nervous habits, fears,

---

[5]Rivlin, Harry N.: "The Role of Mental Health in Education," *Mental Health in Modern Education,* Fifty-Fourth Yearbook of the National Society for the Study of Education, Part II, Chicago, 1955, University of Chicago Press, pp. 22-23.

[6]Reprinted from *Mental Hygiene in School Practice,* by Norman Fenton, with the permission of the author and of the publishers, Stanford University Press. Copyright by the Board of Trustees of Leland Stanford Junior University, pp. 159-160.

temper tantrums, overactivity, faulty eating habits, nail biting, sensitiveness, bashfulness, tics, and enuresis are examples. The problems of the second level are more serious in their personal or social consequences. They include reading retardation, speech defect, repeated truancy, marked seclusiveness, and other evidences of maladjustment. The third level includes problems of children who are acutely disturbed or otherwise seriously handicapped personally. . . . These include a variety of difficulties, of which some, like dangerous aggressiveness or destructiveness, juvenile delinquency, emotional instability, and actual mental or nervous illness, need to be studied and treated for the protection of society as well as for the welfare of the individual.

There is always a reason if a child causes trouble. He is seeking to satisfy his fundamental emotional needs in ways that bring satisfaction to him. The teacher must, therefore, search for these needs which are being unmet in the child's life. However, he needs to be aware that child behavior is most complex and that, in the more serious situations, psychiatric consultation and guidance may be necessary in coming to an understanding of the child's problem. On the physical side, what seem to be the symptoms of a beginning cold may be the initial stages of measles or whooping cough. Similarly, identical forms of overt behavior may arise from widely different underlying causes. For example, hostility in a child may be due to feeling either unwanted, unloved, or inadequate.

Conversely, a single unmet emotional need may be expressed by a variety of forms of behavior. Different children may react to a single cause, such as lack of love and affection, in various ways—by withdrawal, by aggressiveness, by thumb sucking or by stealing. One adolescent who fails in his class work may be nonchalant and quit trying, while another may be deeply hurt, grow tense and worried. A third may make the effort to discover and remedy the cause. When fundamental needs are not met specific symptoms may disappear, only to reappear in other forms. A child may stop stealing, only to run away from home. Since a behavior pattern is not caused by a single factor but by many interrelated factors that have occurred in the life experience of the child, it may be helpful to the teacher to ask such questions as (1) why does the child behave in this manner, (2) what satisfaction does his behavior tend to secure for him, (3) in what ways is his life unsatisfactory to him, (4) why has he become the type of individual he is, (5) what combinations of circumstances have caused this particular reaction, and (6) what will help him to adjust?

Techniques for learning more about children

There are many opportunities within the school day and in his contacts with parents when a busy teacher has opportunities to study an unadjusted child's behavior. Four approaches which have proved helpful in understanding a child are mentioned here:

1. *Observation.* As a teacher "learns to listen more and talk less," and watch a child's behavior at work and at play, he learns how situations look to the child and what his behavior means. It is important for the teacher to record what he sees and hears at the time an event occurs, to determine the significance of his observations, and to discover patterns

of relationship and change which are revealed. Such anecdotal records may serve as a conference tool both with the child and with the parents.

2. *Informal contacts, conferences, and interviews.* An informal talk with a child helps a teacher to see how things look to him. It is important to carry on conversations with children whenever possible—before school, at recess, at lunch time, after school. Informal conversations with parents over the telephone, upon incidental meetings, both in the community and at school, may give important clues to a child's behavior. Parents may be encouraged to come to school for conferences. Some school systems now have periodic conferences with parents instead of sending out report cards in the earlier grades. At such times teachers may ask specific questions which will assist in understanding the child.

3. *Sociometry.* This is a device for the study of social acceptance and relationships between children within the classroom. Children are asked to nominate other children for associates in various situations, such as seating arrangements, committees, attendance at a movie, or for a party. Only positive items should be used. The results will indicate children at the extremes of acceptance and nonacceptance, and the subgroups within the total group. It is very common practice to place the details on a sociogram, in order to view the relationships within a class in graphic form. Informal contacts and interviews can be used to follow up the sociogram and help a teacher understand its significance. Steps can then be taken to improve the social structure of a group.

Teachers need adequate preparation in using and following up information acquired in this way. A number of manuals are now available which will be of assistance to teachers.

4. *Projective techniques.* In projective tests there are no right or wrong answers. They help to give an insight into child behavior by the responses which are given to standard materials. The Rorschach test, the Thematic Apperception Test, based upon responses to pictures, and forms of the sentence-completion test are widely used. Olson and Wattenberg[7] state:

> Because of the sophistication needed to understand and interpret most projective tests, their use by classroom teachers is not generally advocated. On the other hand, the principles involved are of general usefulness and applicable to much of a child's production in the classroom. For example, a child's choice of what to do in a non-directed period in a classroom tells a teacher something about him. Thus, a child's selection of colors and theme in painting or drawing with a possible running, soliloquy gives insight into a thought and feeling process. Some supplementary interrogation may add additional facts. Children, while writing stories in the classroom, have told much of themselves and of their perception of the world, of the family, of the classroom, and of the teacher.

---

[7] Olson, Willard C., and Wattenberg, William W.: "The Role of the School in Mental Health," *Mental Health in Modern Education*, Fifty-Fourth Yearbook of the National Society for the Study of Education, Part II, Chicago, 1955, University of Chicago Press, p. 112.

Sources of help

There are some children having deeply rooted emotional problems with whom the classroom teacher needs help. He frequently does not have the time or the facilities nor does he have the technical skills for making a thorough study of the problems of such children. In such cases, there are other members of the professional team, of which he is a very important member, upon whom he can call. The members of this team may include such specialists as the guidance counselor, the physician, the nurse, the visiting teacher or social worker, the school psychologist, and/or the staff of a child guidance clinic—the psychiatrist, clinical psychologist, and psychiatric social worker.

The personnel and services available will vary with the locality. There is, however, no substitute for an adequately staffed *child guidance clinic* for dealing with serious emotional problems. It often takes a prolonged period of time to study a child's background, determine his assets and liabilities, analyze his difficulties, arrive at a tentative diagnosis, evolve a tentative plan of treatment, try out the treatment, evaluate the results, and replan in light of the results obtained. Emotional difficulties which have evolved over a period of years cannot be corrected in a few weeks. The teacher has a valuable contribution to make to such work in recognizing the types of problems which should be referred to a child guidance clinic, in helping the staff to gain insight into the child's problems, and in assisting with therapeutic measures. In turn, the child guidance clinic may help the teacher to understand the child better and to deal with him more effectively.

It must be recognized that, even with an understanding, highly competent teacher and the aid of skilled professional staff, some pupils are so deeply disturbed that they should not remain in a regular classroom. Educators face an increasingly difficult problem in meeting both the educational and mental health needs of the seriously disturbed pupils who, in spite of every effort on the part of the schools, fail to make a satisfactory adjustment.

Compulsory education is practically universal in the United States and in most areas is vigorously enforced. Furthermore, most parents strenuously resist any attempt by the schools to exclude the socially maladjusted, emotionally distburbed, or recalcitrant child. Educators, on their part, often have feelings of failure and guilt when unable to cope with the disturbed child and help him to adjust. This has placed an exceptionally heavy burden on many classroom teachers and school administrators.

There is also a tendency on the part of parents to hold the schools responsible if the child is uncontrollable at school or failing in his school work. This lack of understanding on the part of some parents and their unwillingness to face up to the problems being created by their undisciplined or actually disturbed child frequently present real difficulties. Some school districts are adopting or experimenting with various measures for helping these disturbed children and at the same time relieving the teacher and the other pupils in the classroom of an intolerable situation. To this end they have established special rooms for emotionally disturbed pupils, in the charge of master teachers, with a norm of 8 or 10 pupils per teacher.

This special placement frequently jolts the parents into recognizing that their child has a serious problem in which they are involved. Pupils assigned to these classes are given as complete a diagnostic study as the facilities of the community and the resources of the parents can provide. In some districts twenty-four-hour schools with separation from the parents have been found to be the best answer in meeting the emotional and educational problem of the seriously disturbed school child who, in spite of every effort on his behalf, cannot adjust to a regular school situation.

References

Association for Supervision and Curriculum Development: *Fostering Mental Health in Our Schools,* 1950 Yearbook, Washington, D. C., 1950, National Education Association.

Beers, Clifford W.: *A Mind That Found Itself,* New York, 1953 ed., Doubleday & Company, Inc. (The fascinating autobiography of the founder of the modern mental-hygiene movement.)

Bernard, H. W.: *Mental Hygiene for Classroom Teachers,* New York, 1953, McGraw-Hill Book Company.

Bullis, Harold E., O'Malley, Emily E., and Jastak, Joseph: *Human Relations in the Classroom: Kindergarten—Twelfth Grade,* Wilmington, Delaware, 1947, Delaware State Society for Mental Hygiene.

Fenton, Norman: *Mental Hygiene in School Practice,* Stanford, California, 1943, Stanford University Press.

Havinghurst, R. J.: *Developmental Tasks and Education,* New York, 1952, Longmans, Green & Company

Joint Commission on Mental Illness and Health of the National Institute of Mental Health: *The Role of Schools in Mental Health,* a report by Wesley Ali Smith and George W. Goethols, New York, 1962, Basic Books, Inc.

Joint Committee on Health Problems in Education of the National Education Association and the American Medical Association, with the cooperation of the National Committee for Mental Hylgiene, Inc., and the American Orthopsychiatric Association, Inc.: *Mental Hygiene in the Classroom,* Chicago, 1950, American Medical Association, 71 pp., 15 cents.

Moak, Helen: *The Troubled Child,* New York, 1958, Holt, Rinehart and Winston, Inc.

National Association for Mental Health, 1790 Broadway, New York 19, N. Y., will supply lists of references and pamphlets.

National Society for the Study of Education: *Mental Health in Modern Education,* edited by Nelson B. Henry, Fifty-Fourth Yearbook, Chicago, 1955, University of Chicago Press.

Peck, Robert F., and Mitchell, V., Jr.: *Mental Health,* Washington, D. C., 1962, Department of Classroom Teachers, American Educational Research Association of National Education Association.

Redl, F., and Wattenberg, W. W.: *Mental Hygiene in Teaching,* ed. 2, New York, 1959, Harcourt, Brace and Company.

Wickman, E. K.: *Teachers and Behavior Problems,* New York, 1955, The National Association for Mental Health, 40 pp.

World Federation for Mental Health (Funkenstein, Daniel A., et al., editors): *The Student and Mental Health,* Cambridge. Mass., 1959, The Riverside Press.

Chapter vii

Health promotion and health education through a hygienic school program

Both health and health education can be promoted through organizing a healthful school day for the child. The pressures of school work are increasing as the knowledge explosion adds to the amount of information which society desires the school to give its children. Emotional and physical health will help the child to carry the load. A healthful school schedule is produced by the establishment of sound administrative policies and through the wise conduct of classroom activities by the teaching staff. Let us look at the factors involved and the possibilities available in giving to the pupil's school day the greatest possible healthfulness. We will be concerned with the health aspects of program arrangement, the physical activity program, various routine procedures, and the methods of conducting many academic activities.

Health aspects of administrative policies

The well-balanced day for young children demands a balance of activity and rest, opportunity for vigorous physical play, preferably out-of-doors, a hot, well-balanced lunch, and a scientifically planned and skillfully directed program of learning based on firsthand experience within their interests and abilities.

The *length of the school day* is adjusted to the age of the child. Providing a school day that is long enough for some children and not too long for others presents problems. At any age level, the school day should be made as short as is consistent with adequate instruction. Some authorities recommend a single session for kindergarten and Grade I. The practice of holding afternoon kindergarten is especially detrimental to the health of many children of this age, as the afternoon nap is prematurely abolished.

The practical difficulty of dismissing children early in the lower grades must be recognized and met. Unless younger children can safely go home unattended by older pupils or parents, supervision must be provided during the interval until all are dismissed.

In this country, *homework* is rarely assigned in the first three grades.

Suggestions for sharing school experiences with the family are sometimes made. However, the sharing should not be a task to be done but a pleasure to be enjoyed. As the pupil grows older, there is increasing value in the development of self-direction and responsibility for independent study; but assignments, when given, should be clear and not so long as to interfere with health.

Suggestions regarding homework will often help the student to avoid ineffective study and unwholesome health habits which may result from such conditions as: (1) poor lighting, heating, and ventilation; (2) unsuitable study table and chair, leading to bad posture; (3) frequent interruptions; (4) lack of reference materials; (5) lack of an organized plan for study at home; (6) too much time given to radio and television, with resulting procrastination and late hours for study; (7) unsuitable location for study; (8) lack of needed guidance and supervision.

The student who has returned to school after an absence due to illness should not have his daily schedule overloaded with make-up work. Ample time is allowed for such make-up work in recognition of the student's impaired health condition. At no grade level is excessive pressure put on the slow-learning child to keep pace with his mentally more capable classmates. Such pressure imperils both the physical and the emotional well-being of the pupil.

After-school activities are considered when teachers work with individual children. The child is nervously tired at the end of the school day. He needs activities which are recreative and different from his school program. He needs time and suitable space and equipment for play. Home duties and responsibilities are satisfying and educationally desirable. They are encouraged and not disparaged. Evening functions during the school week are commonly discouraged by the school authorities even at the secondary school level.

A good principle to follow is that the *arrangement of school work* should provide variety of activity to relieve physical tension and mental boredom. Similar subjects, such as reading and literature or writing and drawing, are not placed in direct sequence. Physical education is preferably not scheduled just before or just after lunch or just preceding or just following a recess. Writing or drawing, with their requirements for delicate muscular control, are not scheduled immediately after a recess period.

The *number of subject areas* per day is adapted to the age of the pupil. Traditionally, American schools have probably given too many different subjects. An effort to adjust this difficulty is seen in the use of long teaching units and in the more effective integration of learning experiences.

Time is provided for short, snappy *drill* periods as needed in appropriate subjects. Time used to *evaluate* what has been done, what needs to be done, and how to improve the doing is well spent in the feeling of self-direction and satisfaction aroused in the pupil. Time is allowed for pupil-teacher, teacher-nurse, and teacher-parent *conferences*.

In high school *adequate time* is allotted *between classes* for students to

(E. Galloway)

Fig. 24. Fruit, not candy, at school provides a nutritious snack.

go from one class to another. Time is needed during the day for *social contacts* between secondary school boys and girls. Time is allowed for proper *toilet habits.*

Special *adaptation of the school program* is made for under-par and handicapped children. Adjustments in seating, lighting, activity, or rest are made in the class for children with visual, auditory, cardiac, or orthopedic defects.

There are both health implications and practical difficulties in the *grouping of pupils* on the basis of their learning ability. The child who is superior in mathematics may be very poor in English and music or in physical activities. The children in the top 10 per cent of the group with respect to mental ability are likely to develop feelings of superiority or to become lazy or restless when the assigned tasks are too easy and when they find themselves in a group of children, many of whom can master these apparently simple tasks only with a great expenditure of time and effort. Contrariwise, the slowest children need a separate grouping if they are to make the progress of which they are capable without discouragement, loss of interest, and feelings of inferiority. When the size of the school permits, it seems desirable from the standpoint of mental and emotional health, as well as from the standpoint of general education, to group children on the basis of learning capacities.

Class periods, or periods of concentrated class attention, vary in length depending upon the age of the pupils, the character of the class activity and the emotional stability of the class. For a 6-year-old engaged in close intensive work a ten-to-fifteen-minute period should be the maximum. If the work is less concentrated a longer period is possible. An increase of a few minutes in each grade thereafter is made for average children. Where freedom to move about is allowed, there is less likelihood that children will suffer from stress. It is commonly recommended that recitation periods should not exceed thirty-five minutes in Grades V and VI, and forty-five to fifty minutes above this grade level.

One hundred per cent *attendance* at school has been unduly emphasized. Remuneration from state funds on the basis of average daily attendance is responsible in part for this. Some states, recognizing the hazards to health in pressuring children to attend school while ill, have ruled that absence due to illness shall not be regarded as absence in computing average daily attendance. When a child is ill, he should be kept at home, or be sent home if the illness occurs at school. Common colds and infections can be partially controlled, at least, if parents and teachers cooperate in excluding ill children from school. Criticism for absence, plus make-up work, may cause children to attend school when really sick.

Feigned illness, on the other hand, may be a pupil's means of escaping an unpleasant situation at school. The distinction which must be drawn between safeguarding the health of childen and coddling them is difficult in many instances. Too much emphasis cannot be laid on the value of good working relationships among pupils, teachers, and parents in meeting problems of attendance. The school nurse can render invaluable assistance in these matters.

The teacher likewise should remain at home when ill, under a plan whereby a substitute is provided to relieve the ill teacher for a reasonable period of time without loss of salary.

Policies concerning *examinations, grades, and reports* are a continuing subject of discussion. We should like to avoid the worry, fear, anxiety, emotional stress, and unhappy comparisons which result from grades, tests, and reports. And yet we need some measure of accomplishment and progress. Selection exists in employment, in sports, and in the creative arts; and selection implies competition. Our school procedure seeks to avoid unnecessary emphasis on competition, examinations, and grades and to provide appropriate emphasis on individual accomplishment and progress.

Examinations represent for the pupil a self-check, a measurement of accomplishment, and a guide to study. They should be made a natural and casual part of the school work, not emphasized to the point where the pupil feels that everything depends upon them.

Sometimes examinations are conducted under undesirable conditions. The teacher adds to the anxiety by predicting a certain number of failures. The environmental conditions are poor. There are frequent interruptions. Unnecessary anxiety and emphasis are often associated with long final examinations given at the end of the school year. This time is a fatigue period for all pupils and a period of rapid growth in height for younger children. Fairly satisfactory practice is to limit examinations in primary grades to frequent ten-minute class exercises and to give frequent objective tests, using perhaps ten minutes, and less frequent tests of thirty minutes in the middle and upper grades.

On high school levels, examinations, final and others, should not exceed two hours, and in most courses should be of shorter duration. It is especially important that the several examinations to be taken by any one student be scattered over a period of two or more days.

Grades are difficult to determine and cannot accurately and precisely represent the pupil's ability. The teacher is not always satisfied that the test adequately reflects the pupil's knowledge. The grading of an essay-type test is a subjective process, and widely different grades are likely to be assigned to the same test by different teachers or even by the same teacher at different times. It is difficult for the teacher not to be influenced in grading by acquaintance with the pupil. It simplifies the teacher's task to distribute grades according to the natural curve of distribution, but statistics from large populations do not necessarily apply to small groups. Despite these limitations, the series of grades accumulated by the student does present a useful record of accomplishment. He can be helped to understand what they mean.

In many school systems periodic *reports* for younger pupils have become more general in nature. Some schools have substituted teacher-parent conferences for formal reports. In other schools a statement of satisfactory or unsatisfactory accomplishment has been substituted for a scale which purposed to indicate the percentage of perfection. This change has been made in order to emphasize the personality and effort of the pupil, rather than his comparative ability. Grading on effort alone, however, gives no indication of the child's capacity and possibilities. For the parent, as well as the teacher, a grading process which reflects the child's relative success in different subjects and his relative ability as compared with other children is essential for the helpful educational guidance of the child, especially in the higher grades. A rating on behavior, health habits, and citizenship is frequently included. These ratings are valuable although highly subjective.

It is desirable that reports should indicate the different phases of the child's progress and give some basis of comparison between his present and past accomplishment. Some report cards allow space for comments by the parent. As the pupil grows older, it is increasingly important that he should have a complete record of his accomplishment in the various departments of academic or professional work. Schools are seeking to develop reports that will reflect ability and accomplishment, and also indicate personality, conscientiousness, and dependability.

Intelligence test scores constitute a part of the cumulative record of the child but are not known by him. The scores are available to teachers. They understand the meaning of intelligence and have a deep respect for the potentialities of any normal child regardless of how high or low his marks are on an I.Q. test. This attitude toward child personality is basic, and only as a teacher believes in the worth of all children can schools be truly democratic. Intelligence tests must be used wisely.

What policy should the teacher follow with respect to *discipline and punishment* in the routine conduct of classroom work?

The school wishes to develop an atmosphere where fear is eliminated and where self-confidence, self-respect, and self-direction are developed. The pupil's classroom experiences should develop respect for the rights of others and teach him to work with other people. We should like the school to be so organized that the child would experience desirable outcomes from sound or "social" behavior and undesirable outcomes from unco-operative or belligerent behavior. We do not wish the pupil to look upon the school as a place where one must "obey the teacher or be punished." It is a place where the child develops a wholesome personality, not one where he merely learns to obey.

Quiet and orderliness promote pupil health, as well as pupil efficiency. Standards of pupil behavior should remain constant. The teacher's atti-tude toward behavior standards should be reasonable and consistent. Teacher threats or other attempts to induce behavior through fear are educationally and hygienically unsound. The child is helped most when the results of misbehavior are prompt, inevitable, consistent, and reason-able. Work is a useful punishment, but it should not eliminate needed recreation.

The need for the correction of individuals, which is the common mean-ing of discipline, lessens as right conditions for children's growth increase, as teachers accept the concept that all education is guidance, and as the school becomes adequate in applying the democratic concept in all aspects of its program. The following suggestions apply directly to this concept.

1. Discipline should be regarded as order, system, or arrangement for the common good, to ensure maximum consideration for the individual and efficiency for the group. Emphasis upon punishment, negation, curbing, or withholding only stimulates the child to rebellion. The positive, helpful, constructive values of discipline are acceptable to most people and also to children. Through an understanding and acceptance of society's or the school's discipline, the child grows as a well-disciplined personality. For the mental health of the pupil, acceptance of his world and its arrange-ments, not hostility toward them, should be sought.

2. The process of becoming a self-disciplined individual is enhanced when the child is motivated thereto internally; that is, when he himself wants to do what would be sound procedure for the group. External con-trols, such as penalties and punishments imposed by teachers and school authorities, may secure temporary compliance but do not favor genuine improvement or right personality development. Hence, it is recommended

that time be given to discussion of the whys and wherefores of discipline in order that the child, through understanding, may accept it.

3. Inasmuch as the school is a social institution in which the child meets a number of standards, regulations, and disciplines which ideally he should come to accept, every precaution should be made against establishing any rule or regulation for which the teacher cannot provide sufficient reasons. In fact every standard might well be accompanied or prefaced by the reasons and purposes for it, and insofar as possible it should be agreed upon by the groups expected to live up to it.

The above consideration of educational problems and procedures emphasizes the importance of teacher relationships with the individual pupil with respect to his health as well as in respect to his school progress.

Physical education

Essential physical activity for the child is provided by the physical education program; but physical education contributes much more than muscular exercise. It contributes to strength, vigor, vitality, and endurance; to competencies in interpersonal relations; to emotional development through self-mastery and self-expression; and to the establishment of recreational interests which continue into adult life. In modern school living, the teacher welcomes physical activities as an attractive means of bringing joy and relaxation into the child's school day through appeal to his natural interests. In free, big-muscle activities the child finds release from the tensions of sitting and of the continued use of small muscles in various tasks.

The teacher sees success in physical achievement linked with improved self-control, increased self-command, poise, and coordination. This success in physical skills often leads to increased security, the development of courage, and to more desirable psychological reactions due to improved status with his peers. Progress in that area points the way to other achievement.

Thus, physical education contributes not only to the growth and development of the individual but also to his ability to adjust to groups. An understanding interest in play and physical activities on the part of the teacher tends to promote a closer pupil-teacher relationship. Naturally, physical education situations abound in opportunities for emphasis upon sound health habits and healthful living.

Kinds of activities

The classroom teacher and the physical education teacher should never be at a loss for material, since there is a wide variety of activities that may be selected to meet the needs and interest of students. There is no excuse for a class being allowed to play the same game or carry on the same activity for weeks at a time. Physical education literature classifies activities in a variety of ways. They have been organized here under six headings: games, rhythms, self-testing activities, and conditioning activities including body mechanics, aquatics, and camping.

I. **Games, team sports and athletics.** A game is a contest in which there are definite rules established for the purpose of providing safety and fair competition for the players. Games make up a large part of the physical education program at both elementary and secondary levels. They have appeal for both boys and girls because they satisfy the need for competition as well as for vigorous action. They develop strength, skill, coordination, cooperation, leadership, followership, tolerance, sportsmanship, and character. We may mention six major types.

1. *Team games* range from the relatively simple to the complex.
2. *Lead-up games* develop skills that are valuable in the more advanced team games, as captain ball for basketball, newcomb for volleyball, hit pin baseball for baseball.
3. *Individual and dual games* are those games experienced by one or two individuals. They include, among others, golf, tennis, horseshoes, shuffleboard, and badminton.
4. *Chasing games* are active games in which one group chases another or one individual chases the other members of the class. As each child is caught, he becomes a chaser. Such games provide for vigorous activity in a limited amount of time without the element of team competition.
5. *Relays* are excellent activities for all grade levels but especially for the elementary grades. Modified relays are used for the young children.
6. *Recreational games* may be used successfully for children whose program in physical education is limited to less active participation. They include quiet games, such as object touching, beanbag throw, boiler burst, and table croquet, and mental games, such as ghosts, checkers, anagrams, and puzzles.

II. **Rhythms.** While all physical activities are fundamentally rhythmic, there are certain ones in which the rhythmic factor is predominant. They are bodily responses made to some type of rhythmic accompaniment. They satisfy the child's desire for creative self-expression, and provide opportunities for children to work together in groups. They encourage and stimulate the development of physical, social, emotional, and mental qualities essential to the child's well-being. They include:

1. *Fundamental rhythms,* or free rhythms such as walking, running, skipping, turning, sliding, hopping, and swinging, and such nonlocomotor movements as pushing, pulling, and striking. In the primary grades, provision is made for spontaneous individual play set to music which changes in tempo, accent, tune, and mood.
2. *Creative rhythms* allow children to portray their ideas and emotional experiences. Little children may identify themselves with trains, cars, or animals. The more advanced techniques in modern dance are presented at the secondary level.
3. *Singing games* are traditional activities that reflect the culture of the people with whom they originated. They are simple in patterns and skills and are appealing to all ages even though they are used in play periods and instructional periods of the primary grades. They provide opportunities for dramatization, together with the satisfaction experienced through repeated melodies. Group cooperation and relation are enjoyed.
4. *Folk dances* are traditional dances which reflect the spontaneous spirit of the people they represent. Such dances are appealing to all ages because they contain simple, vigorous movements, compelling rhythms, and group participation with a spirit of fun and gaiety. They contribute much to the objectives of physical education. The more skilled couple or solo dances are so intricate as to challenge the most skillful dancer.

5. *Square dances* are traditionally American and contain some of the values of folk dancing. They are vigorous and appealing to all ages.

6. *Social dancing* is very important for the preadolescent and can be especially enjoyed if there has been a natural sequence of the types of dances described above.

III. Self-testing activities. These activities challenge the individual to test himself. They provide the child with an opportunity to attain status within a group. They are a happy means of letting the student and the teacher note progress and development. Mastery of a special skill has a marked mental and emotional effect in assisting the person in social development. They are basic to the development of the big muscles of the body, to strength and balance, and to the full range of motion for agility and flexibility. Self-testing activities which also contribute to good body mechanics include stunts, tumbling, rope jumping, apparatus games, and weight training.

IV. Conditioning activities including body-building activities and corrective exercises. These are specially designed to develop body mechanics, the large muscles, endurance, mental alertness, self-confidence, and perseverance. Calisthenics, gymnastics, group activities in stunts, tumbling, and apparatus work are considered a part of the conditioning and fitness program in the secondary school.

V. Aquatics. These activities are listed separately because of their nature, although individual activities could be placed in the groups mentioned above. They deserve special mention because of the rapid growth of swimming and other water sports in the school program. An aquatics program contains a wide variety of activities. Swimming brings into use nearly all the muscle groups and is excellent for developing lung capacity and circulatory efficiency. The resistances involved are such that strained muscles or pulled tendons are most unlikely. In fact, the tank is a place where weak or partially paralyzed muscles can safely begin their rehabilitation. Swimming is also a safety skill. Protection for the ears is desirable in diving or underwater swimming.

VI. School camping. A camping program in which teacher and students spend a week or more together in a desirable camp situation has many contributions to health. Sound habits of activity, sleep, rest, bathing, eating, tooth-brushing, and maintaining neatness of clothes and bedding may be strengthened. Desirable attitudes in sharing, showing consideration for others, following safety precautions, and living by the rules of the camp are developed. New skills are acquired in the directed physical activities which are available and in the camping procedures, such as building fires, erecting shelters, making beds, and perhaps cooking. Teacher-pupil understanding and friendships are strengthened in these days of balanced living.

School camping has been practiced in some parts of Europe for many years. It is becoming more common in this country, and it has been estimated that perhaps 5 per cent of our school children enjoy organized school camping experiences. Public support for this valuable activity is growing.

Physical education in the elementary school

We may review briefly the types of activity commonly provided at different grade levels. Authorities have recommended one period per day for physical education, its length to be consistent with the established length of class periods. These should be chiefly instructional periods. It is advisable from the health and safety standpoint that the children wear sneakers and clothing that will permit sufficient freedom for activity.

In the first three grades, desirable natural activities include running, chasing, throwing, catching, and jumping. Muscles are being developed and vigorous activity is needed. However, overexertion is avoided. Games

Fig. 25. Physical activity at camp, as well as at school, contributes to health, relaxation, coordination, and friendliness.

are of short duration, gradually increasing in length. Skills are developing, and games should gradually increase in complexity as the maturity level changes. Since the interest span of the child is limited, he is not ready for activities which take considerable time for explanation and organization.

Suitable rhythmical activities include fundamental rhythms, creative rhythms, singing games, and very simple folk dances. Story plays are helpful in providing an opportunity for vigorous movement of the whole body. They also appeal to the creative and imitative nature of the child. Boys and girls have approximately the same abilities, and they play together in the planned physical education program. It is important at this age level to give attention to body mechanics during play periods and to posture throughout the school day.

In the intermediate grades, physical education periods are somewhat longer. Play clothes are desirable for freedom of movement. From the standpoint of preference and because boys engage in more vigorous activities, it is desirable that boys and girls should participate in physical education in separate groups for the most part, but not entirely. Square dances, folk dances, social dances, and volleyball are activities which they can enjoy together. Opportunity is provided for creative expression, dramatics, and free play. Imitations are enjoyed.

Boys wish to test their strength, speed, and endurance in climbing, jumping, wrestling, racing, swimming, team games, and skating. They are thrilled by the achievement of older athletes and are willing to practice in the quest of such skills.

Girls develop coordination and skills readily at this preadolescent period. Their program usually contains stunts, tumbling, and team games, as well as rhythms. Undue strain is avoided. Friendly competition and desirable attitudes are encouraged.

Both boys and girls play vigorously at this age, and rest periods are important. Attention to body mechanics helps provide for muscular development with good body alignment. Camping is an excellent informal activity which is appealing to children of this age.

Physical education in the secondary school

At the secondary school level, students are taking over more and more of the responsibility for self-direction. Their habits in regard to health, physical education, and recreation are likely to be continued into adult life. Unfortunately, it is not uncommon to find that, aside from the scheduled physical education period, students have pratically no time for physical activity. Carrying a part-time job or giving the major portion of free time to social affairs or to other types of extracurricular activities may crowd out physical exercise almost completely.

The continuance of some form of physical recreation after graduation will depend largely upon the degree of interest and the skills which the student has gained in school. One naturally tends to continue that which brings enjoyment, but one can really enjoy a physical activity only after he has gained a certain degree of proficiency.

On the secondary level it is important not only that the student should gain mastery of certain recreational and physical skills, but also that he understand the facts about physical and nervous fatigue and how to offset them through rest and relaxation, how to budget one's time in terms of balanced living, and how to become thoroughly familiar with community health and recreational resources.

At the *junior high school* age, physical education contributes to the development of cooperation for both boys and girls through team play. Boys are energetic and desire activities which test physical strength, courage, and endurance and, at the same time, develop skills. They are given stunts, tumbling, and lead-up games for the major sports. Endurance is limited, and the program should avoid undue stress, both physical and emotional.

For girls, junior high school represents the somewhat critical preadolescent period of development. They are energetic, excitable, and often spend too much physical and emotional energy. They like team games and are overanxious about winning. Their physical education program includes lead-up games for field hockey, basketball, softball, and soccer. Stunts, tumbling, and creative dancing form a part of the program.

Both boys and girls are developing the spirit of sportsmanship and fair play at this age. Each should begin to develop skill in one or more individual or dual games. Tennis is a good game to start at this age. Other coeducational activities include social dancing, square dancing, badminton, and volleyball.

Senior high school boys have greater physical capacity and an increased interest in highly specialized competitive games. Gymnastics and conditioning activities have a place in their program. Intramural competition in the track and field sports, as well as baseball, football, basketball, hockey, and tennis, provides good activity for the majority of students, while interscholastic athletics provide opportunities for the better athletes. Every boy should extend his skill in at least one individual or dual sport and know something about many.

Senior high school girls play field hockey, basketball, and softball. Gymnasium activities consist of calisthenics and creative dancing. Rhythmic activities are very popular. They encourage the development of poise, balance, grace, and the ability to relax. Unfortunately an increasing number of high school students, especially girls, lose interest in vigorous physical activity. Interest in social affairs increases and coeducational activities, such as social dancing, square dancing, badminton, tennis, and recreational games, are of increased importance.

Swimming is an important activity for both groups. It is a safety skill and a source of enjoyment throughout life. In most secondary schools where adequate facilities are available, the ability to swim the length of the pool is a graduation requirement for both boys and girls.

The physical fitness program

Supplementing the existing program of physical education, led by an able physical education profession in this country, are the proposals of the President's Council on Youth Fitness. The Council was established following the finding of a high percentage of physically underdeveloped children in studies involving several of our city school systems. There follows a brief description of four valuable and widely used publications of the Council. They may be purchased from the Superintendent of Documents, U. S. Government Printing Office, Washington, D. C., 20402.

Youth physical fitness is prepared for schools serving grades four to twelve and presents the suggested elements of a school-centered program. It gives a brief perspective of a "comprehensive program of health education and physical education" and suggests administrative policies and practices for implementing programs of youth fitness. It gives screening tests for identifying physically underdeveloped pupils and activities to improve their performance. It further suggests a detailed series of tests and activities for boys and girls in grades four to twelve. 111 pages. Price 40¢.

Vigor is for boys twelve to eighteen years of age. It presents a complete physical fitness plan, including a basic workout and sections on isometric exercises and weight training. Suggested tests help boys to check their fitness against that of other boys their own age. 24 pages. Price 25¢.

Vim is for girls twelve to eighteen years of age. It presents a complete physical fitness plan for girls of these ages. It includes a basic workout and tips on figure development, plus information on diet, weight control, and posture. It further explains how being physically fit helps to develop beauty and poise. 24 pages. Price 25¢.

Adult physical fitness presents an activity program for teachers and other adults. It is designed to help the individual feel better, look better, and perform more efficiently. It contains two simple exercise programs, one for men and one for women; and it explains how exercise can help overcome chronic fatigue, improve the functioning of the heart and lungs, aid in weight control, and possibly prolong active years. Isometric contraction exercises are illustrated and described as a valuable supplement to vigorous physical activity. The booklet also describes various daily or incidental opportunities for adding to fitness. 64 pages. Price 35¢.

Posture and body mechanics

A day-to-day responsibility which the classroom teacher, especially in the elementary school, shares with the physical education program in making the school day a healthful one is the maintenance and promotion of sound posture and body mechanics.

We have discussed defects of posture (see page 91). A few of these are due to faulty structure, while others arise from some condition such as malnutrition, recent illness, cumulative fatigue, poorly developed musculature, poor sight, or defective hearing. In most of these situations, the first step is the removal of the underlying cause, following which the child may need special corrective exercises. The classroom teacher cooperates with the school health services and the physical education department in the program prescribed for the improvement of the health and posture of children with such defects.

Apart from these postural defects, we recognize that many children develop changes in their musculo-skeletal structures as the result of *poor posture habits* such as sleeping or sitting in a poor position, habitually carrying books under one arm, wearing inappropriate shoes, poor habits of gait, wrong mechanical use of legs and feet, or the use of incorrectly constructed furniture. Pupils at each stage of growth and development should be given correct standards of good posture when standing, sitting, and walking. Appropriate training in good posture habits should be a continuous process from kindergarten throughout school life. A tendency to poor posture, if persisted in, develops into a habit and eventually into unattractive posture or the ineffective mechanical use of the body.

Proper attention to the body mechanics of the entire group of pupils is reflected in their characteristic bearing both in school and out of school. Here are some suggested classroom activities to promote good posture:

1. Emphasize good posture occasionally throughout the day while the students are reading, writing, or carrying on other class activities
2. Hang pictures in the classroom showing persons with ideal posture
3. Have the children make posters on good posture

4. Have children walk around the room with books balanced on their heads
5. Let older children check themselves for posture by standing beside a pole to see if a straight line would pass through the ear, shoulder joint, hip joint, knee, and ankle
6. Send home booklets on posture in order to arouse the parents' interest
7. Make posture a subject of discussion at a parent-teacher meeting
8. Have a long mirror available for students to check their own posture
9. Post a list of suggestions on important points in good posture, such as: (1) stand tall, (2) shoulders easy, (3) abdomen up and in, (4) lower back flat, (5) weight on balls of feet, (6) toes pointing straight ahead, and (7) think tall.

Routine activities of special health significance

The regular weighing and measuring of pupils, the daily observation of pupil health, the lunch at school, and relaxation are routine activities which make especially important contributions to pupil health.

Watching growth. Regular gain in weight is a sign of health. All young animals grow unless they are ill. People watch the growth of babies from week to week, and if growth stops, they immediately inquire the cause. The farmer watches the growth of his crops and his stock, and if they do not grow, he seeks the reason. It is logical to *watch the growth of school children in the elementary school.*

Every child wants to grow. This desire is a splendid motivating force in encouraging the child to maintain those habits of behavior which are hygienic. The monthly or frequent weighing gives the child a chance to watch for himself the relationship between habits and growth. Frequently he will know the reason for an unusually good gain or for failure to gain. Encouragement, not criticism, should be given to the child who does not gain.

Weighing done by the teacher and the class is an educational procedure. It is not a diagnosis of health status, although failure to gain for each of three successive months suggests that something is wrong. Three-month intermittency is not determined in June, because the seasonal influence is greatest then, because weighing tends to be made early in the month, and because the closing of school makes follow-up impossible.

Proper *methods of weighing and measuring* are important. Regular weighing is done once a month, on about the same day and at the same time of day. The measuring of height is carried out at least twice during the school year, at the beginning and in February. Pupils should be weighed in their indoor clothing, without shoes, coats, or sweaters.

If the scales are moved from one room to another, care should be taken to keep the platform nearly horizontal so that the adjustment of the mechanism under the platform is not disturbed. Before *weighing,* the scales should be tested for balance by pushing the balance weights back to zero. When found to vary from an accurate balance, they must be adjusted.

The pupil being weighed should stand quietly in the middle of the platform with his hands at his sides. The weight should be recorded to the nearest quarter of a pound. The children should participate in all

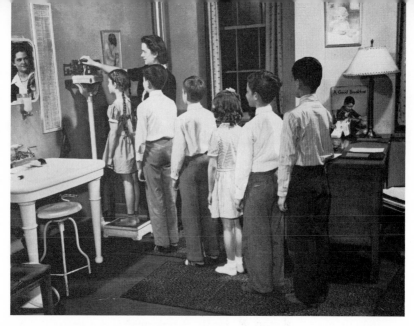

Fig. 26. Interest in growing motivates children toward healthful living. (Courtesy of "Spectrum," published by Pfizer Laboratories.)

these activities as much as their ages will permit. Older children may take charge of weighing and measuring themselves.

Two instruments are necessary for *measuring height:* (1) an accurate scale against which the child can stand to be measured, and (2) a leveling device that can be placed on his head to secure a right-angle measurement against the scale. A convenient scale is secured by tacking a tape measure accurately against a flat wall. An empty chalk box may be used as a leveling device by placing the end flat against the tape on the wall and lowering the box until it rests upon the head. A single flat surface, like a book or a board, cannot be used satisfactorily, because one cannot be sure that it will make a right angle with the scale on the wall.

The pupil being measured should stand as "tall" as possible, with heels together and with his back and head against the wall where the scale is placed. His arms should be at his sides and his eyes straight ahead. Height is recorded to the nearest quarter of an inch.

Data on weighing and measuring that are to be used in scientific research should be taken by the same individual. The technique is not sufficiently simple to provide accurate data when children are weighed and measured by several different persons.

Individual weight cards are used to keep the *records* of heights, monthly weights, and gains. These records are sent home regularly, signed by the parent, and returned.

The cards should not contain any statement of what the child should weigh. Nobody knows how many pounds any individual child should weigh. It is better to omit from the child's card a statement of average weight for height and age and indicate only the child's weight and his gain from month to month, because people are still likely to make the absurd assumption that all children should be of average weight—to assume that "average" weight is "normal" weight in the sense of "proper" weight.

Classroom weight records (wall charts) may well be kept for every class in the elementary school. They are valuable to teacher and pupils when checking the growth progress of the class and are usually the only means of replacing individual records when a card is lost. The classroom record should be kept up to date and should be left hanging where pupils can refer to it.

After being weighed, each child should know his actual weight and how much he gained or lost. He should be helped by the teacher to understand the relation of his health habits or health status to his gain or loss in weight. There are seasonal as well as individual variations in growth rates.

Weighing is done in regular health class time. When teachers object to weighing and measuring children, it is usually because they have not been shown the method or because they think they must do it after school or at recess or take the time from some other subject. There is no time in the school program when teachers get so near to the individual child and his health behavior as at the weighing period. This is a splendid opportunity for friendly encouragement of the child by the teacher.

Many children are encouraged to keep a graph of their growth. Such a graph may contain only actual height and weight lines for the child from month to month; or a standard chart, which shows average growth status for age, may be used. (See pages 45 and 46.)

Daily observation of pupil health. In the primary grades, where children's diseases are most common and where habits of cleanliness are being established, many schools provide a brief period for health at the opening of school. This allows time for checking the personal appearance of individual children for signs of communicable disease and selected items of cleanliness.

Teacher observance of these conditions is of recognized importance. Preference varies as to procedure. Of course, departures from normal health and cleanliness should be noted whenever they occur, but regular morning checking is helpful. Some teachers prefer to stand near the door in good light and greet each child as he comes in or to have the children come to him individually as they enter the room. Other teachers observe as they move about the room, while others make a health club or game of this checking.

The teacher will decide which items he wishes to check. Cleanliness and clothing factors may include part or all of the following: cleanliness of hands and nails; cleanliness of face, neck, and ears; cleanliness of teeth; neatness of hair; cleanliness and neatness of clothing; carrying of clean handkerchief; removal of rubbers, overshoes, rubber boots, and extra sweaters.

There is a difference in the health value of cleanliness habits. Hand-washing and the avoidance of the nail-biting habit, for example, are valuable practices in preventive hygiene. The value of keeping clothing clean and neat, however, is largely aesthetic and social. It lies more in the realm of mental health than in that of disease prevention. The maintenance of cleanliness, neatness, and proper personal appearance contributes to the comfort, the social ease, and the self-respect of the individual. It contributes to the pleasure of the other individuals with whom he is associated.

At higher grade levels, teacher observation of pupil health continues to be important. The capable teacher develops both skill and alertness in detecting changes.

Skillful teacher observation involves many things.[1] Like the parent, the teacher is close to the individual child and knows his individual differences. To him each child is unique. He has a real fondness for the child. He knows when John looks tired or happy or scared or worried or pale or flushed. He considers John as a whole—as an individual. He knows when John is not "like himself."

The skillful teacher has practiced the art of observation. He has observed individual characteristics, such as eye color or posture or complexion or hair condition. The characteristic has become familiar to him and interesting in its variations. He has unobtrusively studied individual children for a few minutes at a time as though he were going to describe the child's characteristics from memory.

It is either the parent or the teacher who gets needed medical attention for a child by asking the aid of the family doctor or the school nurse or physician. In a school without medical service, the teacher expresses his concern to the parents. The teacher is often more skillful than the parent in observation because he sees the child at work and knows his work habits, learning ability, and school behavior. The parent may overlook a developing defect because of his very familiarity with the child who has always "been like that."

The school lunch. Wherever the noon lunch or a mid-morning lunch is provided at school there are important opportunities for health education as well as for improving nutrition.

The *noon lunch* demands attention in the matter of cleanliness before eating, etiquette while eating, a proper length of time for eating, and provision for rest and relaxation for the remainder of the noon hour.

Administrative provision is needed for adequate supplies, equipment, and services. Those selected to be responsible for the preparation of food for the school lunch should: (1) know and apply nutritional standards in meal planning, (2) practice desirable standards of cleanliness of person, of storage, preparation, and serving of food, (3) be able to prepare foods without loss of food values and serve them so they will appeal to the eye, (4) meet regulations of state and local health authorities governing the health of persons who handle food, (5) have a cooperative attitude toward all who assist with the program. (See also page 190.)

---

[1]Valuable and widely used aids in pupils observation are the pamphlet on "What Teachers See" and the filmstrip on "Teacher Observations of School Children," issued by the Metropolitan Life Insurance Company, 1 Madison Ave., New York, N. Y.

The school lunch should provide an enjoyable meal and also a laboratory where all pupils learn practical facts about foods and nutrition.

The *mid-morning* lunch of fruit or crackers and milk offers an opportunity to give children an extra feeding of milk and to make milk drinking popular with them. This should never be considered a substitute for a proper breakfast, however.

It is commonly observed that many children gain better in weight when they have the extra feeding of milk. Teachers frequently notice that this mid-morning nutrition relieves fatigue and that children who have it do better work in the later part of the morning. Early studies by Haggard and Greenberg[2] with children, older students, and industrial workers indicated less fatigue and greater muscular and occupational efficiency with mid-morning and mid-afternoon lunches. Parents often report that a child who has refused milk at home learns to like it by drinking it with his classmates at school.

Milk should be an important part of the diet for every child except, of course, those children who have an allergic reaction to milk proteins. The extra feeding at school is particularly important for children who are very thin and who do not gain well. Teachers should make special effort to have such children take milk regularly.

[2]Haggard, H. W., and Greenberg, L. A.: *Diet and Physical Efficiency*, New Haven, 1935, Yale University Press.

Fig. 27. The milk lunch.

Most children profit by the milk lunch and should be encouraged to take it. Occasionally one finds a child who cannot take milk during the forenoon without losing his appetite for the noon meal. Such a case should be left to the judgment of the parent. Some schools give orange juice or tomato juice for a mid-morning lunch. Each is refreshing, rich in vitamin content, and a source of quick energy according to the limited amount of fruit sugar it contains.

The majority of children have inadequate daily milk intake. Since milk provides so many of the elements necessary for the growth and health of children, it seems preferable, both from the standpoint of education in milk drinking and provision of the extra feeding, to serve milk rather than fruit juices at the mid-morning lunch, keeping in mind the exceptions referred to above.

Plain salty crackers or graham crackers are usually served with the milk. They make the milk more appetizing and are wholesome for children because they require thorough chewing and are not sweet enough to spoil the appetite for the noon meal. Sweet crackers or cookies should never be served. Milk should be served at a palatable temperature in both summer and winter. It should never be served later than ten-thirty; some schools find it preferable to serve it as early as ten o'clock. It is better to serve the milk before recess than to ask the child to give up some of his recess for the lunch period. Only pasteurized milk should be used.

The tops of milk bottles should be wiped and the caps removed or flaps lifted before the milk is served. The straws should be handled in a sanitary way. It is desirable to have pupils assist in serving the milk, and they should be taught to do it with proper regard for cleanliness. The children who take the milk lunch should be allowed to wash their hands before eating, thus providing incidental teaching by example. Of course, hands do not touch the milk if straws are used, but they do handle the crackers.

The lunch period should be a pleasant time. Children should be seated during the period and should be encouraged to eat slowly and to develop good manners.

Some of the more important values of the mid-morning milk lunch may be summed up as follows:

1. Insufficient milk is a common dietary fault among children, and the mid-morning lunch increases the amount taken.
2. Many children appear to be refreshed by the mid-morning milk lunch, while without it they become faint and tired. The child seems to profit physiologically from the extra feeding.
3. Many children learn to drink milk at school where other children are drinking it.
4. Milk is a good food for growth.
5. Many children want something to eat in the middle of the morning, and if milk is not available, they will substitute something less desirable, such as candy.
6. The serving of the mid-morning milk lunch offers an opportunity for training in certain health habits connected with cleanliness and with eating. This in itself would not be a reason for maintaining the mid-morning lunch, but it is a value arising from it.

The chief objections which have been advanced against the milk lunch are the possible dangers that the child will substitute it for a good breakfast, and that it may interfere with the appetite for the noon lunch.

Relaxation. The activity provided in the physical education program offers a restful change from the continued sitting position by freeing one group of muscles and putting other large muscle groups in action. Either prone or sitting relaxation is restful, and the ability to relax the various muscle groups and to relax completely when lying down is of value. Children may have brief relaxation in the seats. They put their heads forward on their arms, with arms on the desks and muscles relaxed. They should avoid a position that makes breathing difficult. Commonly, both relaxation and stretching exercises are used in the relaxation period.

Such relaxation periods are important because they lessen nervous fatigue. Teachers in the elementary schools who have experimented with the use of brief relaxation periods have, with unanimity, approved the procedure and noted its contributions to health and efficiency in school work.

References

American Association of School Administrators: *Health in Schools,* Twentieth Yearbook, rev. ed., Washington, D. C., 1951, The Association.

Andrews, G., Saurborn, J., and Schneider, E.: *Physical Education for Today's Boys and Girls,* Boston, 1960, Allyn and Bacon.

Cassidy, R.: *Curriculum Development in Physical Education,* New York, 1954, Harper & Brothers.

Cowell, C. C., and Hazelton, H. W.: *Curriculum Designs in Physical Education,* Englewood, N. J., 1955, Prentice-Hall, Inc.

Grout, R. E.: *Health Teaching in Schools,* ed. 4, Philadelphia, 1963, W. B. Saunders Company.

Irwin, L. W., and Humphrey, J. H.: *Principles and Techniques of Supervision in Physical Education,* St. Louis, 1954, The C. V. Mosby Company.

Lowman, C. L., and Young, C. H.: *Postural Fitness—Significance and Variances,* Philadelphia, 1960, Lea & Febiger.

Metropolitan Life Insurance Company: *Pounds and Inches,* New York, 1959, 4 pp., free.

National Conference for Cooperation in Health Education: *School Health Policies.* This is a 1956 revision of a 40-page pamphlet which is available from the American Medical Association.

National Education Association and American Medical Association Joint Committee: *Healthful School Living,* American Medical Association, Chicago, 1957.

Oberteuffer, Delbert and Ulrich, C.: *Physical Education,* ed. 3, New York, and Evanston, Illinois, 1962, Harper and Row.

Schneider, E.: *Physical Education in Urban Elementary Schools,* Washington, D. C., 1959, Office of Education, U. S. Department of Health, Education, and Welfare.

Wheatley, G. M., and Hallock, G. T.: *Health Observations of School Children,* ed. 3, New York, 1965, McGraw-Hill Book Company, Inc.

Chapter viii

Health protection and health education through a healthful school environment

A healthful school environment (as well as adequate school health services, communicable disease control, a hygienic arrangement of the pupil's day, a good program of physical education, adequate safety precautions, and the maintenance of a healthy staff) provides a means of teaching health indirectly. These indirect health learnings are a vital part of the child's health education.

The government has the responsibility of providing a school environment in which children can work safely and effectively. Failure to provide and maintain a healthful school environment invalidates the teaching of sanitary principles. Schools that teach the important health practice of hand-washing before eating and after using the toilet, but fail to provide adequate hand-washing facilities, are not likely to develop the habit in their pupils. A healthful environment must be coupled with good instruction, each aiding and reinforcing the other, in order to secure the best results.

Urbanization and improved facilities for the transportation of children in rural areas are resulting in larger schools and better school buildings. These schools are located where public water supplies, sewerage systems, and other sanitary facilities are available. Remarkable modern school buildings are being constructed. At the same time we have many small school buildings in rural areas and older buildings in cities which have such difficulties as cross lighting, inadequate window shades, inadequate temperature control in the classrooms, lack of properly adjustable seats, lack of cloakroom space, inadequate hand-washing facilities, lack of hand-drying facilities, too few bubbler fountains of sanitary construction, lack of drinking facilities and paper cups where bubbler fountains are not possible, lack of sufficient properly kept toilet facilities, lack of adequate and attractive lunchroom space, and lack of scales for the regular weighing of the pupils.

Serious as are some of the structural defects of school buildings, the not infrequent failure of the school staff to make the best use of existing possibilities is equally a cause for concern. Much can be done to provide healthful living in very modest school buildings, if teachers understand the health problems and needs and have creative imagination and leadership. Teachers do not have responsibility for setting architectural, structural, and budgetary requirements; but they do wish to know what are the environmental problems related to health and working efficiency and how these problems are met.

The school site and school grounds

Satisfactory planning for school buildings and grounds is different, of course, between urban and rural schools. In town it is desirable that the building be located near bus lines and paved streets, and within walking distance of the younger children. It should be located away from noise, traffic, railroad tracks, airports, and factories, with a consideration of the future development of the district. Every school building should be located, if possible, where power, water supply, and sewerage systems are available. The ground around the building should be dry, either naturally or by artificial drainage, and with sufficient space for recreation. Walks leading to the school should be of cement or other hard surface. Trees and shrubbery give attractiveness, coolness, and shade.

The size of the *school site* is affected by local circumstances such as property costs and availability of land. For the minimum site for an elementary school the recommendation is 10 acres; for a junior high school, 20 acres; and for a senior high school, 30 acres. To each site an additional acre is added for each 100 pupils of predicted maximum enrollment. Thus, for example, the site for an elementary school of 200 pupils would be 12 acres. Under circumstances where school facilities are combined with recreational facilities of the community, even more space is required. Play space of 100 square feet per child is commonly recommended.

Desirable playground requirements are:

1. Proper drainage and surfacing, to avoid both mud and dust.
2. Removal of all stumps and rocks.
3. Play areas fenced or at least so situated as to prevent children from running into the street.
4. 100 square feet of space per pupil.
5. Provision for supervision of the use of the playground and arrangements by grades to ensure safety of younger children.
6. Provision for frequent checking of apparatus for safety.
7. Arrangement to utilize neighboring parks and playgrounds if the space around the building is inadequate.

Schools should provide, where possible, all-weather play areas so that play periods will not be affected by rain, snow, or excessive dust. Many state departments of education set standards for playground equipment.

Adequate school sites are available at the edge of smaller cities but are obviously difficult to obtain in the largest metropolitan areas.

School buildings

Today, it is increasingly common practice for the teaching and administrative staff who are to use the new school building to cooperate with the state department of education and the school architect in the development of plans. It is their function to indicate the educational and service activities which are to be carried out in the school. This statement provides the architect with the basis for the design of the building.[1]

Most state departments of education have a division of school architecture or a division dealing with the construction and maintenance of school plants. This division does not ordinarily prepare the plans for the school building, but it does approve the plans which have been prepared by the consulting architect. There are now many architects who have specialized in the construction of school buildings and who are expert in planning structures which meet all of the requirements of safety, sanitation, illumination, and climate control.

New school buildings are structurally arranged with great care to facilitate the temporary joining of classes through the raising of soundproof separation partitions between the rooms; the movement of groups to the auditorium, gymnasium, or playroom; and the functioning of special services and activities.

Standard requirements are prescribed for fireproof materials, safety exits, and other elements of construction. Corridors are usually required to be 12 feet in width. If there are stairs in the building, they are built with 6-inch risers and 12-inch treads.

Traditionally, classrooms were rectangular, but many recently built classrooms are more nearly square. Some structural requirements demand a ceiling 13 feet high, and aisles at least 18 inches wide between rows of seats and 20 inches wide between the rows of seats and the walls. At least 6 to 8 feet are usually required between the front row of seats and the front wall. In school operation, unused seats and desks are removed from the room. The seats are so placed as to take advantage of the best lighting. Single seating is required by law in many states.

An important agency in the improvement of school buildings has been the National Council on Schoolhouse Construction, which was organized in 1921 to promote the establishment of reasonable standards for the school plant. Present suggested standards for the construction of school buildings are set forth in its excellent publication entitled *Guide for Planning School Plants*. This book is purchasable from the secretary-treasurer, Floyd G. Parker, 409 Erickson Hall, Michigan State University, East Lansing, Michigan. The copyrighted 1964 edition (second printing 1965) contains 156 pages. Its twelve chapters deal with the planning of educational facilities; educational plant programming; educational build-

---

[1]The State Department of Education in Florida has provided an excellent guide called "Educational Facilities Planning 1965" for the use of the local school systems in setting forth, for the benefit of the architect, the educational requirements which the new school building is expected to meet.

ing sites, instructional spaces; spaces for services auxiliary to instruction; noninstructional facilities; spatial, aesthetic, and safety factors; the sonic environment; the thermal environment; the visual environment; principles of economy in planning and construction; and educational plant planning resources.

School water supply

It is of major importance to health that the school shall provide an adequate supply of safe and palatable drinking water. The sanitary quality of water used from other than a public supply should be tested periodically by the local health department at the source and at the point of use. The great majority of schools today are served from a municipal water system.

If a well is used, it should be so located, constructed, and maintained that it is not in danger of pollution from surface drainage or from nearby cesspools or underground drains. In some schools of the world, well water is lifted to the top of the building by an automatic pump or by a hand pump in order to supply running water within the building. One of us (C.E.T.) visited a small rural school in the Philippine Islands where the children "manned the pump" for a few minutes each day under a well-planned schedule as one of their physical activities.

(H. Armstrong Roberts)

Fig. 28. Bubbler fountains are at the right height and meet standards of sanitation.

Water from any school supply which is of doubtful quality should be boiled or chlorinated according to procedures approved by the health department.

A possible source of danger to the water supply in city buildings is a connection between the drinking water system and the drainage pipes or pipes carrying impure water for fire protection. There should be no cross-connections anywhere within school buildings. A cross-connection may be defined as "any physical connection whereby the safe water supply is connected with any other water supply of unsatisfactory or questionable quality in such a manner that a flow of water into the safe water supply is possible, either through the manipulation of valves or because of ineffective check or back pressure valves, or because of any other arrangements or circumstances."

The state of Kansas has suggested the following requirements for sanitary drinking facilities:

1. Common drinking cup prohibited.
2. Individual drinking cups not satisfactory as they will becomes dirty and will be exchanged.
3. Single service paper cups acceptable.
4. Sanitary drinking fountains recommended:
   a. Minimum of one fountain for each twenty-five children and at least one on each floor.
   b. Fountain should conform to the following specifications:
      (1) The fountain should be constructed of impervious material such as vitreous china, porcelain, enameled cast iron, other metals, or stoneware.
      (2) The jet of the fountain should issue from a nozzle of nonoxidizing, impervious material set at an angle from the vertical. The nozzle and and every other opening in the water pipe or conductor leading to the nozzle should be above the edge of the bowl, so that such nozzle or opening will not be flooded in case a drain from the bowl of the fountain becomes clogged.
      (3) The end of the nozzle should be protected by nonoxidizing guards to prevent the mouth and nose of persons using the fountain from coming into contact with the nozzle.
      (4) The inclined jet of water issuing from the nozzle should not touch the guard, and thereby cause spattering.
      (5) The bowl of the fountain should be so designed and proportioned as to be free from corners which would be difficult to clean or which would collect dirt.
      (6) The bowl should be so proportioned as to prevent unnecessary splashing at a point where the jet falls into the bowl.
      (7) The drain from the fountain should not be a direct physical connection with a waste pipe, unless the drain is trapped.
      (8) The water supply pipe should be provided with an adjustable valve fitted with a loose key or an automatic valve permitting the regulation of the rate of flow of water to fountain.
      (9) The height of the fountain at the drinking level should be such as to be most convenient to persons utilizing the fountain. The provision of several steplike elevations to the floor at fountains will permit children of various ages to utilize the fountain.
      (10) The waste opening and pipe should be of sufficient size to carry off the water promptly. The opening should be provided with a strainer.

5. When a pressure water supply is not available, provide fountain supply tank constructed of impervious material such as stainless steel, aluminum, or stone-ware.
   Tank should be easily accessible for filling and cleaning.
   Tank should have overlapping cover.
   Water in tank should be disinfected with chlorine compound after each filling.
   Tank must be high enough above fountain to furnish adequate pressure for operating fountain. (Minimum height, bottom of tank above fountain discharge, approximately one foot.)
   Provide fountain as previously specified.
   Provide waste line to carry away waste water.
   Clean tank thoroughly and air it at least once a month.
6. If coolers with faucet are used, the district should provide paper cups of a type which can be used only once.
   This equipment is less desirable.
7. Water should be cool. Temperature always less than 75° F. (If ice is used, it should be stored and handled in a sanitary manner.)

Food sanitation

School feeding programs are now common and the sanitation of the school lunch, as well as its nutritional and educational aspects, is of recognized importance. Persons in charge are commonly those who have had training in dietetics and who apply the best practices in food sanitation.

An interesting change in food service has appeared in some cities in recent years with the introduction of central food preparation. The food is prepared in large central kitchens and shipped to individual schools in ready-to-serve sealed containers or in large dishes from which individual servings are dispensed. Some schools have served individual lunches from hot-food carts which go to individual classrooms.

Instruction in food sanitation should be provided for all food handlers. Most local health departments are prepared to organize or conduct such courses. Some items which should be checked in the handling of foods in schools are food-handling and food-serving facilities, dishwashing methods, health of those handling and preparing foods, refrigeration, storage of food and utensils, rodent and insect control, employes' locker space, and availability and use of pasteurized milk. Sanitary standards established by state or local health departments should be followed with care.

Inadequate refrigeration and unsatisfactory dishwashing procedures constitute major health hazards in the school lunch program. All perishable food or drink should be kept at or below 45 degrees Fahrenheit. Special precautions should be taken with such foods as custards, cream-filled pastries, milk, sauces, and dressings.

Safe dishwashing requires immersion of dishes for at least two minutes in water at 180 degrees F. or an equally effective sanitizing procedure, such as immersion in a chlorine solution. Mechanical dishwashers that have their own enclosed, automatically-controlled hot water tanks solve the problem of maintaining a constant supply of sufficiently hot water. In the absence of a dishwashing machine, a three-compartment sink is recommended, using the first compartment for cleansing with a detergent, the second for rinsing, and the third for sanitizing with water heated to 180 degrees F.

Adequate hand-washing facilities are essential both in the kitchen and in the toilet rooms used by the food handlers.

Although the prime object of good sanitation in the serving of food at schools is to protect the health of the pupils and teachers, a very important secondary objective is the education of pupils in the proper methods of food preparation, storage, dishwashing and similar subjects, in order that such procedures may become common practice in the home and throughout the community. Whenever food is served at schools, the facilities provided and procedures employed should be the best known to nutritional and sanitary science. Children who bring their lunches should have a suitable place in which to eat them. Food service areas should be pleasant, quiet, and attractive. Table tops should be of smooth impervious material. The highest standards of cleanliness should be maintained. Leisurely eating and courteous eating habits are to be encouraged.

Garbage containers should be conveniently located and maintained in a clean and sanitary condition. Pupils should be held responsible for keeping school grounds free from trash and discarded food. A pupil sanitation committee is often most helpful in developing pupil cooperation.

Hand-washing facilities, bathing facilities, and swimming pools

Minimum hand-washing facilities for both rural and urban schools should provide an opportunity for every pupil to wash his hands after going to the toilet, before meals, and at other times when necessary, with a reasonable expenditure of time and effort and with satisfaction to the pupil.

To achieve this it is important that there be warm running water, soap, and sanitary towels. The equipment should be easily accessible to classrooms, toilets, and lunchrooms. Sanitary hand-washing facilities are desirable in the classrooms of kindergartens and primary schools.

Pupils and personnel should be encouraged to conserve materials intelligently, but there should not be such pressure from boards of education and those in charge of supplies as to limit the desirable use of such materials. Pupils should be allowed adequate time for hand-washing.

One lavatory is needed for every twenty-five pupils and at least one lavatory in each toilet room. They should be adapted to the height of the pupil and equipped with a mixer faucet for hot and cold water. The lavatory has no stopper and the pupils wash their hands in running water. Wash fountains may be used in place of wash basins. Paper towels should be within the reach of small children. Liquid or powdered soap should be available, and a mirror should be located low enough for convenient use. Studies show that bar soap without antibacterial additives does not spread bacteria,[2] but it is less convenient to use.

---

[2]Bannan, E. A., and Judge, L. F.: "Bacteriological Studies Relating to Handwashing," *American Journal of Public Health*, vol. 55, no. 6, pp. 915–921, June, 1965.

Fig. 29. Many kindergarten and lower grade classrooms have their own hand-washing facilities.

The success of hand-washing depends upon carefully rubbing the soap into the skin of hands and wrists and around nails after hands have been wet, then rinsing off the lather and thoroughly drying the hands. This requires careful supervision of little children by the teacher until both monitors and hand-washers thoroughly understand and carry out the procedure.

Common towels should be completely eliminated.

Bathing facilities are ordinarily found in schools only in conjunction with athletic or physical education programs, and usually in the larger schools. Where showers are provided in connection with gymnasium classes, the minimum number of shower heads provided should equal at least one-fourth the number of pupils in the largest gymnasium class. There should be 10 to 12 square feet of floor space for each shower head.

Dressing and shower room floors should be kept scrupulously clean to protect pupils against athlete's foot and other infections. Shower room floors are preferably of nonslip tile and are washed daily, using hot water and soap. A final wash with a disinfectant such as a solution of Purex or Clorox, 1 to 8, is used and left to dry.

Recent studies support the point of view that athlete's foot is not as easily acquired as formerly supposed, and that the most important preventive measure is good foot hygiene. This involves daily bathing of the feet with thorough drying between the toes. In highly susceptible individuals, foot powder may be helpful. All students with fungus infections of the feet are placed under treatment.

All *pools* should be designed, constructed, and operated so as to meet any requirements that may be set forth in the regulations of the Board of Health for approved pools. In general, these regulations require a recirculating system equipped for chlorination and filtration having a turnover period not to exceed eight hours, and frequent tests for chemical and bacteriological characteristics of the pool water. A chlorine content of 0.4 parts per million is maintained.

The temperature in pools being used for instructional purposes is usually between 72 and 78 degrees F. Air temperature should be three or four degrees warmer than water temperature. All pupils using the pool should be free of infectious conditions. A warm-water shower in the nude with the use of soap should be required before entering the pool.

Toilet facilities and sewage disposal

Adequate sewage disposal demands convenient facilities, adequate capacity, freedom from odor nuisance, and the avoidance of any danger of contamination either of soil or of water supply.

The water carriage system most desirable is one which has its outlet in a city sewerage system. For rural schools, drainage into a septic tank with overflow into underground pipes is satisfactory if properly constructed and supervised.

Toilets should be located convenient to classrooms on each floor, with separate units for boys and girls. They should be well lighted, clean, screened, and well ventilated in accordance with local or state plumbing codes. Only open-front toilet seats should be used.

In some of the newer elementary schools small toilet rooms adjoining each primary grade classroom, for use by both boys and girls, have been provided. Separate toilet rooms are needed for health service suites, locker rooms, and administrative offices.

On the basis of minimal standards there should be one toilet seat for each 50 boys and one urinal for 30 boys. For girls, one toilet seat for 30 girls is minimal. In some cities plumbing codes permit a slightly higher ratio in secondary schools. Minimal standards should be exceeded wherever funds are available.

Few rural schools still employ outdoor-type toilets. They can be used without danger to health if standards of construction and operation set by health departments are followed. There is always danger that proper maintenance will be neglected. Students frequently defer using such toilets to their own physical detriment, because of remote location and unsanitary conditions. Inside flush toilets with drainage into a septic tank are to be preferred.

Climate control

Modern methods of air conditioning make it possible to provide the kind of climate desired for classrooms, shops, gymnasia, and other areas of the school building. In contrast to the traditional little red schoolhouse, we now have many schools in which all air is supplied by the air conditioning system. What kinds of procedures are involved in climate control, and what air conditions are desirable?

Heating refers to raising the temperature of air. *Ventilation* refers to the process of supplying or removing air by natural or mechanical means to or from any space. Climate control or air conditioning in its broadest sense implies control of any or all of the physical and chemical qualities of the air, for example, temperature, humidity, air motion, and purity.

It was once thought that the effects of poor ventilation were due to air which had lost oxygen and accumulated carbon dioxide. It is now known that these changes are of no physiological concern because they are too small to produce appreciable effects even under the worst conditions of schoolroom ventilation. Air should be free from unpleasant odors and excessive dust, but modern science has taught us that it is the physical or thermal properties of air rather than its chemical properties which are important in ventilation.

The air in properly ventilated rooms assists the body in its function of maintaining a balance between the heat produced in the tissues and the heat lost to the environment. Thermal comfort is dependent, however, not only on air temperature but also on humidity, air movement, and on the nature and amount of clothing. All of these factors have an effect on the rate of heat loss. A little heat is lost from the body with the breath, and a little is lost in warming cold beverages and foods that are taken into the body. Most heat is lost, however, from the slightly moist surface of the skin. When a person is too warm, the evaporation of moisture from the surface of the body is a major source of heat loss. Thus the dryness, or conversely the humidity, of the air is a factor in heat loss.

When heat is lost too rapidly, the person feels chilly and uncomfortable. Comfort is restored by increasing his activity or by supplying warmer air. If heat is lost too slowly, the person perspires and is likely to feel drowsy and depressed, with the possible onset of headache. Overheated classrooms slow up pupils' work and tend to lower resistance to colds and other respiratory infections. While the most comfortable temperature will depend somewhat on the humidity, it is commonly recommended that classrooms should be from 68 to 74 degrees F. Gymnasium temperatures of 55 to 65 degrees, playroom temperatures of 60 to 65 degrees, lunchroom temperatures of 65 to 70 degrees, and shower room temperatures of 70 to 75 degrees are recommended.

Air movement increases evaporation and carries away body heat so that it is a factor in the cooling effect of the air. Air movement which is just barely perceptible is provided in air conditioning.

The ordinary dry-bulb thermometer does not tell us the humidity or the rate of air motion, but it is the only instrument ordinarily available in

HEAT LOSS THROUGH SKIN   HEAT PRODUCTION

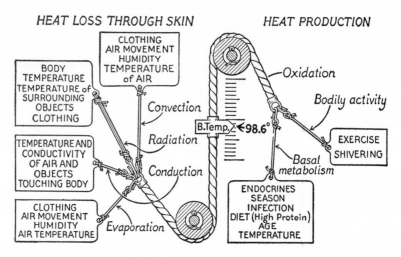

Fig. 30. This diagram shows the factors affecting heat production and heat loss. When the rate of heat production in the body is balanced by the rate of heat loss, the body temperature remains at 98.6° F. Heat production through oxidation within the body pulls toward the raising of body temperature. The rate of oxidation, or heat production, is determined by the basal metabolism of the individual and by his bodily activity. Heat loss tends to pull down the body temperature. Heat is lost through convection, radiation, conduction, and evaporation. In each case the rate of heat loss is determined by the factors listed in the diagram. We keep comfortable by adjusting the room temperature or other factors. For example, when we are working in a warm room the body may be producing more heat than it is losing. Body temperature rises. We perspire; we take off our coats; we open the window to let in cool air. In these ways we increase the rate of heat loss and pull the body temperature back to 98.6° F.

the classroom. Discomfort of the teacher and pupils from an overheated room may not be noticed promptly when one's attention is centered on school work. For this reason regular thermometer inspection (carried out by pupil monitors in Grade III and above) is desirable.

The amount of air needed in a classroom depends on many factors, including the number of pupils, size of the room, type and degree of activity, objectionable odors, and the system of ventilation. From 11 to 38 cubic feet of air per minute per pupil is an acceptable standard, the higher rate being indicated under conditions of greater activity.

Natural ventilation is adequate for small buildings. Inside air is replaced by outside air which makes its way through walls, around doors, and windows. Radiators are placed under windows with window boards to avoid drafts.

Large school buildings and auditoriums require a mechanical system of ventilation in which air is provided by the use of ventilation ducts and fans. In mechanical air conditioning we can wash the air by pulling it through a sheet of water, heat it from the furnace or cool it by refrigerating machines, and adjust the rate of movement as desired. Washing removes dust, pollen, and harmful gases. Water carried mechanically by the air is separated by eliminator plates before the air is heated to the desired temperature for distribution throughout the building.

Lighting

The provision of good school lighting is a highly technical task, requiring the guidance of lighting specialists. Responsibility for its provision rests with architects, engineers, and school officials. Teachers and school health personnel, however, should understand what constitutes good school lighting in order that they may make wise use of the facilities provided.

School lighting should be considered in terms of both quality and quantity.

Schoolroom lighting of good *quality* avoids sharp contrasts between bright and dark surfaces. It avoids reflected glare from working surfaces such as shiny chalkboards, glossy desk tops, glass table tops, or glazed paper. Ideally there should be more light on the task than on the eye. The usual task area confronting the student should be as bright as the surrounding visual environment, or somewhat brighter. Chalkboards and some art and shop tasks are situations where the immediately adjacent surfaces may be brighter than the work areas. In avoiding too great contrasts, the brightness of any surface in the surrounding field should not be greater than ten times nor less than one-third that of the task area.

The *quantity* of light is measured in foot-candles—a foot candle being the amount of light provided by a standard candle at a distance of one foot. One candle power is about equal to one watt consumption in a tungsten lamp. It is difficult to set a fixed standard for the desired quantity of illumination because the amount of light required varies with the work surface and the type of work or activity.[3] The brightness of a surface depends upon the illumination provided by the source of light and the reflection factor of the surface. It is measured in *foot-lamberts*. For example, if 30 foot-candles of light fall upon a green chalkboard with a reflection factor of 50 per cent, 15 foot-lamberts of brightness will be produced.

The amount of *daylight* available varies widely according to the elevation and seasonal course of the sun, whether the sky is clear or clouded, and the location of the room. The distribution of daylight to all parts of the room depends upon its reflection from walls and ceiling, the kind of shades used, and the dimensions of the room itself.

Windows are placed toward the rear of the room and should stop at the line of the front row of desks or some five feet from the front wall. They should be on one side of the room or on one side and at the rear. The tops of windows are as near the ceiling as possible, and the glass area should be in excess of 18 per cent of the floor area.

---

[3]*American Recommended Practice of School Lighting*, which may be obtained from the American Standards Association, 70 East Forty-Fifth Street, New York 17, N. Y. ($0.25), presents standards acceptable to professional groups, as does the NCSC "Guide for Planning School Plants."

Some form of shielding must be provided against direct sunlight and glare from exterior surfaces. Hanging *shades* of proper density are commonly used. They are usually light tan in color and hung at the middle of the window. The rollers are placed one above the other with the upward operating shade on top. In showing motion pictures the room is darkened by a dark shade hung at the top, which is rolled up entirely when not in use.

Venetian blinds, although somewhat more expensive, are used in many schools because they can control lighting and at the same time permit air movement through the windows.

The reflection characteristics of all room *surfaces* is a factor in the amount and kind of light diffused in the room. The percentage of the light reflected by different colors varies sharply. For example, white gloss paint reflects about 81 per cent, ivory 79 per cent, light cream 74 per cent, light buff 58 per cent, light green 47 per cent, and medium gray 30 per cent. Obviously, the accumulation of dirt or dust on a surface reduces its reflectance.

Light-toned surfaces contribute to the lighting and cheerfulness of the room. *Ceilings* are given a nonglossy or flat finish with white paint having a reflectance factor well above 75 per cent. *Walls* are given a reflectance factor of 50 to 70 per cent. Walls between windows may be made somewhat brighter (75 to 80 per cent reflectance factor) and a wall in front of which the instructor commonly stands may be made somewhat darker (50 to 70 per cent reflectance range). *Floors* are of finished light wood or of light uniformly colored tile with a reflectance factor of 20 to 50 per cent.

Chalkboards should be dark enough to allow chalk writing to be readily visible. Reflectance should not exceed 20 per cent. Green nonglare chalkboards and yellow chalk give good results. *Desk tops* should have a nonglossy finish with a reflectance of 35 to 50 per cent.

We should avoid *reflected glare* from glass-covered pictures and from glass panels in cabinets or doors. We can remove the picture or the glass and sandblast or curtain the glass panels.

The School Lighting Committee of the Illuminating Engineering Society, in the 1959 edition of the I.E.S. Lighting Handbook, recommended 30 foot-candles of illumination for reading printed material and 70 foot-candles for reading pencil material. Fifty foot-candles of illumination or more are recommended for sewing rooms, drafting rooms, or situations where speech reading is required. An illumination of 10 foot-candles is suggested for halls, stairways, washrooms, locker rooms, and cafeterias.

Artificial illumination can provide whatever illumination is required, and it is being used increasingly. Indeed, some school buildings have been built without any windows at all. There illumination and climate control are both artificial, and noise is effectively excluded. In some schools which use natural lighting, artificial lights are turned on automatically if the degree of illumination drops below the required standard.

Fluorescent lights, although somewhat expensive to install, provide effective lighting for large rooms with a low operating cost. Properly placed they provide illumination that is steady, even, free from deep shadows, bright, and cheerful. They have largely replaced incandescent lights.

In *indirect lighting* the source of light is not visible to the eye, all of the light being reflected from the ceiling. Indirect lighting is of excellent quality, but it is expensive and *semidirect lighting* is more commonly used. A common type of semidirect lighting uses fluorescent lamps running nearly the length of the room and suspended 2½ to 3 feet below the ceiling. Light is dispensed from a frosted type of glass below the lamps as well as being reflected from the ceiling.

In the maintenance of satisfactory illumination, the teacher and pupils watch natural or artificial lighting to see that objectionable conditions are promptly remedied. They check periodically to see that shades are properly adjusted and that seating arrangements are adjusted to lighting for right-handed and left-handed pupils and for children with eye difficulties. They see that chalkboards are kept clean and that artificial lights are not blackened or dimmed.

Acoustics

Increasing attention is being given to noise control and soundproofing in school buildings. Partitions with low sound transmittal are used. Sound control ceilings reduce the noise from shops and other rooms. A room in the health services suite is soundproofed for the testing of hearing. In some rooms a special sonic floor covering is used.

Seating

Since there is such a wide variance in schools and classrooms, it is not expected that any specific set of standards can be set up and universally followed by all classrooms whether they are of the one-room rural school type or the rooms in a city school system. Each school should set a goal for each classroom that is in keeping with the type of work which is to be done in that particular room. Certain recommendations follow:

1. Select only some good standard make of seat, chair, or table. Various types of seats and desks are available in both wood and metal. Either is very satisfactory when well constructed. Most makes of seats and desks come in sizes one to five or six, number one being designed for students seventeen or over. Movable desk chairs and table chairs come in several sizes. The sizes should be carefully selected, depending on the sizes of the pupils who will use them.

2. When tables are used, the individual type rather than the group type seems preferable because the light for each pupil is then the same and there is less need of shifting chairs to face the teacher. Tables with drawers in which the tablets, pencils, etc., may be kept, are, of course, very desirable.

3. Good posture while seated should always be kept in mind. Each seat should be the correct height for the pupil. The seat should be low enough so that, when the pupil sits well back in it, his feet rest flat on the floor, and high enough that his thighs are in contact with the seat. The desk or table should be placed so as to give the pupil's knees ample room, and the back of the

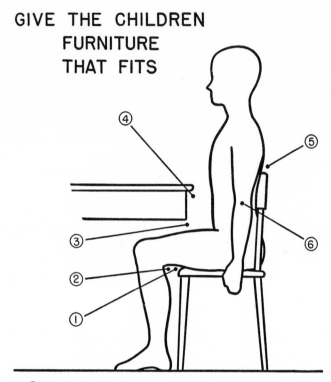

GIVE THE CHILDREN FURNITURE THAT FITS

1. NO PRESSURE UNDER THE KNEES
2. FREE SPACE BACK OF INSIDE ANGLE OF KNEE
3. ROOM ABOVE THE THIGHS
4. BACK EDGE OF TABLE OVERLAPS FRONT EDGE OF CHAIR
5. LOW CHAIR BACK, OPEN AT BOTTOM; SUPPORT FOR HOLLOW OF BACK ONLY
6. TABLE TOP HIGHER THAN ELBOW WHEN ARM IS STRAIGHT

Fig. 31. From the Yearbook, *American School Buildings.* (Courtesy American Association of School Administrators.)

seat should fit the natural contour of the student's back. Where the teacher finds no chair or seat the proper height for some child, then a board or platform footrest should be improvised to suit the child's needs.

4. The desk or writing surface should be at the proper height so that the student may write while seated squarely and without having to elevate one shoulder out of line with the other while writing. The teacher should realize that he is dealing with a growing child, and the seat and table assigned at the beginning of a term should be periodically checked to make sure it is satisfactory.

5. The eyesight and hearing ability of each pupil should determine the location in the room where he should sit, irrespective of his height. The policy of arranging seats and desks so the short ones are in front and the tall ones are in the rear gives a pleasing appearance, but does not always meet the individual needs of children. The physical comfort and proper seating of growing children should always be kept in mind.

6. Seats should be placed in such a way that the pupils using them will get the best possible light. The diagonal seating arrangement is advisable in some classrooms to secure better lighting results and often is preferable to the orthodox rectangular method.

7. Best modern practice endorses movable seats. They are specially important in rural schools where the one room may be needed for games, entertainments, and parties.

8. Seats should be placed in a manner which will permit a thorough cleaning of the floor each day.

9. The surfaces of the tables and desks should be kept smooth, clean, and well finished, but free from glossy varnishes.

10. Seats should not be placed too close to a radiator or stove or in a place where the student will be in a draft.

11. Ample space should be provided for a student's books, either in a desk or in a locker. In cases where hall lockers are provided, there should also be a book-rack or some other arrangement in each room where books can be placed while not actually being used. Books under chairs have not proved satisfactory, as the books fall out whenever chairs are moved.

Custodial care

In the modern school building, the custodian is better described as a maintenance engineer than as a janitor. He needs an understanding of the problems of environmental health which we have discussed in this chapter. Educational requirements are set for his appointment, and many states now provide short courses of in-service training for these men, dealing with such subjects as basic bacteriology, cleansing agents, cleansing and sanitizing methods, pest control, and other problems.[4]

Checking environmental conditions

As has been indicated, the best use of available facilities by the school staff is most important. Teachers and children can do many things to maintain a healthful school environment, even though major structural changes must be made by school authorities.

A stimulus for keeping sanitary status at a high level is the periodic inspection of buildings and grounds by appropriate health authorities. Such an inspection should be made at least once a year. The person who makes the inspection will vary according to the size of the community, the organization of sanitary and school health services, and the health personnel available. Commonly it is a sanitarian from the health department. It may be the school physician or school nurse. In some instances it may be the health officer. It is highly desirable that the principal accompany the person making the inspection. The school administration should be made aware of all deviations from health standards. The principal, health teacher, health coordinator, or school nurse may well make informal and unofficial sanitary inspections of the school with pupils to

---

[4]An outline of such a course is to be seen in "Sanitation in School Housekeeping," a custodial training course available from Manager, Publications and Textbook Services, State Department of Education, Tallahassee, Florida, Price 50¢.

check conditions and demonstrate environmental health factors. Pupils may also observe the collection of samples of water for analyses, and inspection of school wells, toilets, and food-handling facilities by the inspecting health official.

A school health appraisal form may be secured from health authorities or prepared from such standards as are given here. (See also Chapter 19.) The rating or scoring of a school environment is a stimulus to improvement. Sometimes an organized community campaign may be required to present the need and secure better environmental conditions.

Educational values

In a good school health program pupils gain a sense of responsibility and respect for the care and proper use of property and the rights of others involved. The difficult task of maintaining a clean school and the responsibility of each pupil and teacher for preventing unnecessary dirt and litter become clear. Pupils realize the contribution to the discomfort of other pupils and possible danger to health by such personal practices as placing lips and mouth on drinking fountains, spitting, improper disposal of rubbish, and improper use of toilets and sinks. They gain satisfaction from attractive surroundings, and learn to appreciate a clean, wholesome, and healthful environment. The study of the sanitation of his school and community is a valuable part of the pupil's education in health.

References

American Association for Health, Physical Education, and Recreation and National Education Association: *Health Aspects of the School Lunch Program,* Washington, D. C., 1956, National Education Association.

American Association of School Administrators: *American School Buildings,* Twenty-Seventh Yearbook, Washington, D. C., 1948, National Education Association.

American Public Health Association: *Recommended Practice for Design, Equipment and Operation of Swimming Pools and Other Public Bathing Places,* New York, 1949, American Public Health Association, 56 pp.

California State Department of Education: *Check List for a Healthful and Safe School Environment,* rev. 1957, Sacramento, California. Prepared by Patricia J. Hill, Consultant in Health Education.

Carrier, W. H., Cherne, R. E., and Grant, W. A.: *Modern Air Conditioning, Heating and Ventilating,* ed. 2, New York, 1950, Pitman Publishing Corporation.

Ehlers, V. M., and Steel, E. W.: *Municipal and Rural Sanitation,* ed. 6, New York, 1965, McGraw-Hill Book Company, Inc.

Hopkins, E. S., and Schulze, W. H.: *Practice of Sanitation,* Baltimore, 1954, The Williams & Wilkins Company.

Illuminating Engineering Society: *American Standard Practice for School Lighting,* New York, 1948, Illuminating Engineering Society.

Linn, H. H., et al.: *The School Custodian's Housekeeping Handbook,* New York, 1948, Teachers College, Columbia University.

National Council on Schoolhouse Construction: *Guide for Planning School Plants,* East Lansing, Michigan, 1965, the Council, Floyd G. Parker, 409 Erickson Hall, Michigan State University, 156 pp.

National Education Association: *Common Sense in School Lighting,* Washington, D. C. 1956, the Association.

National Education Association: *Planning America's School Buildings,* Washington, D. C., 1960, the Association.
National Education Association and American Medical Association Joint Committee: *Healthful School Living,* Chicago, 1957, American Medical Association, 535 North Dearborn Street, Chicago 10, Ill.
Perkins, L. B.: *Workplace for Learning,* New York, 1957, Reinhold Publishing Corp.
School Plant Section, State Department of Education, Tallahassee, Florida: *Sanitation in School Housekeeping, Resource Manual Custodial Training Course.* Available from Manager, Publications and Textbook Services, State Department of Education, Tallahassee, Florida. Price 50 cents.

Part four

Health services and health problems

Chapter ix

Health protection and health education through school health services

In general, school health services are preventive or protective, advisory, and educational. They do not take over the responsibility of the family for medical care. Preventing the spread of communicable disease and the medical examination of athletes were early functions. They are still important, as is also the arrangement for emergency care in case of accident or sickness. The appraisal of pupil health makes possible professional advice to the pupil and his family on personal health, and advice to the school on the adaptation of the school program to the needs of the individual child. The school system also profits from the advice of health experts on environmental control and the organization of the program. School health services contribute to the health education of children, not only through informing the child concerning his own health assets and liabilities, but also through the child's contact with medical and allied personnel. The work of the physician, dentist, and nurse in the school determines, in large measure, the pupil attitude toward medical service. It provides many poignant pupil experiences which contribute to his education in health.

It is important to make the most of learning opportunities presented. Teachers must know what the school health services are, if they are to cooperate effectively and make use of the services educationally. The teacher needs to know what each of the health specialists does for the child, what he does for the teacher, and what he expects of the teacher. The medical, dental, and nursing professions and the parents should also know what the school health services are. The school administrator makes provision for correlating the work of the health services with the instructional policies of the school.

The direct contribution of the physician to the education of the child will depend upon his background and experience in school health work and also upon the amount of time available. In many school systems the number of health examinations required of the physician makes it impossible for him to give the child anything like the individual attention which he would have provided in his own office. It is unfortunate when the physician's contact with the child must be so hurried as to be impersonal and abrupt. There is then little possibility of persuading that child that physicians are thorough, scientific, friendly persons whose guidance should be sought in health as well as in disease.

The school nurse is an interpreter of the medical service, health conditions, and health needs to teachers, parents, and children. But only when teachers join her in the educational aspects of school health services does she become most effective.

The teacher, because he is with the class day after day, can best prepare the children for their contact with physician and nurse. He can tell them what to expect and how to cooperate. He can assure them in advance that physicians and nurses are their friends. The teacher can clarify the experience the child has had with the school health service, making it more meaningful, and prevent misunderstanding. If a child has secured glasses, it is the teacher, not the physician or nurse, who can see that he wears them every day. The nurse-teacher conferences regarding the health of individual children and the cooperative efforts of both teacher and nurse which grow out of these conferences are most valuable links between health education and health services.

Six major activities of school health services are: (1) the health appraisal of pupils and school personnel (2) follow-up and promotion of the correction of health defects (3) the prevention and control of communicable diseases (4) the provision of emergency care in case of accident or sudden illness (5) the provision of special health services for exceptional children and (6) the supervision of environmental sanitation. The control of communicable disease and problems of environmental health are considered in Chapter 10 and Chapter 8 respectively. The other activities of school health services are discussed in this chapter.

Health appraisal

Health appraisal is the process of determining the health status of the child, using not only medical and dental examinations, but also health histories, screening tests, the observations of teachers and nurses, and psychological examinations. Of basic importance are the health examinations made periodically for all pupils and the examinations of individual pupils referred for special reasons. These examinations make use of information acquired by teachers and nurses in their observation of pupils. Data from intelligence tests and other psychological examinations are usually available. The parent can provide information about the health of the child if he or she is present.

The school physician is a health advisor. His examinations are made to determine the health status of the child and to detect the presence of physical defects or impaired health. He uses the opportunity presented by the health examination to advise pupils and parents regarding needed hygienic procedures. He decides whether there is a condition which needs attention. If so, the child is referred to the family physician or the clinic for diagnosis and treatment.

Preschool examinations are highly desirable. If the examination of children from infancy to school entrance is neglected, many children will enter school with defects and health problems detrimental to their normal growth and general health. Adjustment to school life is difficult enough for the young child without the unnecessary burden of visual defects, decayed teeth, diseased tonsils and adenoids, poor nutrition, or other handicaps. Schools, public health authorities, private physicians, and voluntary health agencies cooperate in stressing the importance of regular health supervision during this period. Such groups cooperate in a campaign for the examination of preschool children. These examinations take place during the early summer in order that there will be time for the correction of defects before the child enters school in the fall.

A procedure for giving these examinations is often worked out with private physicians, and the findings are transmitted to the school. It is helpful if the school health record form is used for such examinations, as it assures accurate and uniform information regarding the health status of the children.

In *school examinations* the present tendency is to give a limited number of routine examinations to all children and to give priority to the examination of children in special need of attention. In most states, the frequency of medical examinations of school children is determined by law. Many states require an examination at or just before school entrance and an examination of all children every three or four years thereafter. In addition, individual children and certain groups of children are referred for health examinations. Children new to the school district who have not had examinations are usually examined upon arrival.

In *individual referrals*, the teacher commonly initiates the action which will ultimately result in the selection of a given child for nonroutine examinations. The teacher should have the benefit of consultation with a school nurse, and the two should then work together in selecting pupils for referral to a physician or dentist. The closer the cooperative relationship between the teacher and nurse, the better will be the results obtained. Children who have failed to gain any weight for several months or who have had repeated absence for illness should be considered for referral. Examinations are also given for children who fail to secure grade promotion, for children leaving school and requiring work certificates, and for high school athletes. Special attention should be directed toward determining and correcting physical, mental, and emotional defects of children *failing to make their grades*. The teacher has firsthand knowledge of these facts and should relay the information to the school nurse or urge the parents to have a special physical examination of the child.

The examination of children *leaving school and requiring work certificates* should comply with principles evolved for health examinations

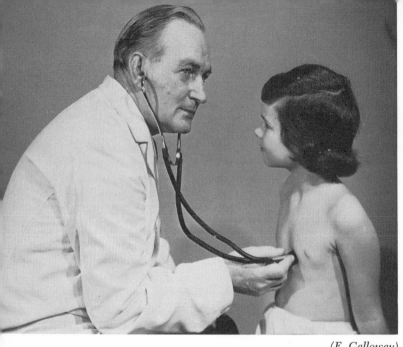

Fig. 32. The health examination is a learning experience.

(E. Galloway)

generally. The physician should know the type of activity into which the child expects to enter.

All candidates for the *school athletic teams* should be examined by a doctor of medicine. The physician should state that the pupil is or is not physically fit to take part in the designated sports. If the pupil is unfit for the sport in question, the physician should indicate the activities in which he may safely engage. Following an injury or an illness during the same season, the pupil should be re-examined before participating again. Examinations should be repeated each year and approval for participation in one sport should not be transferable to a more strenuous sport.

The teacher should have an intelligent understanding of the health examination. If he creates the proper setting and atmosphere in which the examinations are carried out, the children will not fear the examination; indeed they will be eager and interested. If the pupil does not have the right attitude, the school physician will be working under a handicap.

The nature of the examination. The examination should be as thorough and comprehensive as possible with full realization that it cannot be diagnostically exhaustive.

It should be broad enough in scope to discover all abnormalities which can be detected by observation, and should include: (1) a careful physical examination and a careful history, with tests (which may be done by teacher or nurse) for vision, hearing, and speech; (2) a consideration of those subjective and behavior problems called to the examiner's attention by the teacher, nurse, or parent; and (3) the presentation to both parent and pupil of a practical amount of health information concerning conditions or defects found. It is desirable to record in some detail the condition of teeth, vision, hearing, nutrition, and state of mental or social development. The parent should be present at the examination of the elementary school pupil, in order to learn what parental action may be needed. The school nurse does the recording and later can intelligently discuss and review cases with the teacher and parent. There is special need for the primary school teacher to be present, because of the intimate knowledge he has about the child. He has participated in tests for vision, hearing, and speech. He has weighed and measured the pupils, noted the causes for any absences they have had, and observed departures from normal health or behavior. His presence at the examination further increases his knowledge of the child. If he is not present, the physician's findings and recommendations should be reported to him.

School health examiners should take as much time as is practical to make the examination interesting and educational to the child, teacher, and parent; and the entire procedure should be a pleasant health experience which should influence the child and parent to demand good medical care and motivate them to more healthful living.

Commendation is freely given for correct posture and good health habits. Detailed individualized education is not the primary objective on the part of the physician. However, the examiner should take time to explain the implication of serious defects, and to answer all questions. It may at times be desirable to talk to the group or class as a whole on important or prevalent defects or problems.

The reaction of pupils and parents will be determined by the personalities and professional relationships of physicians, nurses, and teachers and by the administrative conduct of the examination quite as much as by the specific advice given and received. The absence of confusion and undue noise, the efficient working of the staff, the courteous treatment of pupils and parents, calm discussion, the maintenance of friendly and confidential relationships, and an interest in the child's mental and emotional as well as physical welfare are all important elements in a good health examination.

The examination should take place in a room which is warm and quiet. It is not given in the presence of other pupils. The child cannot be properly examined when dressed. In some examinations the child strips to the waist and removes shoes and stockings, a slip-over or other chest covering being provided for the older girls. In other schools all clothing is removed and, in addition to the slip-over for girls, each is given a garment to cover the genitals. Privacy is easy to obtain in the physician's office; it is sometimes difficult in a one-room school.

The pupil should be examined from head to foot, including an examination for hernia in the boys. With sufficient privacy, a stethoscope, otoscope, nasal speculum, tongue depressor, and a good light, the examiner can observe the expression, mannerism, alertness, skin texture, and muscle firmness, as well as physical defects. He gives consideration to the history, subjective symptoms, and behavior.

The number of students examined per hour. In general it is recommended that an average of from ten to fifteen minutes per child be allowed

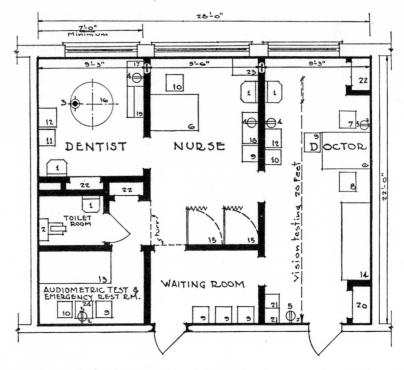

Fig. 33. Suggested plan for conversion of the regular classroom into a health unit for doctor, dentist, and nurse. Scale: 1 inch = 1 foot.

1. Lavatory.
2. Water closet.
3. Floor outlet.
4. Outlet for sterilizer.
5. Duplex outlet.
6. Desk.
7. Chair, doctor.
8. Chair, parent.
9. Chair, child.
10. Chair, nurse.
11. Chair, dental assistant.
12. Recording table.
13. Cot.
14. Examining table.
15. Dressing table.
16. Dental chair.
17. Sterilizer.
18. First aid cabinet.
19. Dental cabinet.
20. Closet, blankets, linen.
21. Locker.
22. Closet, cupboard.
23. File case.
24. Audiometer.

This plan is recommended by the Department of Health and the Department of Public Instruction of Pennsylvania. (Courtesy Department of Health, Commonwealth of Pennsylvania.)

as the period during which the parent and child are with the examiner, exclusive of the time necessary for vision, hearing, and speech testing, weighing and measuring, and time consumed in other routine preparatory work. Notes are made at the time. If more than six examinations per hour are scheduled, all parties concerned should clearly understand that some valuable features of a health examination are being sacrificed. If there are several examiners (perhaps dividing the examination according to specialties) the number of pupils examined per hour will be somewhat increased. The time needed for individual pupils will vary, of course.

Health examinations in the physician's private office. Experience has shown that promtional work by health personnel, educators, and others tends to motivate a large percentage of people to take their children to their own physicians for routine physical examinations.

If the examination is to be made by the family physician he should be well informed regarding the objectives of the school health program. He should record his findings on the health record card furnished by the school in order that examinations may have the same scope.

The main advantages of this plan for pupil health examinations are that:

1. It accomplishes the objective of getting the pupil under the supervision of the family physician by one direct move.

2. It retains the valued individual physician-patient relationship.

3. It maintains or develops the sense of parental responsibility for such services.

Reaching all the family physicians of the community is not always an easy task. School Health Councils and school health committees of local medical and dental societies are helpful in planning school health programs and in developing mutual understanding and cooperative relationships. Many family physicians are overburdened with the acute emergencies of a busy private practice and have little time for the health examination of an apparently well child. As a result there is often oversight in reporting findings to schools and reluctance to fill out school records. These difficulties can be greatly lessened by mutual planning as mentioned above. Although many physicians and dentists are taking time for the health supervision and health education of their young patients, there is usually a tendency to underemphasize health education possibilities.

Dental examinations. Beginning at the age of 3, each child should have his teeth examined, and thereafter as frequently as advised by the dentist. Certainly every child should have his teeth examined and correction of dental defects made before entering school for the first time. Dental inspection should be made at least once (better twice) each year after the child starts to school. An x-ray examination should be made when the dentist finds it to be needed.

Local dental groups in cooperation with school authorities should decide where dental examinations are to be held—whether in the schools or in the offices of private practitioners. In many communities satisfactory cooperative programs were developed in which all school children went to private dentists or dental clinics for dental examinations and needed dental care.

In the larger cities, having all the children go to the office of a private dentist or dental clinic, desirable as it is, is usually an impractical procedure. Examination by a dentist at school can be a highly motivating experience in educating children to seek corrections, especially when the program is correlated with classroom instruction. The school dentist, as a resource person in health education, can render an important service through dental health talks and demonstrations of oral hygiene methods and techniques.

Medical examinations for school personnel. As we have noted earlier, the health appraisal activities of the school health services provide medical examinations for school personnel. This activity is in the interest of the health of teachers and other employed persons and in the interest of the health of the pupils. No school employe who is not in sound health and free from communicable disease should be permitted to work in direct contact with the boys and girls. This means a pre-employment examination for all school employes within six months prior to the date that work begins. A re-examination should be made if serious illness occurs after the original examination prior to starting work.

The extent of the examination is decided by the employing agency. Many boards of education prefer to have the examinations given by the school physician. In other school systems, the examination is made by the applicant's own physician, and the school systems provide forms upon which the reports of such examinations are made. Some states have a legal requirement that all new employes must submit a health certificate from a physician licensed to practice medicine in all its branches within the state.

In-service examinations of teachers and other school employes, similar in scope to the pre-employment examination, are usually required at regular intervals. All information in these examinations is regarded as strictly confidential and the detailed health records remain in the custody of the examining physician. Some states recommend that a statement of physical fitness signed by a physician should be presented to the school board annually and that the physician's fee should be paid by the board if the employing board specifies the physician.

In addition to these routine examinations teachers may be expected to have an examination following illness. In returning to school following a communicable disease, teachers and other school employes should be subject to the same checks and clearances as those established for pupils.

Follow-up and corrective activities

Examinations are of little value unless there is a planned follow-up program. Parents, teachers, and pupils should be informed as to the findings of the examinations. The most effective plan includes a health conference at the conclusion of the examination, at which time the physician discusses the status of the pupil's health. After findings are thoroughly understood, then all concerned should work together for meeting health needs. The parent should consult the family physician for verification or for extending the scope of the examination if needed.

With proper safeguards, children should be excused from classes to meet appointments for correction of defects, such as those of teeth or eyes, when requested by doctors making the corrections. In many instances,

Fig. 34. If corrections are to be effected, parents must understand the condition needing attention.

corrections should be made in the early part of the day when the child is rested and emotionally more fitted to submit to treatment.

The teacher has a major responsibility for stimulating an interest in having corrective work done. In the instance of difficult cases, the nurse instructs the parents in regard to the importance of medical advice and treatment. After corrective work has been finished and the report of these corrections has been received, the teacher and the nurse again confer in regard to the child's progress.

The use of clinical facilities will, of course, vary according to the economic status of the individual pupils and the socio-economic resources of the various communities.

In most communities there are, economically speaking, three groups of pupils to be considered: first, those who can afford to make use of the services of physicians and dentists; second, those who can pay in part for these services; and third, those who must have the necessary medical and dental work done without charge.

Each group presents an entirely different problem to the school health service. The first group needs only the routine of informing pupil, parents, and physician or dentist, and a check-up to see that the defect has been remedied or is receiving treatment. For the second and third groups it is recommended that the school, health department, welfare department, and allied agencies examine their resources and organize a system which will bring needy and marginal children under medical and dental care and make available to all, as needed, other, related community services and facilities.

Some communities have solved this problem through a connection with the city welfare department which makes home investigations and keeps available a city-wide file of family economic information. On the basis of this information the various schools recommend partial-payment patients to clinics. Some schools have set up service-club-sponsored health loan funds to help in such programs. The bill is paid from the fund at once, and the pupils or their parents repay the fund over a period of months, or the pupils work out the bill as student aid. In certain instances no repayment is required.

Certain school-wide clinics or services are carried on in many schools regardless of economic status. These provide tuberculosis case-finding, vaccination against smallpox, inoculation against diphtheria, and nutritional guidance. Many cities have a dental clinic, either endowed or tax-supported, to provide dental care for children from medically indigent families, either free or for a token payment. All resources available in the community should be used in order to carry on an adequate and effective program.

Prevention and control of communicable diseases

This major activity of school health services is discussed at length in Chapter 10. Appendix A presents a suggested set of rules and regulations indicating school procedures with respect to each disease.

School emergency services

The emergency care of pupils who become sick or injured on school premises is a responsibility of the school. Every school should have well-defined procedures for pupil protection. Plans should be in effect to cope with major disaster, whether from flood, fire, tornado, earthquake, or other cause. Preparedness for such events involves cooperative planning with local major disaster and civil defense authorities.

For handling day-by-day illnesses and accidents, every school should:

1. Require teachers and other school personnel to have had recent training in first aid and in the recognition of the early signs and symptoms of communicable disease.
2. Provide a health office or nurse's room in each school with standard first-aid equipment and supplies.
3. Provide first-aid kits in all departments of school where special hazards exist, e.g., laboratories, home economics rooms, shops, gymnasiums, school buses.
4. Provide an isolation room or facility with screened-off cots for pupils suspected of communicable disease and awaiting transportation home.
5. Use a pupil record card, signed by the parents, for reference in case of illness or accident to a pupil, indicating whom to call and where to take a pupil if the parent cannot be reached. Such a card should include the following information:
   Parent's home address and telephone number
   Father's and mother's place of business and telephone number
   Address and telephone number of relative or neighbor in case parent cannot be reached

Address and telephone number of family physician
Hospital which parent prefers to use

6. Keep at hand an emergency hospital card. In cities where such facilities are available, the address and telephone numbers should be on a card beside the school telephone.
7. Use a system of accident reporting and records for protection of the school staff and the district in event of legal complications.
8. Provide a statement of emergency procedures for the care of accidents and acute illness. This may be developed by the school district in cooperation with the local health department, the hospitals, or the medical society.

General policies for emergency care of illness and accidents at school

1. Immediate and adequate first-aid care should be given. In serious cases the school physician or nurse, if available, should be called.
2. Contact the parent and have the parent take charge as soon as possible.
3. If parent is home but cannot provide transportation, the school should have a staff member take the child home. If attention en route may be needed, the school nurse should accompany the child.
4. A sick or injured child should never be taken home and left unless a responsible adult is there to care for him.
5. When a sick or injured pupil is taken home and further care is needed, the parent should be instructed to call the family physician. If the parents have no family physician or cannot afford private care, they should be instructed how to proceed in order to obtain the services of a physician or hospital.
6. In serious emergencies requiring prompt medical attention or hospital treatment, if parent is not available or emergency procedures previously agreed upon with the parent cannot be followed, send for ambulance or take the child to the nearest public facility or receiving hospital.
7. In serious cases, a follow-up home call by the school nurse to determine whether the parents have arranged for the necessary professional attention will, in some instances, avoid neglect of the child and future misunderstanding.

First aid.[1] Every school, regardless of size, should be adequately equipped to give first aid for the major or minor accidents which occur on school premises. The larger schools are built with a health office or suite as a part of the administrative unit. The first-aid facility is usually equipped with a medicine cabinet, hot and cold running water, a heating unit, a counter or dressing table, a cot, a stretcher, and two blankets.

The following supplies are suggested for the *first-aid cabinet.* Quantities are on the basis of 100 pupils.

STANDARD UNIT	DESCRIPTION
1 Bottle	Alcohol, 70% (water 30%) or rubbing alcohol
1 Bottle	Ammonia, aromatic spirits of, U.S.P. (4 oz.)
1 Box	Applicators, throat, wooden (865 to box)
12 Rolls	Bandage, gauze, 1-inch (10 yd.)
12 Rolls	Bandage, gauze, 2-inch (10 yd.)
8 Packets	Bandage, triangular
2 Packages	Cotton, absorbent, sterile (¼ lb.)
1 Carton	Cups, drinking, paper (100 to ctn.)
1 Box	Dressings, finger, ⅜-inch, Band Aid (100 to box)

---

[1] Appendix B presents a manual of first-aid procedures.

STANDARD UNIT	DESCRIPTION
1 Box	Dressings, finger, 1-inch wide, Band Aid (100 to box)
2 Packages	Gauze, sterile, (1 sq. yd.)
1 Packet	Gauze, sterile, plain, pad 2 by 2 inches, in germproof envelope (100 to pkt.)
1 Packet	Gauze, sterile, plain, pad 3 by 3 inches, in germproof envelope (100 to pkt.)
2 Bottles	Germicide solution, for first aid (4 oz.) (local preference)
1 Can	Magnesium sulfate, tech., crystals (Epsom Salts) (5 lb.)
1 Bottle	Oil, castor, U.S.P. (1 oz.)
1 Bottle	Oil of cloves (1 oz.)
2 Tubes	Petrolatum, plain white (2 oz.)
4 Cards	Pins, safety, No. 2½, 1½-inch (8 to card)
2 Bottles	Soap, green tincture, U.S.P. (8 oz.)
1 Pound	Sodium bicarbonate, U.S.P. (bulk)
4 Each	Splints, for arm, 3 by 17 inches Yucca No. 1 or equivalent
2 Each	Splints for leg, 3½ by 30 inches Yucca No. 1 or equivalent
2 Each	Splints, for thigh, 3½ by 20 inches Yucca No. 1 or equivalent
4 Rolls	Tape, adhesive, ½-inch (10 yd.)
4 Rolls	Tape, adhesive, 1-inch (10 yd.)
4 Rolls	Tape, adhesive, 2-inch (10 yd.)
10 Each	Thermometers, clinical, Fahrenheit, 1-min.
2 Packages	Tongue blades (100 to pkg.)
1 Roll	Toweling, crepe paper, 18 inches wide, (110 ft. to roll)
1 Package	Toweling, crepe paper, approximately 30 by 40 inches, ¼ fold (24 sheets)
1 Pair	Scissors
1 Pair	Forceps, splinter
2 Pair	Forceps, dressing
1 Dozen	Eye droppers
1 Each	Hot water bottle
1 Each	Icebag
1 Each	Wash basin
2 Each	Dressing basins
1 Each	Red Cross First Aid Textbook

The *first-aid kits* provided in the laboratories and other departments of the school are usually equipped from the cabinet of first-aid supplies in the health office. A member of the school staff, preferably the school nurse, is given the responsibility of inspecting and maintaining the first-aid cabinet and kits. She recommends to the principal when additional supplies should be requisitioned.

In all serious accidents the most qualified person available should administer first aid. If a school physician or nurse is in the vicinity, he or she should be summoned. As indicated above, every effort is made to contact the parent and get the child under competent medical attention.

Minor first aid should be given whenever possible by the teacher, school clerk, or other member of the school staff. The school nurse's time (which is often limited) can usually be used to better advantage in carrying out her more important professional duties of health counseling, follow-up, and health education.

When a principal, teacher, clerk, or other nonmedical school employe administers first aid, he can be held responsible, legally, only for the exercise of common sense and good judgment which might reasonably be expected of any layman in a similar situation. From the legal point of view it is extremely important that duplicate copies of accident reports be kept, giving full details of the nature of the accident and all the procedures which were followed for the protection of the pupil. The "Standard Student Accident Reporting System of the National Safety Council" is recommended.[2]

Health services for exceptional children

Some children need special health services and educational adjustments because of physical defects, recent illness, or emotional maladjustment. We have discussed these individual problems in Chapter 5, indicating the kind of supervision and guidance which is needed in each case. In the majority of instances, the child continues in the regular class. He may follow an adjusted program of work under the continued observation of teacher, nurse, and physician.

A special program is needed for children who, for some health reason, cannot be instructed in the regular school program. The problem of placing physically exceptional children in special schools or special classes is often vexing. Some persons feel that to remove a child from a regular classroom is to brand him as an abnormal child. Others argue that every physically exceptional child should be removed from the regular grades to prevent his having to compete with children who are not handicapped.

A good general rule to follow is to enroll a child in a regular classroom if his physical or mental condition permits and if he can get a sound education there. If his condition requires constant medical supervision, or if he is apt to do himself injury, he must be enrolled in a special class. Special teaching procedures can be provided by enrollment either in a special class or in a regular class with part-time special teaching.

Special classes make provisions for sight conservation, the mentally advanced or retarded, the cardiac, speech reading, speech improvement, rest and nutrition, and problems of social maladjustment.

Health records

Adequate, accessible, and continuous health records are needed to reflect the activities of school health services in respect to health appraisal, follow-up, communicable disease control, emergency care, and the health guidance of exceptional children.

The most important single record is the *health record of the individual child*. This is sometimes called the medical record. The school health record suggested by the Health Records Committee of the School Health Section of the American Public Health Association is shown here as an

---

[2]Available, with instructions, from the National Safety Council, 425 North Michigan Ave., Chicago 11, Ill.

SCHOOL HEALTH RECORD*

M □ F □ Mo.............Day.............Yr.............

| Last name | First | Middle | Sex | Birthdate | | | Birthplace |

| Addresses | | Home phone | Schools | | Rm. (pencil) |

Parent or guardian.........................Business address.................................Phone..........
Father's occupation.........................Mother's occupation.............................Phone..........
Family physician.........................Address.................................Phone..........
Family status: F............M............Bro. No.........Ages.........Sis. No.........Ages.........

Personal history, illnesses, operations

Date or check		Date or check
Accidents	Mumps	
Allergy	Operation	
Chorea	Poliomyelitis	
Diabetes	Rheumatic fever	
Ear infection	Speech defect	
Epilepsy	Tuberculosis—Self	
German measles	Tuberculosis—Family	
Headaches	Upper respiratory	
Heart disease	Others	
Hernia	Others	
Measles	Others	

Immunization history

	Basic	Booster	Booster
Diphtheria			
Tetanus			
Whooping cough			
Polio			

	Date	Result	Date	Result
Smallpox				
Tuberculin				
Chest X-ray				

Teacher or nurse observations and tests

Date	Grade	Height	Weight	Vision Without Glasses R	L	Vision With Glasses R	L	Plus sphere	Speech	Behavior	Scholarship	Attendance	Hearing Date	R	L	Dental record Date	Obv. decay	Cleaning	Gums	Irreg. teeth

Date	Teachers', principals', or coordinators' notes (please initial)

*Prepared by the Health Records Committee of the School Health Section of the American Public Health Association.

Last name .... First .... Middle ....

Mo.............Day.............Yr.............
Birthdate

Physician's record of examinations

Date	Grade	Eyes	Ears	Nose-throat		Teeth	Gums	Glands	Heart		Lungs	Abdomen		Genitalia	Nervous system	Nutrition	Orthopedic			Skin, scalp	Other	Name of Physician
				Tonsils	Mouth Breath.				Organ.	Funct.		Hernia	Other				Posture	Feet	Other			

0—Normal, no defect
x—Slight defect, keep under observation
xx—Defect recommended for treatment
xxx—Gross defect, immediate attention urged
Circle defect symbol when corrected

G1—Wearing glasses
(xx)—Defect cured
T—Under treatment
I—Irremediable

Physicians' comments, recommendations, physical education assignments

Nurse's follow-up notes and home call records

(Back)

example. Record cards are usually 8 inches by 10 inches or 5 inches by 8 inches for convenience in filing and are printed on both sides. They contain space for recording family data, communicable disease experience and immunization, the various physical defects, and the status of growth, vision, hearing, teeth, and diet. If a preschool health record for the child is available, it accompanies the school record or the essential facts are transferred to the school card. Some space is left on the school card for recording unusual conditions and recommendations.

The degree of the physical defect is commonly indicated. You will note that in the code on the card shown here, O is used for normal, × for a minor defect which should be checked from time to time, × × for a defect which needs correction, and × × × for any condition demanding immediate attention. A corrected defect is indicated by circling the code item, as ⊕

The purpose of this card is as follows:

To provide a summary or history of the child's development and health through the infant and preschool period. (This summary may be transcribed from the *infant and preschool record* by the public health nurse.)

To provide a guide for selecting children for whom immunizations should be advised.

To provide the teacher with information on the immunity status of individual children. (This information should be referred to when school children have been exposed to a communicable disease or during an epidemic. Susceptible children manifesting symptoms should be excluded from the group early.)

To provide the public health nurse with information on which to base investigation of home contacts of children.

To provide a record of the school physician's findings in order that advice may be given the parents regarding need for medical care.

To aid the teacher in understanding the relation between physical well-being and behavior.

To provide information which the public health nurse will use when home visits in the interest of the health of the child are indicated.

To provide information on the most essential foods in the child's diet.

To provide for the study of the growth record of individual children in order that remedial measures may be instituted when indicated. (A separate record card may be used for monthly weighing.)

To provide information on the visual acuity of individual children in order that parents may be advised regarding need for eye examinations by an ophthalmologist when this is indicated, and in order that adjustments in lighting and seating may be made for children having defective vision.

To provide for information on the ability of individual children to hear. (Children with symptoms of defective hearing should be placed under treatment of a specialist as early as possible.)

To provide information on dental health status in order that parents may be advised regarding the implications of abscessed teeth, diseased gums, or lost teeth and so that corrections may be made.

Various *sources of information* are used in making the record.

Information on immunization and history of communicable diseases is obtained from parents at the time children register on the opening day of school. Parents are encouraged to bring certificates of immunization to school. A record of subsequent communicable disease is made concurrently during the school year. Some school systems have used a health history form like the one shown here, which includes data on immunization and the communicable disease history. These forms are filled out by parents when registering the child or are taken home and later returned to the school. The information is transferred to the child's health record by the teacher or school nurse.

The physician's findings are recorded at the time of the examination. The recording may be done by the school nurse, the teacher, or a volunteer worker. All recordings should be signed and dated by the individual making the examination, report, or observation. School health records are often called for in connection with litigation involving the school child. Only abbreviations or symbols should be used which will be understood by all school personnel.

The results of vision and hearing tests are recorded by the teacher or nurse.

Disease records show the year the child had the disease. Immunizations are recorded when the series of required doses is completed. Month, day, and year should be stated when this information is available. Tuberculin tests are recorded as positive (pos.) or negative (neg.)

Dental defects are recorded in terms of decay, abscessed teeth, or lost permanent teeth. Malocclusion and diseased gums are recorded by "yes" or "no." If a dentist makes the examination the record will be more specific. Some dental services use what is known as the DMF index, which refers to the number of teeth that are decayed, missing, or filled. This index gives an indication of the general level of the child's dental health; but it does not have the meaning for primary school children that it does for students who already have their permanent teeth. The reason is that teeth from the primary set are coming out.

In some schools it is customary for the child to bring his individual record with him when he comes to the medical room or principal's office or other assigned place for a conference with the physician or nurse. Since the child reads his own record, information recorded should not be psychologically injurious to him. This system has obvious weaknesses, as it seriously limits the nature of the information which the physician might wish to make available to the school counselor, psychologist, or teacher.

Individual health records are usually *filed* in the central office in the larger schools, where they are available to the teacher as well as to the staff of health workers. In some schools they are kept in the classroom or home room or in the guidance department. They are filed with the permanent academic record and transmitted with it at the end of the year or when the child moves to a new school.

Sometimes separate and more extensive records covering such items as behavior or dental health accompany the health card.

One other individual record which has come into common use is the *Teachers Observation Record* or *Pupil Referral Card* containing such items

HEALTH HISTORY FORM*

Dear parent: Your answers to the following questions will help the school to meet your child's needs in planning his school program and provide valuable information for our school records. Please fill out the answers and bring this form with you or send it with your child.

School.. Room no.........................

Date..

Name........................... Address..Phone.........................

Birthplace................... Birthdate....................................Grade.........................

Family doctor..................................... Address................................,.......................Phone.........................

Date of last visit...

Please check any of the following conditions that your child has had (give age and date):

Asthma..	German measles..........	Fainting—when?.........................
Eczema..	Heart disease.............	Recent bed wetting..................
Hayfever..	Hernia (rupture).........	Growing pains............................
Chorea..	Measles...............................	Operations—what?....................
Diabetes...	Mumps..................................	
Diphtheria......................................	Poliomyelitis.............	Accidents—what?......................
Ears, running...............................	Rheumatic fever..........	
Epilepsy (convulsions)...............	Scarlet fever............	Other serious illness, what?...........
Frequent colds (how often).........	Speech defect............	....
Frequent coughs (how often)........	Tuberculosis—self........	....
Frequent headaches (how often).....	Tuberculosis—family.....	....
Frequent nosebleeds (how often).....	Wears glasses............	....
Frequent sorethroat (how often).....	Tires easily?............	

Has the child been immunized against the following?

	No	Yes	If yes, give date or dates
Diphtheria...............			
Tetanus (lockjaw)...........			
Whooping cough...........			
Smallpox..................			
Poliomyelitis.............			
Others...................			

Family history:

	Yes	No	Health condition
Who lives in the home?....................			
Father......................................			
Mother.....................................			
Brothers—ages..............................			
Sisters—ages...............................			
Others.....................................			

Health habits:

How much milk every day?...
Any food allergies?..
What does child eat for breakfast?...
Usual bedtime on school nights?..
Give any other health information you feel we should have...
....
....
....
....
....

....
Signature of parent

*Prepared by the Health Records Committee of the School Health Section of the American Public Health Association.

as those shown on pages 55 and 56. The purposes of this type of record are as follows:

> To provide a guide for the teacher in selecting children who are to be examined by the school physician and/or those who should be referred to the family physician.
> To provide specific information upon which the teacher-nurse or teacher-physician conference is based.
> To provide information which the public health nurse will use when follow-up home visits are indicated.
> To aid the teacher through observation to understand the relationship between behavior and health.

This is the teacher's record, based upon his own observations and recorded (with the date) as the conditions are noted. If, at the end of the year, the record shows items still needing attention, the data are transferred to the permanent record or this card also goes along with the other records of the pupil.

Records and forms used in follow-up. Health needs may be hidden away when record cards are filed, and some device is neded to show which children need attention and what progress is being made. In some elementary schools a notebook is kept in each teacher's desk. The defects needing correction are listed, and both teacher and nurse record corrections and other developments of health significance as they occur. In other school systems the nurse keeps a blue book in the principal's office in which she records home visits, pupils sent home ill, correction of defects, and other items. Some secondary schools use follow-up cards in the hands of the home-room teachers. These cards have space for notes and the signature of the teacher at the end of the year. Nurses sometimes use tabs of different colors on the health cards themselves to call to their attention cases in need of follow-up.

Unfortunately it is not always possible to have the parent present for the health examination by the school physician. Various forms of home notices, therefore, are needed for conveniently informing the parents of the health status and health needs of the child. Such a notice may be in the form of a letter with blank spaces and room for a longhand note of four or five lines. These letters are in simple, nontechnical language, adapted to the educational background of the person receiving them. They do not give a diagnosis or indicate the degree of departure from normal health. Instead they inform the parent concerning the condition which, in the opinion of the school physician, needs to be brought to the attention of the family physician for further investigation or treatment. Home notices should never be used to notify parents of heart conditions or any health problem which might occasion acute anxiety. Such matters should always be reserved for a conference with the school doctor.

Work records. Various other blanks are needed by physicians, dentists, nurses, dental hygienists, or other health specialists for making daily or monthly reports of work done and for indicating the number of pupil exclusions, defect corrections, and other items which reflect the work of the health and medical staff. Such forms can be obtained from larger school systems or from state school departments or health departments. They are of technical or professional interest to the health specialists who use them, but need not be considered here.

Confidential records. The question of how much information concerning mental health should be recorded on the pupil's school health record card is of importance. Teachers, administrators, and counselors are looking to school physicians and nurses for more assistance and guidance in helping the child with emotional disturbances and behavior problems. Physicians on their part are increasingly aware of psychogenic or psychosomatic aspects of many disorders and problems of school children. In many cases family problems of an extremely personal nature are affecting the child's school progress and behavior. Case conferences cannot always be held on short notice for the oral transmission of confidential information, which other school personnel should have in order to understand fully the child's problem. It becomes increasingly apparent that some system must be used in schools for locking up records of a highly confidential nature if the school physician, the school psychologist, nurse, counselor, and social worker are to make their most effective contributions in the field of mental health.

Supervision of school sanitation

School health services have the responsibility for advising the school administrator concerning school requirements in the sanitation of the environment and in the maintenance of sanitary conditions. Chapter 8, dealing with the healthful school environment, discusses the problems of environmental health.

Duties of members of the school health team

We have discussed health services in terms of the activities involved. It may help to clarify this phase of the school health program if we state briefly the duties of each member of the school health team, starting with the key person—the classroom teacher.

The classroom teacher. Health education must remain mainly in the hands of the teacher because he is the only person with the child long enough to modify his habits, and because health education is a part of general education, not a series of special lectures by a group of specialists. Contributing to the development of the individual child is one of the chief delights of teaching. A growing understanding of the physical, mental, emotional, and moral nature of the children is the essence of professional teaching ability.

Some of the specific activities of the classroom teacher with respect to pupil health are the following:

1. To assist in interpreting the school health program to the home and in developing parent-school cooperation.
2. To participate in the health appraisal of pupils, providing helpful information to the school nurse and the examining physician.

3. To observe departures from normal health and possible signs of communicable disease, and to refer the child to physician, nurse, or parent as indicated.
4. To support and further the work of the school health services through the program of health education in the classroom.
5. To assist in maintaining hygienic and sanitary working conditions in the classroom.
6. To weigh and measure pupils or to supervise the children in doing it.
7. To observe children daily for health status.
8. To supervise the school lunch if brought by the pupils.
9. To conduct relaxation periods where necessary.
10. To supervise organized play as planned with the physical education supervisor.
11. To teach health.
12. To develop special habit-forming activities in the field of health, related to the observed needs of pupils.
13. To make screening tests for vision.
14. To furnish an example of health in himself.

The school administrator. Today the school administrator, with the aid of his professional staff, plans, administers, and interprets to the community with increasing efficiency the health program which is under way in the schools. Through formal education and professional experience, he has acquired a broad knowledge of health activities in the school and community. It is his responsibility to coordinate the phases of the school health program and to secure an adequate budget for these activities. He cooperates with the health department and other community agencies; appoints the health specialists employed by the school; and arranges desirable working relations among school personnel, parents, and health agencies. He arranges a working schedule which makes health activities possible and promotes sound record-keeping and the coordination of health services with health instruction. He promotes a healthful physical, mental, and social environment for children and staff.

The physician serving the school. The first requirement is that "physicians serving the schools should above all be fine human beings and good doctors." School medical service is a specialized field. It is desirable that, in addition to sound medical training and clinical experience, he should have a background in public health and school health procedures. The well-qualified school physician has a sound knowledge of the growth and development of the child, the philosophy of modern education, and the nature of the health curriculum. He is experienced in handling children with special problems, in developing good pupil relations, and in working with pupils, parents, health authorities, and community groups.

Medical examinations, with the advisory conferences they entail, are, together with immunizations, the most time-consuming activities of the school physician. His total list of activities, however, is broad. He advises the administration regarding all the policies and procedures which we have discussed in connection with health services. He works closely with the athletic program, examining all high school players who are to be on interscholastic teams. A physician is usually present at all major sports. He participates in planning the health curriculum and in the development of in-service health training for teachers or other school personnel. His health advice extends to the school staff as well as to the pupils. He helps to clarify the nature of the school health program to physicians in the community and to the general public. The educational values of school health services, as well as the medical aspects, receive his careful attention.

The nurse in the school. In some states, the nurse in the school is employed by the school authority and gives all of her time to school nursing. In other states or communities school nursing is carried out by public health nurses employed by public health authorities. These nurses include school nursing as a part of general public health nursing.

The nurse works intimately with the teacher in solving the health problems of individual children. Through teacher-nurse conferences she helps to develop a clear understanding of individual health needs. She is also an important link between the classroom, the home, and other health resources in the school and community. She has a major responsibility for counseling parents with regard to the health needs of children as revealed by teacher observation and the health appraisal findings of the school health specialists.

In addition to her professional training in basic nursing and in public health nursing, the schol nurse needs special preparation for understanding the school program, for her part in the testing and health examinations of children, and for cooperation in the educational activities of the school.

The school nurse carries out such nursing and first-aid acitvities as are assigned to her, assists in the control of environmental health and curriculum planning, aids in developing understanding of the school health program by both parents and community agencies, and keeps appropriate medical and nursing records. Her most significant educational activities take place in her home-visiting and in her work with individual teachers. Health education in the classroom is in the hands of the classroom teacher, and nurse-teacher cooperation is primarily in relation to individual children. However, the interest and cooperation of the school nurse in what the children are doing in health is most stimulating to the health program. At the request of the teacher, the nurse often discusses the health activities of the class with the children, showing appreciation and perhaps supplying further information. She may talk to appropriate age groups on health topics in the broad area of nursing. Sometimes she cooperates with the teacher in explaining the forthcoming medical examination. She may participate in the in-service preparation of teachers for their first-aid activities. If she has had adequate preparation in education, she may teach home-nursing classes.

The physical educator. The physical educator is a teacher, expert in the educative processes and especially skilled in the development and conduct of the activity program. He has studied the physical, physiologic, hygienic, and therapeutic aspects of physical education. He has had basic education in personal and community health and in the nature and relationships of the school health program.

The physical educator provides:

1. A plan for a sound, graded, adapted activity program contributing to the broad objectives of physical education.
2. Direct instruction in special skills and sports.
3. Guidance and help for the classroom teacher in developing physical activity with the class.
4. Posture-building activities for well children who have minor departures from good body mechanics.
5. Corrective training for children under the care of the orthopedic surgeon.
6. Leadership in school recreation and sports, for pupils and teachers.

The nutritionist in the school. In the field of nutrition many schools have the services of a nutritionist or home economist, with professional preparation in the basic sciences, in the physiology of nutrition, in the preparation of food, and in the selection of an adequate diet. The school lunch program may be under the supervision of a full-time dietition.

The schools look to these specialists for:

1. The teaching of nutrition and home economics in the upper grades.
2. Help in integrating these special subjects with the other aspects of health education.
3. The conduct of school lunches and cafeteria in the interest of health, economy, and health education.
4. Assistance or instruction to teachers, as groups or individuals, in nutrition or the nutritional aspects of health education.

The dentist in the school. The school tries to see that every child gets (1) effective dental health education, (2) a dental examination by a dentist at least once a year, and (3) the needed dental care. Dentists employed to serve school children commonly:

1. Make dental examinations of the pupils.
2. Do oral prophylaxis or supervise this when done by hygienist.
3. Supervise preventive dental work.
4. Assist the superintendent or principal in the selection and preparation of curriculum material in dental hygiene.
5. Advise classroom teachers and school nurses on subject matter in dental health and the dental health problems of children.
6. Do such work in a dental clinic as may be demanded by the school dental program.
7. Develop cooperative relationships between the schools, local dentists, the health department, and other community health agencies and groups.

School districts which do not employ school dentists usually can arrange through the local dental society for a dental consultant or a dental advisory committee which will provide professional guidance for the development and supervision of the school dental program.

The school audiometrist. The school audiometrist renders a specialized service requiring a high degree of technical competence. The audiometrist should be prepared to carry out the following responsibilities and duties.[3]

---

[3]Based upon *Hearing Testing of School Children and Guide for Hearing Conservation Programs,* California State Department of Public Health, 2151 Berkeley Way, Berkeley 4, California.

1. Select and use audiometric testing equipment.
2. Assure periodic check of all the testing equipment for calibration or function.
3. Perform both individual and group hearing screening tests and individual threshold tests with a wide variety of instruments approved for use in the schools.
4. Explain the tests and the manner in which the children should respond (e.g., oral, written, or hand signal) during the testing procedure.
5. Recognize factors which might interfere with securing a valid test, for example, problems and difficulties which may arise in the test site of the instrument during test procedure, or unusual responses on the part of the child.
6. Record the child's response to the test; note also any defects in speech, any unusual responses during the testing procedure, and any other obvious physical deviations.
7. Keep appropriate records.
   a. Record results of all screening tests on forms provided for this purpose.
   b. Accurately record results of all threshold tests.
8. Assemble the data on children suspected to have a hearing loss and supply the hearing test results to those individuals who will be responsible for educational and/or medical follow-up.

The nature of the service requires not only technical competence in the field of audiometry but a warm, friendly personality, the ability to work comfortably with other school personnel, with parents, and with children at various age levels, and the ability to work with these children individually and in groups. The school audiometrist needs to have great patience, as well as a sound knowledge of child growth and development, and needs to be sensitive to the health needs and problems of children.

The dental hygienist. Dental hygienists are used in many of the larger cities. Their time is devoted largely to:

1. Assisting the dentist in organizing and conducting the dental inspection program.
2. Giving oral prophylaxis and, in some areas where permitted by law, applying fluorides to the teeth as a decay preventive measure.
3. Assisting the classroom teacher in dental health education by giving tooth-brushing drills to small groups, and by providing approved dental health education materials.

As dental hygienists have demonstrated their value on the school health team in conserving dentist and school-nurse time, there has developed a trend toward a four-year college course for dental hygienists, so that they can assume a greater responsibility for the dental health education program, assisting in in-service training for teachers and in parent education programs through the P.T.A. and other organizations. They are also assuming greater responsibility for dental health counseling of school personnel, parents, and children with regard to dental defects and their correction.

The director or supervisor of health education. The Supervisor of Health Education in the school system should be an able educator with special professional preparation in the various aspects of hygiene, public health, school health, curriculum development, and health education. He should meet the criteria in general education which are set for all supervisors or directors. This professional background in education plus the needed professional education in the health sciences (physiology, nutrition, mental hygiene, the hygiene of activity, physiologic hygiene, growth and development, sanitation, biostatistics, communicable disease control, and social-work relations) will require, in addition to basic undergraduate instruction, one or more years of study following the bachelor's degree, in addition to teaching experience.

This person provides leadership:

1. In developing a strong health education curriculum.
2. In aiding the teacher in developing health education activities and in measuring results.
3. In coordinating the work of the teachers with that of the health services, so that there will be more integration in both the direct and the indirect health education of the pupils.
4. In establishing healthful relationships between health education in the school and in the community.

The health coordinator or health chairman in the elementary school. A faculty health committee under the chairmanship of a teacher who serves as health coordinator has been found to be an effective procedure for the promotion of school health and health education. The assignment of a teacher to the chairmanship of this committee is comparable to assignments for other faculty committees. A teacher of well-adjusted personality, with facility in working with others and an interest in health, is appointed to this post and assumes such duties as are assigned by the principal. In a small school, the health chairman may have on the committee only the school nurse and the chairman of the P.T.A. health committee. In large schools, the committee may be enlarged by the addition of persons serving the school as classroom teacher, teacher of physical education, guidance supervisor, librarian, lunchroom manager, or head custodian. In some instances the committee may have in its membership a parent who is a physician or dentist. Serving as health coordinator represents a major extracurricular assignment for the teacher.

The coordinator is working under policies set by the health committee and approved by the principal. He promotes health activities and health education and provides a liason between the school, the health department, and other community resources. He assists other teachers in the development of health education activities and in securing health education aids and teaching materials. He assists in setting up a schedule of nurse-teacher conferences, in facilitating the operation of health services, and in keeping faculty members informed of special health programs, such as immunization or special testing for vision or hearing. The state of Florida has asked every school to appoint a school health coordinator and has prepared an excellent suggested guide for their use, titled *Handbook for School Health Coordinators.*

The health coordinator in the secondary school. As the school health program has grown in complexity, the need for better coordination of the activities of all school health personnel has become more apparent. In large secondary schools, especially, the function of coordination is indispensable to the realization of an effective school health program because many of the school health personnel (physicians, nurses, dentists, attendance supervisors, or visiting teachers) are part-time employes who visit the school once or twice a week or even once a month. Their contact with classroom teachers is sporadic. Yet they are all trying in their respective spheres to do something helpful for the same child. Without coordination their well-meant efforts may be ineffectual or even harmful.

Too often we have found that the school physician's findings never got beyond the health card file in the gymnasium or health office; or children with frequent absences because of health or socio-economic reasons remained case histories in the attendance supervisor's record. Children with mental and emotional health problems were studied by teachers and counselors to no avail because all the facts were not known.

The health coordinator should be a faculty member with a special background, interest, and aptitude in the health field. His most important attributes should be diplomacy, tact, cooperativeness, sympathy, social concern, health, and a sense of humor. His activities are many and time-consuming. If the immediate appointment of a full-time health coordinator is impractical on account of insufficient teaching staff, a minimum of three periods daily should be arranged for this work. How many of the following duties are actually carried out will depend on the amount of time provided for this service.

The duties of the health coordinator are the following:

1. To stimulate healthful attitudes and practices in the lives of pupils and staff by promoting a positive and dynamic health program.
2. To assist the principal in the organization of a health council. In some schools the principal provides the leadership and acts as chairman of this policy-forming body. In others the health coordinator fulfills this function and is responsible to see that the policies of the health committee are carried out. Note that, in the senior high school, there is pupil participation. Personnel of the health council might include as many of the following individuals as the principal deems necessary and desirable for the size of the school and his local situation:

Principal	Social living teacher or equivalent
Guidance counselor	Teachers with special health interests
School physician	Representatives of all other subject field
School nurse	departments
Dentist	Chairman of student health
Dental hygienist	subcommittee
School audiometrist	Cafeteria manager
Attendance supervisor	Custodian
Health teacher	President of student body
Physical education teacher	Health chairman of Parent-Teacher
Home economics teacher	Association
Science teacher	Board of Education representative

3. To help utilize the school physician's services to the best advantage. (The most efficient use of the school physician's time depends on careful planning and the arranging of examinations in order of importance.)

4. To assist in selection of pupils to be examined by the school physician.
   a. By careful follow-up and checking on health cards of pupils transferred from other schools.
   b. By consulting with classroom teachers and school nurse in regard to those pupils with actual or potential health problems.
   c. By conferring with the attendance officers, registrar, and school nurse regarding pupils frequently absent from school on account of illness.
   d. By consulting with the counselor regarding pupils who are maladjusted or have behavior problems.
   e. By arranging screening procedures for the discovery, early in the school year, of pupils with defects of eyes, ears, or posture.
5. To see that the observations of teachers and the findings and recommendations of health specialists relating to pupil health needs and conditions are transmitted to all those concerned and to facilitate appropriate action.
6. To be responsible for care of the pupil health record cards.
7. To follow through on physician's recommendations with regard to placement of pupils in special programs.
8. To check health records of pupils engaged in extracurricular activities.
9. To facilitate the follow-up program for correction of physical defects by checking on all clinic appointments.
10. To discuss with the attendance supervisors or registrars the health and educational factors in truancy and poor attendance.
11. To cooperate with health service staff in arrangements for health surveys.
12. To assist in developing and utilizing the health education values and opportunities inherent in the health services program.
13. To be chairman of subcommittee on health instruction so that duplication and gaps in the health curriculum may be avoided.
14. To arrange student health committees for active participation in the health program.
15. To set up procedures for the evaluation of the health program.

In those schools where full-time nurses are assigned, the health coordinator will have fewer duties connected with health supervision and pupil health counseling. Much more time will be devoted to coordinating the health services with the health instruction program and to developing a comprehensive, coordinated, graded, and functional health instruction program based on pupil needs and interests. It is of the utmost importance for the effective and harmonious functioning of the health program in each school that the respective responsibilities of the health coordinator and the school nurse be clearly defined in order to avoid duplication of effort and misunderstanding. The school health council is an appropriate place for planning and making these decisions.

While smaller secondary schools cannot have a full-time health coordinator it is desirable to have a health council to deal with policy and to have some one member of the staff responsible for the coordination of activities.

The school custodian. The work of the school custodian relates to the health of pupils as well as to the maintenance of school property. Many states and large cities have established special training for these men.

The custodian is concerned with ventilation, heating, lighting, cleanliness, and sanitation in classrooms, lunchrooms, gymnasium, shower room, locker room, swimming pool, and every other part of the building. He is an important factor in safety through his control over the condition of playgrounds, play equipment, floors, walks, exits, fire-alarm systems, fire-fighting equipment, and safety devices on boilers.

References

American National Red Cross: *First Aid Textbook,* Philadelphia, The Blakiston Company.

Anderson, C. L.: *School Health Practice,* ed. 3, St. Louis, 1964, The C. V. Mosby Company.

Byrd, O. E.: *School Health Administration,* Philadelphia, 1964, W. B. Saunders Company.

Grout, R. E.: *Health Teaching in Schools,* ed. 4, Philadelphia, 1963, W. B. Saunders Company.

Haag, J. H.: *School Health Program,* ed. 2, New York, 1965, Holt, Rinehart and Winston.

Hanlon, John J.: *Principles of Public Health Administration,* ed. 3, St. Louis, 1960, The C. V. Mosby Company.

Linn, H. H., and Helm, L. C.: *Check List Forms for Rating School Custodial Service,* New York, 1940, Columbia University Press.

Linn, H. H., et al.: *The School Custodian's Housekeeping Handbook,* New York, 1948, Columbia University Press.

National Conference for Cooperation in Health Education: *School Health Policies.* This 1956 revision of a 40-page pamphlet is available from the American Medical Association.

National Education Association and the American Medical Association Joint Committee: *School Health Services,* ed. 2, 1964, AMA, 535 North Dearborn Street, Chicago, Illinois, 20036.

Nemir, A.: *The School Health Program,* ed. 2, Philadelphia, 1965, W. B. Saunders Company.

School Plant Section, State Department of Education, Tallahassee, Florida: *Sanitation in School Housekeeping, Resource Manual Custodial Training Course.* Available from Manager, Publications and Textbook Services, State Department of Education Tallahassee, Florida. Price 50 cents.

Sellery, C. Morley: "Role of the School Physician in Today's Schools," *The American Journal of Public Health,* **42:**813–817, July, 1952.

State Departments of Education or State Departments of Health may be able to supply publications on school health services.

Wheatley, G. M., and Hallock, G. T.: *Health Observation of School Children,* ed. 3, New York, 1965, McGraw-Hill Book Company, Inc.

World Health Organization: *Expert Committee on School Health Services,* Technical Report Series no. 30, 1951; available from Columbia University Press, International Documents Service, 2960 Broadway, New York, N. Y., price 25 cents.

World Health Organization: *PAHO/WHO Inter-Regional Conference on the Post-Graduate Preparation of Health Workers for Health Education,* Geneva, 1964, Technical Report Series no. 278.

World Health Organization: *Teacher Preparation for Health Education,* Geneva, 1960. Report of a Joint WHO/UNESCO Expert Committee, Technical Report Series no. 193, 19 pp.

Chapter *X*

Health protection and health education through communicable disease control

Communicable disease control is a primary activity of the school health service. It was for this purpose that physicians were first brought into public school work and many communities were slow in extending medical service beyond this activity.

We have seen that there has been a great drop in deaths from communicable disease during the present century. Illness from some communicable diseases, however, is still the major cause of school absence. Studies by the United States Public Health Service, from which the following table was prepared, show that in 1961 the average days lost from acute illness and injuries for children under fifteen years of age was about four days per child. You will notice in the table that over half of the absenteeism was due to respiratory diseases. These included common colds, which accounted for by far the greatest number of absences, influenza, tonsillitis, pneumonia, and pulmonary tuberculosis.

The relative importance of the different diseases as causes of absence does not change much, as shown in Figure 35, which reflects an earlier study (1947) of all causes of absence from school.

The administrative authority

The control of communicable disease is vested by law in state and local public health departments. Each state department of public health, through its communicable disease control division, or Division of Epidemiology, as it is usually known, establishes the rules and regulations relating to isolation and quarantine or other measures for the control of the various communicable diseases. Local departments of public health may establish control measures which are more rigid than those required by the state but may not relax the requirements set up by state authorities.

The procedures are similar whether the school health service is operated by the public health department or by the school system. Communities have secured good results under both of these administrative

187

Table 5. Causes of school absence from sickness and injury among children under fifteen years of age for the year ending in June 1961*

Respiratory diseases	55.0%
Infectious and parasitic diseases	19.5
Injuries	11.0
Other acute conditions	9.3
Digestive disorders	5.2
Total	100.0%

*From data presented in *Illness Among Children,* Children's Bureau Publication No. 405, U. S. Department of Health, Education, and Welfare, 1963.

CAUSES OF ABSENCE IN TERMS OF PERCENT OF DAYS LOST FROM SCHOOL

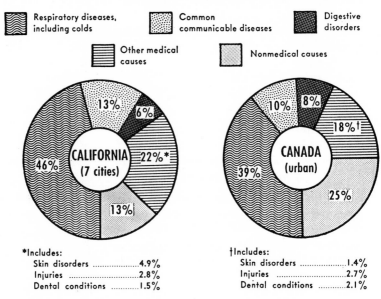

Respiratory diseases, including colds

Common communicable diseases

Digestive disorders

Other medical causes

Nonmedical causes

*Includes:
Skin disorders 4.9%
Injuries 2.8%
Dental conditions 1.5%

†Includes:
Skin disorders 1.4%
Injuries 2.7%
Dental conditions 2.1%

Fig. 35. Chart of absentees, based upon extensive studies in California and in Canada. (Courtesy Metropolitan Life Insurance Company.)

procedures when the relationships have been clear, harmonious, and cooperative. Schools should recognize that public health departments operate under the constitutional police powers of the state and that, in the matter of sanitation and communicable disease control, their authority extends to school properties and personnel.

In those districts where the school services are administered under the Board of Education, school physicians and nurses are frequently deputized by the health department to carry out sanitary inspections and communicable disease control measures. Immunization programs are carried out through joint planning with public health officials. Schedules are planned well in advance, usually during the summer vacation or the preceding semester, so as to coordinate health department activities with school programs. In a cooperatively operated school and public health program the health officer frequently assists with institutes and workshops for the in-service training of teachers and other school personnel.

Educational opportunities

Education of the rising generation for the control of communicable diseases is extremely important. However, the first objective of the school is the control of the disease and not education. Fortunately there is no conflict between these two objectives. Effective control does not interfere with educational activities. In fact the more effective the control, the sounder its educational value. Being sent home in the early stages of an acute cold or sore throat is not only a useful control procedure, it is also a most effective and practical educational experience which the child and his parents will not forget.

Hearing or reading the characteristics of a disease and a list of preventive measures is not a very vital learning experience for the class. The facts can be memorized, but they are soon forgotten. On the other hand, what happened when Mary had the measles is easily remembered. The pupils learn how Mary got the disease, what it was like, and what steps were taken to prevent its spread. The facts learned here are related to many items of personal interest and previous knowledge. They are likely to remain with the individual for life.

Teaching is vital when related to an actual problem. The teaching of hand-washing, which is so frequently disregarded, takes on special significance, meaning, and effectiveness when it is related to a specific disease such as, for example, hepatitis, which in recent years has become more prevalent. Its existence in the form of isolated cases or small outbreaks is frequently reported in the news. Fecal contamination and careless disposal of nose and throat discharges appear to be among the modes of transmission. When there are cases in the community, it is desirable to give pupils helpful suggestions for avoiding the disease.

We want to use actual situations to emphasize those health practices which are related to disease prevention. We do not wish to frighten children unnecessarily. We teach that there is some danger but that hygienic living is a good and usually an adequate protection. In pioneer days when children were in danger from wild animals they were told of the danger and were told how to take care of themselves. Our teaching in the prevention of communicable disease at appropriate grade levels should be similarly realistic.

Basic control procedures

Three basically different procedures are used in communicable disease control. The first is sanitation. Through it, we provide an environment which reduces the likelihood of transferring the disease by indirect contact. The second is immunization. Through it, we protect the well child so that he does not develop the disease even if he does pick up the germ. The third is isolation and quarantine, through which we seek to prevent the direct transfer of the disease by isolating the patient until he is no longer infectious and by quarantining the susceptible contacts so that they will not spread the disease if it does develop.

Sanitation in communicable disease control. Sanitary standards for the school plant are presented in a separate chapter. Water supply, waste disposal, toilet facilities, hand-washing facilities, and ventilation have obvious relationships to the spread of infectious organisms. Certain problems involving school sanitation demand further comment with specific reference to communicable disease control.

The school bus. Like crowded street cars, the school bus brings children together in a crowded area for a considerable period of time. The spread of common cold among the children who ride in the same bus is frequently observed. Studies in the epidemiology of tuberculosis have disclosed instances in which this disease was apparently transmitted from an open case to other children riding regularly in the bus. These dangers will be minimized somewhat by keeping the bus clean. More important, however, is the principle of keeping children home when they seem to be coming down with a cold or some other childhood disease. Tuberculosis must be discovered by specific case-finding methods in order that active cases may be put under treatment.

The school lunchroom. A food-borne outbreak of disease usually arises from one of six conditions. (1) The serving of unpasteurized milk may spread any of the milk-borne diseases, such as septic sore throat, scarlet fever, diphtheria, tuberculosis, typhoid fever, or dysentery. (2) Food handlers with common colds, influenza, dysentery, or some other infectious disease may leave germs on food or eating utensils. (3) Inadequately cooked pork may transmit trichinosis. (4) Botulism may develop from eating improperly prepared or inadequately protected foods (especially nonacid foods) in which *Bacillus botulinus* has been growing under anaerobic conditions. Home-canned vegetables which have not been heated sufficiently are a source of this poisoning. (5) Food infections from Salmonella or food poisoning from Staphylococcus may be caused by foods which have become contaminated and not properly refrigerated. These organisms multiply rapidly in chopped meats, custard, and cream fillings. (6) Occasionally some poisonous substance, like rat poison or insecticide, gets into food through careless handling.

Both respiratory and intestinal diseases may be transmitted from the sick to the well in the lunchroom, directly, as well as through the indirect avenues of food and dishes. Protective steps include the provision of enough room to avoid crowding, the exclusion of food handlers with symptoms of illness, the adequate washing of dishes with rinse water at a temperature of 180° F. or higher, and the use of suitable facilities for keeping foods clean during storage and refrigeration.

As we have pointed out, food handlers should be provided with such facilities for cleanliness as locker space, washbasins, hot and cold running water, liquid soap, and towels. They should be adequately trained in cleanliness of hands and clothing and provided with an ample supply of clean uniforms or aprons. They should understand the importance of refraining from food handling when they are ill.

The protection of food from insects and rodents requires adequate screening and the storing of food in containers with secure covers.

Cleanliness. The ancient practice of fumigating school-houses or other buildings with formaldehyde or sulphur gas, as a means of disinfection, has been abandoned. Fumigation is used to destroy vermin but is ineffective in eradicating the germs of disease. The microorganisms of disease do not stay alive very long on walls or furniture. However, desks, lockers, cots, and other equipment used by a student are usually washed or sunned following the discovery that he has a serious communicable disease.

School books are not believed to be an important agent in the transmission of disease. It is common practice, however, to take books out of use for thirty days in instances where the books have been handled by a patient with a serious disease such as poliomyelitis, diphtheria, or meningitis. In the case of minor diseases, like German measles, mumps, or chicken pox, the books need no special attention unless they have been extensively soiled by the secretions of the patient. Books badly soiled with infectious discharges should be destroyed.

Immunization. An effective program of immunization will eliminate or reduce to a minimum those diseases for which satisfactory immunization procedures have been developed. Immunization against *whooping cough, diphtheria,* and *tetanus* is now commenced as early as 2 months of age, three doses of triple vaccine (DPT) being given one month apart. Early immunization against whooping cough (pertussis) is especially important because 80 per cent of the deaths from this disease occur during the first year of life. Vaccination against *smallpox* is recommended at from 6 to 18 months of age, with revaccination every five years. In countries where smapplox is endemic, primary vaccination within the first three months is advised with revaccinations.

In order to maintain immunity, stimulating or booster doses of whooping cough vaccine and tetanus and diphtheria toxoid are recommended at 16 to 18 months of age and in the preschool round-up or upon entering school. Booster doses against diphtheria and tetanus should be repeated at eight to ten and twelve to sixteen years of age. Reimmunization with a booster dose against tetanus should be given in event of injury where there is a possibility of tetanus. If the child has not had immunization with tetanus toxoid he must receive tetanus antitoxin.

Poliomyelitis immunization is started at from two to four months of age. Two vaccines are available, the Sabin oral vaccine (OPV) types 1, 2, and 3 and the Salk inactivated vaccine (IPV). The Sabin vaccines contain weakened live polio viruses, and the Salk vaccines contain killed viruses. Either vaccine is acceptable, and both are widely used. Some authorities consider the (OPV) vaccine preferable for community-wide vaccination programs for children and young adults, and for routine immunization in infancy, because of ease in administration and the high level of immunity obtained.

The oral polio virus vaccine is administered by mouth in one of two ways. One procedure is to give a separate dose of each of the three monovalent vaccines, beginning with type 2, giving type 1 not less than eight weeks after type 2, and type 3 not less than six weeks after type 1.[1] The other procedure is to give two doses of trivalent vaccine with an eight-week interval between doses.[2] Spacing of doses varies somewhat from country to country and in the primary immunization of infants to conform with the time other immunizations are given. Booster inoculations with either Sabin or Salk vaccine are indicated in time of epidemic, in travel to a hyperendemic area, and at time of entering school. If not previously immunized, the child should be immunized at school entrance.

The procedure for polio immunization may differ somewhat from one community to another, since various methods have been found effective in inducing immunity. Which vaccine is used will depend on the recommendation of the local medical and public health authorities. The major concern of the schools is to educate the public to the advantages of immunization in early childhood, the modes of spread, and the desirability of avoiding excessive physical exertion during epidemic times.

An effective immunizing agent against *measles* is now available. A single injection of a live attenuated virus induces active immunity in 95 per cent of susceptible children for a known five years.[3] The majority of the vaccinated children have mild of unapparent noncommunicable infection with minimal symptoms. Thirty to 40 per cent develop some fever on the fourth to tenth day, which lasts two to five days, but with little disability. A substance known as measles immune globulin, made from human blood and administered at the same time as the measles vaccine, will sharply reduce the symptoms mentioned.

---

[1]American Academy of Pediatrics: *Committee on Control of Infectious Diseases,* Evanston, Illinois.

[2]"Report of the Special Advisory Committee on Oral Poliomyelitis Vaccines to the Surgeon General of the Public Health Service," *Journal of the American Medical Association,* vol. 190, no. 1, October 5, 1964.

[3]American Public Health Association: *Control of Communicable Diseases in Man,* ed. 10, 1965, 1790 Broadway, New York 19, N. Y.

Measles, unfortunately, has been regarded by the public as a relatively innocuous disease. The facts are that, while the death rate from measles is not high, serious complications, such as encephalitis, are not infrequent. In California, for example, in the years 1954 to 1963, there were 405,051 cases of measles reported, with 202 deaths. During this period there were 775 reported cases of measles encephalitis, with 76 deaths.[4] It would appear evident that, with an effective measles vaccine now available, a more intensive program of parent education is needed.

Typhoid fever vaccination is recommended for persons traveling in districts where sanitation is uncertain, and for individuals living in war target areas where sanitation may be temporarily disrupted.

The school nurse performs a major function in communicable disease control by carrying out or promoting the health education phases of the immunization program within the school and with the parents. Since these services are given only to children with parental consent, the number of request slips returned by parents depends largely on the preplanning and the quality of the school's health education program.

Preventing direct contact: isolation and quarantine. Sanitation aids in preventing indirect contact. Immunization is not available against all diseases. Direct contact can sometimes be prevented through the discovery of the disease and the isolation of the sick. Emphasis on "perfect attendance," which encourages children to attend school regardless of their physical condition, not only contributes to the spread of communicable disease but frequently results in more severe illness, with prolonged absence from school. Parents should inspect children before they start for school, keeping at home those who are coming down with a cold or some other communicable disease. When this is done and provision is made for sick teachers to stay home without loss of salary, real progress will have been made.

In many areas the school physician visits the school only periodically, and the major responsibility for interpreting communicable disease regulations to the school staff and to parents and pupils falls upon the school nurse. She makes it her duty to see that the principal and staff are familiar with the communicable disease regulations of the local health department and that quarantine, isolation, and exclusion requirements are available in the principal's office for convenient reference. Many health departments provide a chart for this purpose.

Although a continuous observation of pupils by the classroom teacher is essential, morning inspection is particularly valuable for the speedy detection of children who have come to school in the early stages of a communicable disease. Since nearly all of these diseases start with the same early symptoms, children having any of the following signs should

---

[4]California State Department of Public Health: *Morbidity and Death Records.*

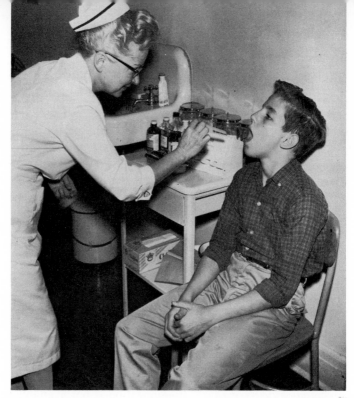

(E. Galloway)

Fig. 36. Careful inspections are made in time of epidemic.

be excluded from the classroom immediately and sent to the principal, nurse, or physician for a possible exclusion from the school:

Unusually flushed face
Unusual pallor
Any rash or spots
Swelling of neck glands
Symptoms of acute cold
Coughing or sneezing
Red or sore throat
Stiff or rigid neck

Nausea or vomiting
Red or watery eyes
Dizziness or headache
Chills or fever
Disinclination to play
Pains in chest, limbs, or back of neck
Diarrhea

Teachers should also be alert to the importance of recognizing the signs which might indicate the presence of a communicable skin disease. While these conditions are more prevalent in areas where low sanitary standards prevail, an occasional case may crop up in any district. The most common skin infections or nuisance diseases found in the schoolroom are impetigo, ringworm (ringworm of the scalp or body and athlete's foot), pediculosis (head lice), and scabies (itch). For the symptoms and control measures see pages 390, 393, 396, and 397. Young girls occasionally complain to the teacher or nurse of vaginal discharge and discomfort. Purulent vulvovaginitis is not uncommon in prepubescent females. In the United States, only about 25 per cent of this disease is gonococcal, the remainder being due to a variety of infectious agents. School personnel should be careful not to jump to the conclusion that the infection is gonococcal. The diagnosis of gonorrhea can be made only by bacteriological examination.

Where school nursing services are adequate, the nurse relieves the principal of much responsibility (1) by seeing children who become ill at school and advising concerning their exclusion, (2) notifying parents and health departments of suspected communicable disease and suggesting private care where indicated, (3) readmitting children who have been absent due to illness, and (4) watching for those children whose convalescence is incomplete or who have not met health department requirements.

There is often a discussion within a community as to whether schools should be closed in time of epidemic. That procedure should be followed which provides the fewest number of contacts between the sick and the well. Children in farming communities are separated by distance, and contacts are few when schools are closed. On the other hand, city schools are usually kept open and children are carefully inspected upon arrival in school each morning in order that early symptoms may be detected and the sick child isolated. When absentees are suspected of being ill, such absences are investigated.

Authorities sometimes delay the opening of schools if an epidemic is prevalent at the end of a vacation period. The present trend, however, is to open schools as usual, advising parents to keep home any child who shows any sign of illness. Schools on their part should alert all staff members to observe carefully all pupils for any sign of the onset of illness and exclude immediately any suspicious cases. Most public health authorities are in agreement that careful supervision at school is more effective in preventing the spread of disease than having children remain home if they are permitted by parents to move about freely, going to theaters, playgrounds, beaches, and swimming pools. It is always important that careful inspection and exclusion should be made by physicians, nurses, or teachers on the first day of school.

Certain specific diseases

Further comments seem desirable concerning certain diseases of special importance to the school.

The *common cold* is highly transmissible and is the most common of the communicable diseases. Its symptoms are the same as those in the early stages of many other diseases. We never know, therefore, whether a child is coming down with a cold or with one of the other infections. Authorities have become increasingly urgent in their demands that the schools should try to control the common cold in the way they do the other communicable diseases. In fact we can only have limited success in the control of other diseases so long as common cold is disregarded.

With such evidence as we have, it seems likely that the serious complications of a cold would be less frequent, total absenteeism less, and scholarship better if children and teachers went to bed at the first sign of a cold.

There is need for better education in preventing the spread of colds, through proper disposal of the discharges of the nose and throat, the prevention of droplet dissemination in coughing and sneezing, and adequate hand-washing. There is also need for a better understanding of the relationship of common cold to such factors as overcrowding, poor ventilation, exposure, fatigue, overheating, chilling, and poor nutrition. Both public education and communicable disease procedures need to be developed more vigorously in our battle against the common cold.

Usually mild, *German measles* (rubella) has assumed increased importance because of the hazard of significant congenital defects in offspring when the mother acquires the disease during early pregnancy. The risk of giving birth to a dead or deformed infant is as high as 20 per cent. These defects include congenital cataracts, heart disease, and deaf mutism. Because of these hazards no attempt should be made to protect female children in good health against exposure to this disease before puberty. Deliberate exposure is recommended by most authorities.

Tuberculosis demands special consideration because the school, like the family, provides continuing and repeated contacts highly favorable to the spread of the disease. Tuberculin testing of school children identifies infected individuals and also provides leads to adult sources of infection. Although there has been a phenomenal decrease in tuberculosis mortality in recent years, from 194.4 per 100,000 in 1900 to 5 per 100,000 in 1962, tuberculosis is still a menace. It is estimated that 35 million individuals in the United States are tuberculin reactors. A significant number of these will develop clinical disease.

The prevalence of infection with tuberculosis in school children as manifested by the tuberculin test varies with the age level of the children, socioeconomic conditions, population congestion, and housing. In 1963–64, 27,160 students in 18 senior high schools in the Los Angeles City School Districts were tuberculin tested. Eight per cent were found to be positive reactors. In 24 junior high schools 6 per cent reacted positively, and, in 12 elementary schools, 4.5 per cent.[5] Myers,[6] in a study made in Minnesota, reports upon 1127 persons who reacted to tuberculin when they were between the ages of thirteen and seventeen, during the years from 1921 to 1941. They were followed for 30,099 person years. Of 899 recently traced, 11.9 per cent had developed clinical lesions. The importance of tuberculin testing in schools and the subsequent follow-up of positive reactors is evident from these figures.

Except by the tuberculin test, early tuberculosis does not show signs or symptoms in the majority of cases. However, the teacher can assist in discovering some cases of early tuberculosis by being alert to: (a) history of tuberculosis in the family, (b) possible contacts in the home, school, or elsewhere, (c) slow recovery from influenza, measles, or pneumonia, fol-

---

[5]Los Angeles City School Districts: *Health Services Branch Annual Report,* 1963–64.

[6]J. Arthur Myers, M. D.: "Eradication of Tuberculosis from the Schools of America," *The Journal of School Health,* vol. XXXIV, no. 10, December, 1964.

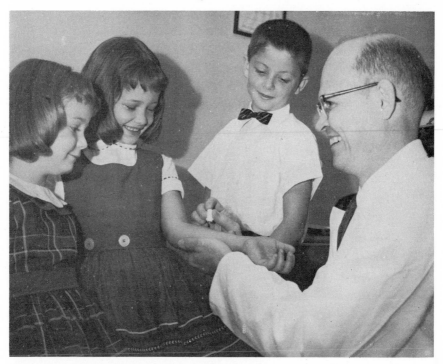

Fig. 37. Tuberculosis control begins with detection. Here a doctor uses the Tine test developed by Lederle Laboratories. (Courtesy Lederle Laboratories Division, American Cyanamid Company, Pearl River, N.Y.)

lowed by a chronic cough, (d) history of protracted chest colds or bronchitis. An occasional case may escape observation and become advanced enough to show one or more of the following: cough, fever, rapid pulse, spitting of blood, loss of weight, night sweats, lack of energy, easy fatigability, chest pain, and pallor.

It is important to remember that absence of the above symptoms does not rule out tuberculosis and that every student should have a tuberculin test periodically during the school years, with x-ray of all positive reactors. Teachers also should follow the same procedure. Instances have occured in which the teacher with tuberculosis has infected several of his pupils before the disease was discovered. In some of these infected children, the disease proved fatal. The regular examination of school personnel either by x-ray followed by other diagnostic procedures, or by tuberculin testing followed by a chest x-ray for all reactors, is now recommended as a universal practice.

The discovery and prevention of tuberculosis is, of course, not merely the responsibility of the schools. As Myers has pointed out, comprehensive and effective programs of eradication must begin with the prenatal period and the examination of all adults who have contact with the new-born baby. Such a program involves the enthusiastic support and cooperation of public health departments, official and voluntary health agencies, the schools, and the medical profession. With modern methods of discovery and the very effective new drugs, this disease could be eradicated in the near future.

Scarlet fever and streptococcal sore throat are caused by Group A hemolytic streptococci, which produce a wide variety of diseases differentiated clinically according to portal of entry and tissue of localization of the infectious agent. Scarlet fever is a streptococcal sore throat in which the infectious agent is capable of producing a scarlatinal rash. If the patient is immune to the toxin of scarlet fever, streptococcal sore throat results.[7] Since both scarlet fever and "strep throat" are highly communicable and there are many carriers with inapparent infections, public health authorities in recent years have stressed the importance of control of "strep throat" whether a rash is present or not.

Scarlet fever and streptococcal sore throat can be controlled promptly and the disease checked by adequate treatment with antibiotics or drugs. Although the severity of the disease has been decreasing in the United States for many years, serious complications, such as peritonsillar abscess, rheumatic fever, and nephritis, may develop if the treatment is inadequate. The potential seriousness of these infections places a heavy responsibility upon parents to keep children home with so-called "colds" and sore throats and necessitates adequate control procedures by the schools.

Mumps does not appear to be as common in school children as measles or chicken pox, possibly because one-third of exposed susceptible persons have inapparent infections. The disease in the preadolescent is relatively harmless. In persons past puberty, however, serious complications may occur, involving the testicles in the male and the breasts and ovaries in the female. Meningoencephalitis may also occur as a serious complication. However, death from mumps is exceedingly rare. Vaccines are available, but since the induced immunity probably does not exceed two years, it is usually not recommended for children. The enduring immunity from infection is preferable, thus avoiding the serious consequences which may occur with the disease during or after adolescence.

Gonorrhea and syphilis are highly communicable venereal diseases spread almost wholly by sexual intercourse. Because of the serious complications which usually develop in untreated or inadequately treated cases, prompt diagnosis and skilled medical treatment are vitally important. Reported infectious syphilis in the United States increased again in 1963 for the sixth consecutive year. The 10 per cent increase brought the count of reported cases up to 22,045. The number of reported cases of gonorrhea in 1963 was 270,076. Since studies indicate that less than 30 per cent of treated cases are reported, experts estimate the incidence of gonorrhea to

---

[7]American Public Health Association: *Control of Communicable Diseases in Man*, ed. 10, 1965, 1790 Broadway, New York, N. Y., 10019.

be at least a million cases per year. The actual number of cases of syphilis is likewise far in excess of the number reported. Among the younger age groups—in children ten to fourteen, in teenagers fifteen to nineteen, and in young adults twenty to twenty-four—infectious syphilis is also increasing each year. As to gonorrhea, the ten to twenty-four age group accounted for 55.6 per cent of all U. S. cases in 1963, which was an increase over 1962 of 4.9 per cent.[8] It should be apparent that there must be an intensified program of prevention, involving a total community effort, in which the schools will have an important educational function.

Rheumatic fever occurs as one of the complications in a small proportion (1 to 3 per cent) of patients with Group A hemolytic streptococcal upper respiratory infections. The symptoms appear two to three weeks after the streptococcal infection, which by this time has usually subsided. Rheumatic fever is not an infection in the usual sense, nor is it communicable. It is probably a sensitivity reaction precipitated by streptococci. The disease has special significance for school personnel because of the frequency of cardiac involvement, the tendency of recurrence, and the important part which the school can play in prevention. Children who have had rheumatic fever must be protected continuously from intercurrent streptococcal infections and maintained on prophylactic therapy, possibly throughout life, in order to prevent recurrences and further damage to the heart.

Infectious mononucleosis, also known as glandular fever and monocytic angina, is an acute infectious disease characterized by malaise, irregular fever, sore throat, enlarged glands, and abnormal blood findings. In children the disease is usually mild and difficult to recognize. Occasionally in older children, and more commonly in young adults, the more severe manifestations of the disease are present, with acute symptoms persisting for several weeks and general malaise lasting several months. Students returning to school during this period of slow convalescence will need special consideration in regard to studies and physical activities.

Rules and regulations

Each school system has its own rules for the control of communicable disease. In the larger school systems these regulations are put in the hands of teachers and other school personnel in printed form. Appendix A gives a statement of communicable disease control procedures suitable for use in public schools. It is always necessary to have any written statement concerning control procedures conform to the policies of the local public health department with jurisdiction in the area where the schools are located. The suggested rules and regulations give some needed definitions,

---

[8]American Social Health Association: *Today's VD Control Problem*, A joint statement by The Association of State and Territorial Health Officers, The Venereal Disease Association, and The American Social Health Association, March, 1964, The Association, 1790 Broadway, New York, N. Y. 10019.

procedures in securing immunization, regulations covering the exclusion and readmission of pupils, and procedures in the case of quarantinable diseases. These statements are followed by more detailed information and specific regulations concerning individual diseases. The examination of such a set of regulations will give you a clear picture of school procedures and responsibilities.

You may not wish to consider each individual disease at this time, important as such information may be to you later should the disease appear in your school system. You will, probably, wish to discuss basic procedures and you may wish to consider the characteristics of important groups of diseases, such as skin diseases (including ringworm, scabies, impetigo, and pediculosis), diseases transmitted through the discharges of the nose and throat (including common cold, influenza, measles, chicken pox, and tuberculosis), intestinal diseases (including dysentery and typhoid fever), and any diseases which may be of special interest to you, such as poliomyelitis or smallpox.

References

American Public Health Association: *The Control of Communicable Diseases in Man,* ed. 10, 1790 Broadway, New York, N. Y., 1965, price $1.50.

American Social Health Association, 1790 Broadway, New York, N. Y., will supply source material on venereal diseases and family life education.

Anderson, Gaylord W., and Arnstein, Margaret G.: *Communicable Disease Control,* ed. 3, New York, 1953, The Macmillan Company.

Bower, A. G., and Pilant, Edith B.: *Communicable Diseases for Nurses,* ed. 8, Philadelphia, 1962, W. B. Saunders Company.

Greenberg, M., and Matz, A. V.: *Modern Concepts of Communicable Diseases,* New York, 1953, G. P. Putnam's Sons.

Krugman, S., and Ward, R.: *Infectious Diseases of Children,* ed. 2, St. Louis, 1960, The C. V. Mosby Company.

Los Angeles City Schools: *Communicable Diseases: Quarantine Rules and Regulations,* No. 359, 1960 (revised).

National Foundation, 800 Second Avenue, New York, N. Y., will supply source materials on poliomyelitis and certain other virus diseases.

National Tuberculosis Association, 1790 Broadway, New York, N. Y., will supply source materials.

State health departments will supply pamphlets and regulations concerning communicable diseases.

Top, F. H., et al.: *Communicable and Infectious Diseases,* ed. 5, St. Louis, 1964, The C. V. Mosby Company.

U. S. Public Health Service: *A Child-Centered Program to Prevent Tuberculosis,* Washingtos, D. C., 1965. Available from U. S. Government Printing Office, Washington, D. C., 20402, 40 pp., price 25 cents.

Chapter xi

The safety problem

W hen a school has no accident for the school year, it is not an accident. It is the result of a good safety program. The prevention of accidents can be secured to a considerable degree, but only through planned and intelligent action. Safety is a health problem, a problem of "life and limb." The teacher's responsibility for the health and welfare of the child certainly includes accident prevention and safety education.

We cannot treat this subject exhaustively because safety involves innumberable details of environmental control and individual practice. A list of safety objectives and detailed, free, or low-cost material is constantly available in this field from such sources as the National Safety Council; the National Commission on Safety Education; state and local safety councils; and state and local health, police, and fire departments. We shall present the framework of an adequate safety program with particular reference to teacher responsibility.

The scope of the problem

Accidents are the leading cause of death for ages one to twenty-four. In 1964, about 7,400 children five to fourteen years old died from accidents. At all ages, 105,000 persons were killed and over 10,300,000 were injured severely enough to be disabled beyond the day of the accident. The estimated cost was $16,700,000,000.[1] Of the disabling injuries, 380,000 resulted in some degree of permanent impairment, ranging from partial loss of the use of a finger to blindness or complete crippling.

Accident rates can be and have been reduced. Organized safety work was begun in schools in 1922. Since that time traffic fatality rates for children have declined while those of adults have greatly increased. There have been over 75,000 fewer traffic deaths among children in the last 25 years than there would have been if these fatality rates had followed the same trend as adult fatalities. We have had plenty of successful experience in accident reduction to argue against an attitude of defeatism and complacency.

---

[1]National Safety Council: "Accident Facts," 1965.

Table 6. Leading causes of deaths, 1962

Children aged 1 to 14

Cause	Number of deaths			Death rates*		
	Total	*Male*	*Female*	*Total*	*Male*	*Female*
All causes	32,664	18,754	13,910	60.5	68.3	52.4
Accidents	11,803	7,604	4,199	21.9	27.7	15.8
Motor-vehicle	4,595	2,909	1,686	8.5	10.6	6.4
Cancer	4,207	2,305	1,902	7.8	8.4	7.2
Congenital malformations	3,067	1,568	1,499	5.7	5.7	5.7
Pneumonia	2,933	1,558	1,375	5.4	5.7	5.2
Gastritis, enteritis	636	337	299	1.2	1.2	1.1
Heart disease	562	281	281	1.0	1.0	1.1
Meningitis	541	306	235	1.0	1.1	0.9

Youths aged 15 to 24

Cause	Number of deaths			Death rates*		
	Total	*Male*	*Female*	*Total*	*Male*	*Female*
All causes	27,345	19,274	8,071	103.5	147.1	60.6
Accidents	14,557	11,809	2,748	55.1	90.1	20.6
Motor-vehicle	10,157	8,028	2,129	38.4	61.3	16.0
Cancer	2,218	1,335	883	8.4	10.2	6.6
Homicide	1,556	1,179	377	5.9	9.0	2.8
Suicide	1,502	1,115	387	5.7	8.5	2.9
Heart disease	946	527	419	3.6	4.0	3.1
Congenital malformations	725	430	295	2.7	3.3	2.2

*Deaths per 100,000 population.
Source: National Vital Statistics Division.
Data from National Safety Council.

An approach to safety

On all levels safety education should be inclusive; it should deal with all phases of the problem. It should be meaningful—related to the needs of students as shown by analysis of their activities, interests, experiences, and accident records. It should be continuous—the task simply cannot be completed overnight, or during an annual safety week or month, because habits, skills, and desirable attitudes develop slowly. It must be the concern of school administrators, curriculum and research specialists, teachers, and others whose responsibility it is to determine the long-range program of the school and who have the professional competence to do so.

The program can be greatly enriched by the utilization of the resources of nonschool agencies. The fire department is a protective agency and can often bring to the school impressive facts and interesting speakers. The traffic division of the police department may render a similar service. Many states and cities have a safety council and in some of the larger cities there are insurance companies with special safety programs. Cities

Table 7. Student accident rates by school grades*

	Total		Kindergarten		1-3		4-6		7-9		10-12	
	Boy	Girl	Boy	Girl	Boy	Girl	Boy	Girl	Boy	Girl	Boy	Girl
Shops and labs	0.7	0.1	—	—	—	—	—	—	1.3	0.2	2.5	0.4
Building—general	1.9	1.3	2.0	1.2	1.2	0.8	1.5	1.1	2.9	1.9	2.6	1.8
Grounds—unorganized activities	2.0	1.1	1.9	1.2	2.7	1.5	3.2	1.9	1.3	0.4	0.4	0.1
Grounds—miscellaneous	0.5	0.3	0.4	0.2	0.5	0.3	0.5	0.4	0.5	0.3	0.4	0.3
Physical education	4.6	2.4	0.5	0.4	1.0	0.7	2.8	2.0	8.4	4.6	10.7	4.1
Intramural sports	0.3	—	—	—	—	—	0.1	—	0.6	0.1	0.9	0.1
Interscholastic sports	1.1	—	—	—	—	—	—	—	1.4	—	5.3	0.1
Special activities	—	0.1	—	—	—	—	—	—	0.1	0.1	0.1	0.1
Going to and from school (motor vehicle)	0.3	0.2	0.4	0.3	0.3	0.2	0.2	0.1	0.3	0.2	0.3	0.3
Going to and from school (not motor vehicle)	0.5	0.3	0.5	0.3	0.5	0.3	0.6	0.4	0.5	0.3	0.3	0.4
Total	11.8	5.8	5.7	3.6	6.2	3.8	8.9	5.9	17.3	8.1	23.5	7.7

The accident experience of nearly 3,500,000 students is summarized in the table above. The figures in the tables are rates, which show the number of school jurisdiction accidents per 100,000 student days. A rate of 0.1 in the "Total" column is equivalent to about 8,000 accidents among the nation's total shool enrollment.

Accidents are those requiring doctor's attention or causing one-half day's absence or more.

*Adapted from figures in the 1964 Accident Facts, National Safety Council.

and industries employ safety engineers. Parent-teacher associations, women's clubs, and service clubs often have safety committees. But nothing such agencies can contribute can substitute adequately for leadership from within the school.

The school safety program

There are three phases of the safety program in school: safe school living, care and reporting of accidents, and safety education.

1. *Safe school living.* The first step is the provision of a safe environment and the establishment of safety precautions through organized activities for accident prevention. This is a fundamental administrative responsibility. It means safe buildings, adequate grounds, good equipment—all maintained in proper working order. Recognized standards of fire safety and structural safety are applied in the construction or selection of new facilities. Specific safeguards are developed where old facilities, such as buildings and school buses, are continued in service.

The administrator establishes the over-all *policies and regulations* necessary for pupil and teacher safety, including the important item of fire drills. He arranges for the compilation of all statutes and rulings which the instructional and custodial staffs are required to observe. Planned and regular supervision of buildings and grounds provides for organized inspection for broken glass, holes, uneven surfaces, accumulation of trash, fruit peelings, tools and nails left around, broken railings, loose boards, blocked exits, dangerous play apparatus, slippery stairs or floors. Inspection also maintains a check upon apparatus in the gymnasium, machines and tools in the workshop, fire hazards about the building, and a neighborhood hazard of any type. Special provisions are made for the handicapped.

If you are to score the safety program in a school, you will want to use a carefully prepared and standardized form such as the "Checklist of Safety and Safety Education in Your School"[2] which contains 325 items organized under the following headings:

General Administration
Construction, Equipment, and Grounds
Daily School Routine and Maintenance
Exit Drills and Fire-Fighting Equipment
Civil Defense Preparedness
Personnel (Faculty, Building Engineers, and Other Workmen)
Street and Highway Safety
School Transportation
Driver Education
Special Activity Areas (Industrial and Home Arts Rooms, Laboratories, Cafeterias, Stage and Auditorium, Playground, Gymnasium, Pool and Shower Rooms)
Safety Education (Supervision, Guidance, and Classroom Instruction)
Instructional Materials
Committee Relationships

---

[2]Available from the National Commission on Safety Education, 1201 Sixteenth St., N.W., Washington 6, D. C., 48 pp.

A major problem in school accident prevention is that of *safeguarding pupils transported to school by bus.* Safe vehicles, competent drivers, safe routes, safe operating or transit practices, trained and disciplined pupil passengers and a cooperative motoring public are essential to the safety of school bus passengers. All school buses should be standard in design and construction and maintained in a safe operating condition. Regular bus inspection, preferably semiannually, by the state police, and daily checks by drivers are also essential to the maintenance of the bus in safe operation. Most states have requirements for the drivers of school buses. They should be careful, experienced, and emotionally stable individuals. Stringent health examinations are essential to assure the selection of bus drivers with adequate vision, hearing, mental alertness, and with freedom from any nervous or circulatory disorder which might result in mental confusion or loss of consciousness. Epilepsy, diabetes, hypertension, or heart disease precludes employment.

The length of the route, kinds of roads, condition of the road, and specific hazards are among the factors to be evaluated in the selection of a *school bus route,* where a choice is possible. A study of these factors may lead to adjustments in the type and size of equipment, passenger loads, and time schedules. The route should be laid out in such a way as to provide safe stopping places and avoid backing and turning, as much as possible. It is desirable that as few children as possible should have to cross the road in boarding the bus. Yearly re-examination of the bus routing is desirable and it is helpful if some member of the school staff goes over the route to see the problems firsthand.

Typical safe operating or transit practices require school bus drivers to observe all state regulations relating to the operation of motor vehicles; define the top speed at which a loaded school bus may travel, ordinarily at a speed considerably below that permitted by the state motor vehicle code; prohibit the driver from filling the gas tank while children are in the bus or leaving the vehicle while the engine is running; prohibit the driver from allowing anyone else to occupy the driver's seat or operate the bus; and require the driver to limit his passenger load to pupils and teachers regularly assigned to the vehicle.

The training and disciplining of pupil passengers is the joint responsibility of school administrators and teachers, parents, bus drivers, and the pupils themselves. School authorities should take the leadership in guiding the development of all rules found necessary to govern the conduct of pupil passengers and in providing maximum opportunities for pupil participation in the program. Self-discipline should be encouraged. Typical rules now in effect for pupil passengers include the following: all pupil passengers are required to obey the bus driver's instructions promptly; passengers remain seated while the bus is in motion; pupils avoid standing or playing in the roadway while waiting for the bus; each passenger is responsible for his own personal property, such as lunch box, books, and wraps.

Many of the accidents involving individual pupils occur when a pupil has alighted from a bus and is attempting to cross the highway to reach his home. The safety of these individuals is affected by the action of automobile drivers on the highway and by the precautions of the pupil himself. Nearly all states have enacted legislation requiring automobile drivers to stop when approaching a school bus which has halted for the purpose of loading or unloading passengers. To secure the observance of this requirement, a constant educational and enforcement campaign is necessary.

To further safeguard the pupil passenger, there must be agreement among teachers, parents, drivers, and pupils on how the pupil is to proceed after alighting from the bus. In many localities, pupils are taught to alight from the bus, step around in front of it, stand there until the driver signals that it is safe to cross, then go directly across the highway. The National School Bus Standards Conference recommended that a safety patrol should accompany pupils to the front of the bus and, on the driver's signal, the pupils should cross the road in front of the vehicle.

The following items include some of the more common *safety precautions in the operation of a physical education program:*

1. Provision of proper supervision during recess, free play periods, and the use of the pool and gymnasium
2. Provision of acceptable first-aid procedures which are approved by the school physician and available at all times
3. Provision of an orderly sequence of skills in activities such as stunts and gymnastics
4. Instruction in the correct use of equipment and the necessary precautions concerning its use
5. Regular systematic inspection of equipment and facilities by the teacher and custodian
6. Provision of "spotters" in the teaching of tumbling and gymnastics
7. Helping each child to feel his responsibility toward the safety of the group
8. Having teams of equal size and ability compete with each other
9. Provision for qualified officials (women officials only for girls' activities will provide the best and safest type of competitive play)
10. Highly competitive sports being reserved for the upper four years of secondary school
11. Arrangements such that children of widely different size and strength do not share the same play area together.

2. Care and reporting of accidents. Procedures in the care of pupils having accidents at school have already been discussed (page 169). Adequate recording and reporting of accidents are also important. The widely used accident report form developed by the National Safety Council is shown on page 207 by permission of the Council. In connection with its use, the Council advises:

A. Use Part A of the form to report all student accidents. Injuries requiring a doctor's care, or keeping a student out of school one-half day or more, should be reported regardless of where the student was when injured (on school property, en route to or from school, at home, or elsewhere).

STANDARD STUDENT ACCIDENT REPORT FORM
Part A. Information on ALL Accidents

1. Name: _____ Home Address: _____
2. School: _____ Sex: M ☐; F ☐. Age:____ Grade or classification: _____
3. Time accident occurred: Hour _____ A.M.; _____ P.M. Date: _____
4. Place of Accident: School Building ☐ School Grounds ☐ To or from School ☐ Home ☐ Elsewhere ☐

5.

NATURE OF INJURY

Abrasion	____	Fracture	____
Amputation	____	Laceration	____
Asphyxiation	____	Poisoning	____
Bite	____	Puncture	____
Bruise	____	Scalds	____
Burn	____	Scratches	____
Concussion	____	Shock (el.)	____
Cut	____	Sprain	____
Dislocation	____		
Other (specify) _____			

DESCRIPTION OF THE ACCIDENT

How did accident happen? What was student doing? Where was student?
List specifically unsafe acts and unsafe conditions existing. Specify any tool,
machine or equipment involved. _____

_____
_____
_____
_____
_____
_____

PART OF BODY INJURED

Abdomen	____	Foot	____
Ankle	____	Hand	____
Arm	____	Head	____
Back	____	Knee	____
Chest	____	Leg	____
Ear	____	Mouth	____
Elbow	____	Nose	____
Eye	____	Scalp	____
Face	____	Tooth	____
Finger	____	Wrist	____
Other (specify) _____			

_____
_____
_____
_____
_____
_____
_____
_____

---

6. Degree of Injury: Death ☐ Permanent Impairment ☐ Temporary Disability ☐ Nondisabling ☐
7. Total number of days lost from school: _____ (To be filled in when student returns to school)

Part B. Additional Information on School Jurisdiction Accidents

8. Teacher in charge when accident occurred (Enter name) :_____
   Present at scene of accident: No: _____ Yes: _____

9. IMMEDIATE ACTION TAKEN

First-aid treatment	____	By (Name) :_____
Sent to school nurse	____	By (Name) :_____
Sent home	____	By (Name) :_____
Sent to physician	____	By (Name) :_____
		Physician's Name:_____
Sent to hospital	____	By (Name) :_____
		Name of hospital :_____

10. Was a parent or other individual notified? No:___ Yes:___ When: _____ How: _____
    Name of individual notified: _____
    By whom? (Enter name) : _____
11. Witnesses: 1. Name: _____ Address: _____
    2. Name: _____ Address: _____

---

12. LOCATION

Specify Activity		**Specify Activity**		**Remarks**
Athletic field	____	Locker	____	What recommendations do you have for pre-
Auditorium	____	Pool	____	venting other accidents of this type? _____
Cafeteria	____	Sch. grounds	____	
Classroom	____	_____ shop	____	_____
Corridor	____	Showers	____	_____
Dressing room	____	Stairs	____	_____
Gymnasium	____	Toilets and		_____
Home Econ.	____	washrooms	____	_____
Laboratories	____	Other (specify)	____	_____

Signed: Principal: _____ Teacher: _____

(National Safety Council—Form School 1)   Printed in U.S.A. Rep 5M 1249

B. Use Part B of the form to report additional information on injuries to students while under the jurisdiction of the school. School jurisdiction accidents, however slight, should be reported promptly. Unless otherwise defined by administrative ruling or court action, school jurisdiction accidents are those occurring while students are on school property, in school buildings and on the way to and from school.

IMPORTANT: In order that maximum use be made of accident reports, it is essential that the accident be described in sufficient detail to show the unsafe acts and unsafe conditions existing when the accident occurred. The description should answer such questions as: What was the student doing at the time of the accident? (Playing tag or football, operating lathe, cutting lawn, etc.) Was he using any apparatus, machine, vehicle, tool, or equipment? How was he using it? Would it have been safer to do it some other way? Was another person involved in the accident in any way?

Adequate records are needed to enable us to study and understand our accident problem and also for information in connection with insurance or possible school liability. In cases where students are insured, the insurance company will give assistance in the development of satisfactory record forms.

Liability in the case of pupil accidents exists where negligence or carelessness has occurred on the part of teachers or other school employees. Such negligence may be failure to take ordinary or reasonable precautions in protecting pupils against accident, or it may be some act on the part of the teacher which any person of ordinary judgment would realize as involving serious risk.

School personnel are expected to act with ordinary prudence. If a teacher fails to do so, a suit for damages may be brought against him by the parents. The principal or other administrative superior is liable in such a situation only if he has directed the teacher to take specific action. The school board, as a governmental agency, is not liable for accidents due to negligence unless the board is willing to be sued or unless the state has enacted special legislation permitting suits against school boards. A few states have already removed this immunity of school boards and some have provided that judgments against teachers may be paid out of school funds. Thus we see that a good safety program is both a moral and a legal responsibility.

3. Safety education. The third phase of the program is education with respect to safety at school, on the street, at home, in recreation, on the farm, and in the factory. Education in safety, as in any other field, takes place through both direct and indirect learning. The indirect learning comes through living in a safe environment and through safe living at work and in play. Direct learning comes through (1) experience in student safety organizations and (2) class instruction in safety.

Safety education, like environmental safety, is a responsibility of the school administration. The administrator, directly or through his representatives, guides the development of the content of the safety instructional program and its placement in the curriculum. He provides class-

Fig. 38. Children in all grades study safety problems.

room teachers with instructional tools or materials, by arranging either for their production locally or for their purchase. He gives standing to the safety program and arranges in-service education in safety for teachers who have not had safety training. He calls for evaluations of the program and for its continuous revision to meet new problems or to attack old ones more effectively.

The administrator also cooperates with and contributes to the community safety effort. He recognizes that, while the school can and does have a large part in the community safety effort, it cannot, unaided and alone, solve the whole accident problem. In safety education, especially, home and school cooperation is important because parents often violate, in their own acts and in directions they give to the child, the very safety principles which the school teaches.

Student organizations. Throughout the country safety is taught effectively through various types of *student organizations.* Their type and scope vary with the needs of the school and the abilities of the students. It is essential that the faculty as a whole understand the needs of the student safety organizations and that each organization be provided with competent faculty leadership.

This faculty leader, or sponsor, should have certain qualifications. He should be a firm believer in student participation in the development and execution of the program of the school. He should be willing to give all of the students opportunities to make their contributions to the program even though they may, at first, do so slowly and awkwardly. He should be capable of providing indirect, sometimes behind-the-scenes, leadership. He should be interested in safety and safety education.

Effective *elementary school safety organizations* operate on a classroom or on an all-school basis.

Ordinarily, *classroom safety organizations* are informal and their organizational structure is quite limited. They concern themselves with good housekeeping and with learning how to act safely as individuals and as groups. Agreements on ways to act so that everyone is safe may be reached as a part of oral and written language work. Reading, writing, arithmetic, and art all may contribute to a group attack on a specific room or playground hazard.

The typical *all-school safety organization,* ordinarily called a *safety council* or club, is composed of two representatives elected from each room. It has an elected president, vice-president, secretary and, perhaps, a treasurer. These safety organization officers function, in general, as do corresponding officers in other school organizations.

The members may be organized into program, publicity, accident-reporting, inspection, and fire-drill committees. The members of these committees collect accident reports and prepare summaries of them for the bulletin board. They survey and prepare spot-maps of hazards in the school neighborhood. They study such problems as "should pupils ride bicycles to school?" and, after consideration, develop rules reflecting the majority opinion. They prepare special appeals to parents who drive cars to school to bring or pick up children. They supervise the loading of school buses and serve as school bus patrols. They assist in daily inspection of school grounds. They assume definite responsibilities in connection with fire drills—closing windows, opening doors into the corridor, aiding the handicapped. They assist in directing traffic in school corridors. They take the leadership in planning for the merry, safe observance of Halloween.

The safety council meets during school hours, perhaps once every two weeks, perhaps once a month. Ideally it meets often enough to maintain interest, but not so frequently that there are no specific or interesting items of business to come before the group. The frequency of meetings varies from one school to another and may be varied profitably from time to time in the same school.

In all cases it is essential that the room representatives on the student safety council be given an opportunity to report back to their rooms. This need results from the fact that an active, effective student safety organization makes decisions affecting the entire student body.

The most popular pupil safety activity, on the elementary level, is that of the *school safety patrol,* and wherever possible these patrols should be a part of the over-all safety organization. This activity is so extensive that it merits special mention. The majority of these organizations function in accordance with the *Policies and Practices for School Safety Patrols* of the National Safety Council. The standard rules now recommended were prepared by a committee composed of representatives of the United States Office of Education, National Education Association, National Congress of Parents and Teachers, American Automobile Association, and National Safety Council. A most important action of this committee was to define the function of the patrol.

The standard rules state that the functions of school safety patrols are:

To instruct, direct and control the members of the student body in crossing the streets and highways at or near schools; and

To assist teachers and parents in the instruction of school children in safe pedestrian practices at all times and places.

Patrols should not be charged with the responsibility of directing vehicular traffic, nor should they be allowed to direct it. They should not function as police. The standard rules cover such additional points as selection of patrol leaders, instruction and supervision, insignia, position and procedure, hours on duty, and relation to police officers. The minimum basic equipment is the regulation white safety patrol belt.

School bus patrols are common in school systems in which pupils are transported to school. These pupils assist in supervising the loading of the bus, checking to see that everyone is aboard, maintaining order during trips, and assisting pupils required to cross highways to reach their homes.

Another type of student safety organization is the bicycle club. Such organizations, popular in schools where many pupils ride bicycles, are frequently limited in membership to bicyclists. They work intensively on three major problems—bicycle inspection, registration, and the development of a code for riders.

Student safety organizations in secondary schools may be (1) all-school safety organizations, (2) safety units within a general student council or commission, or (3) special interest groups such as safety clubs. In a limited number of cities there are active inter-high school student safety councils.

The general purposes of the *all-school safety council* are to plan and carry out a complete safety program designed to reach all students. The activities of the organization are directed by a president, vice-president, secretary, and treasurer. Committees often include those on program, accident-reporting, publicity, inspection, safety codes, bicycle and automobile parking, and permits. This organization, unlike the stamp club or the camera club, but like its counterpart in the elementary school, needs established channels through which to reach the entire student body with reports on its deliberations and decisions and with appeals for cooperation.

The activities of a *safety committee of the general student council* are not unlike those of a student safety council. The chief officer is the chairman of a committee of the student council, instead of being the president of a separate organization. The committee plans and directs the necessary safety activities.

Safety clubs have special interests in such matters as bicycles, automobiles, and shop safety. In some areas school "shop safety engineers" have established friendly contacts with safety engineers in local industries. The members of predrivers' clubs often work with police officials on driver license examining procedures and other matters of mutual interest. Safety is also promoted by certain other clubs, such as gun clubs and swimming clubs, in connection with their other activities.

The general function of the *inter-high school safety organization* is to

Fig. 39. High school safety council.

provide a medium of exchange between the safety organizations of the various secondary schools within the community, and to permit the organization of a city-wide attack on safety problems common to all schools. These organizations have developed codes of behavior for all secondary students; cooperated with police in surveying pedestrian practices adjacent to secondary schools; conducted educational campaigns to secure enactment of city ordinances requiring the registration of bicycles; investigated the handling of teenage driver violation cases in the local traffic courts; cooperated in city-wide fire prevention programs by appearing on local radio stations and by addressing assemblies in elementary schools; handled the scheduling of safety films in school systems not having a visual aids department; received and studied reports on the effect of the city building code on safe housing; studied the effects of long-range city planning on future traffic problems; and carried on many other types of activities. In general, these organizations have been remarkably successful in stimulating adult interest in many fundamental community safety problems.

Safety instruction. In the *elementary school,* safety is usually integrated with established curriculum subjects and only occasionally taught as a separate course.

The basic content of the instruction is determined by a study of the potential hazards and aids to safety in the school community and by an analysis of the potentially hazardous activities in which pupils engage. Potential hazards relate to types of homes and streets, types of public transportation facilities, weather, popular games, and unorganized play activities. Some of the potentially hazardous activities in which elementary school pupils engage are walking; riding in private passenger cars, street cars, and school and public buses; climbing; hiking; using hand tools; and running errands.

The National Commission on Safety Education has published two safety guides to aid the elementary school teacher. Units covered in these safety guides are listed below.

Safety guides for the primary grades

Ensure a Round Trip to School and Home Again (A Traffic Safety Unit)
Play Safe to Have More Fun (Safety in Playtime Unit)
Eat, Drink, and Be Safe (Safe Habits of Eating and Drinking)
"Clothes Make the Man" Safe and Comfortable (Safe Clothing)
No Place Like Home for Potential Accidents (Home Safety Unit)
You and The Burning Facts (A Fire Safety Unit)
You and The Animals You Meet (Safety in Regard to Pets and Wild Animals)
You and Civil Defense (A Statement on Security Measures for Young Children)
Every Day in Every Way You Are Taking A Test in Safety Practices (An Evaluation)

Safety guides for the intermediate grades

Do As I Do—For Safety At School (A Unit on Safety Citizenship at School)
You Can Be Safe in a Crowd (A Unit on Safety in the Widening Community)
You in The Driver's Seat (A Unit on Bicycle Safety)
Safety and Highways and Railways (A Unit on Safety in Transit)
Skyway Safety in the Air—On the Ground (A Unit on the Airways)
All Aboard for Safety (A Unit on Water Safety)
Be A Live Wire Concerning Electricity (A Unit on Electricity)
Forest Fires are Everybody's Business (A Fire Safety Unit)
You and Civil Defense (A Statement on Security Measures for Children)

Safety is commonly correlated with social studies, elementary science, language, reading, arithmetic, health, and art. The classroom program is supplemented and extended, almost universally, by faculty-supervised pupil organizations such as those already described.

In the secondary school the student desires adventure and dislikes restraint. He wants to get away from rules and rigid control of his earlier years. He feels almost adult and must have a program of suitable maturity and adaptation to his present interests. The methods as well as the subject matter should be such as to command interest. The student wants practice, participation, demonstration, and visualization.

New objectives appear. There is an increased interest in the protection of life, health, and property, in the safety of the group, and in the mechanisms of society through which accidents are controlled. There is an increased interest in occupational hazards, the scientific factors underlying accidents, and in special problems, such as safe driving, wounds, poisoning, and fractures. The bicycle is a safety problem in junior high school and the automobile in senior high school.

In the secondary school safety is taught (1) as an integrated subject, (2) as a part of one or more established courses, or (3) as a separate course with credit toward graduation.

Many subjects present an opportunity to *integrate* safety education. General science often gives instruction in the cause and prevention of fires. Biology deals with alcohol and narcotics in their relation to accidents. Physics deals with electricity and explosives. Chemistry is concerned with chemical hazards and laboratory accidents. Safety procedures are presented in connection with home management and cooking. Social studies investigate the work of police and fire departments, community safety activities, and forest conservation. Public speaking classes may prepare speeches on safety problems. Such integrated activities along with the student organization and special projects previously mentioned help to keep safety a continuing and live interest.

Physical education and *industrial arts* are established courses which teach safety in relation to their own problems of accident prevention. In the secondary school, specific standards for using the gymnasium and swimming pool are developed. Student leader corps are given responsibility for maintaining these standards. Coaches safeguard the sports under their control. Specific instruction is given in swimming and water safety.

In *industrial arts* machines are provided with proper safeguards and students are given lessons in safe machine operation. Specific consideration is given to such details as proper sleeves and aprons, the removal or fastening of neckties, goggles, hammers, shop cleanliness, and the proper covering of machine gears.

Increasingly some direct instruction in a *separate safety course* is provided, but care should be taken that it does not replace integrated instruction in other subjects. Special credit courses in safety education in high schools ordinarily are built around such general subjects as: safety in sports and recreation, including commercial recreation; safety and housing; community planning for safety; building safety into streets; cars, drivers, and pedestrians; community fire prevention and control; the conservation of human and natural resources; federal, state, and local governmental safety agencies; community organizations for safety; vocational opportunities in the safety field; and first aid.

Driver education, like general safety education, is taught as an integrated subject, a unit in a required course, or as a special course. Where driver education (classroom instruction) and driver training (behind-the-wheel instruction) are offered together, a special course ordinarily results. The driver education course may be made up of units on the automobile in modern life; engineering for traffic safety; the driver and his responsibilities; the pedestrian and his responsibilities; the function and operation of traffic courts; alcohol and traffic accidents; the reasons for driver licenses; how they are acquired, how they may be lost, why they are required; the causes and circumstances of traffic accidents; and many other topics of interest to the individual approaching the legal driving age. The primary objective of driver training is to give students an opportunity, under the direction of a trained instructor, to learn to drive. Driver skill alone will not guarantee the avoiding of accidents. The student must also learn the meaning of social responsibility.

Fig. 40. The Aetna Drivotrainer in use.   *(A. Devaney, Inc.)*

Driver education courses are increasing in importance and in number. The difficulty and importance of developing the right attitudes toward safe and courteous driving are recognized. Traffic engineers and other experts in traffic control are making increasing contributions to this instruction. In large schools where it is impossible for the city to own enough machines to give every student driving experience on the highway, trainer units like those shown in the accompanying illustration (Fig. 40) are used. They do not give exactly the same learning experience as driving on the road; but they do teach many students at once, and some emergency situations can be presented on the screen which cannot safely be produced on the road.

References

American Automobile Association: *Teaching Driver and Traffic Safety Education,* New York, 1965, McGraw-Hill Book Company.

Florio, A. E., and Stafford, G. T.: *Safety Education,* ed. 2, New York, 1962, McGraw-Hill Book Company.

Haddon, W., Jr., Suchman, E. A., and Klein, D.: *Accident Research Methods and Approaches,* New York, 1964, Harper & Row Publishers.

National Commission on Safety Education, 1201 Sixteenth Street, N. W., Washington, D. C., will send a list of their publications covering all phases of safety education.

Stack, H. J., and Elkow, J. D.: *Education for Safe Living,* ed. 3, Englewood Cliffs, New Jersey, 1957, Prentice-Hall, Inc.

Publications of the National Commission on Safety Education
National Education Association
1201 Sixteenth Street, N. W., Washington, D. C. 20036

General interest

Schools and Civil Defense. This publication outlines the civil defense responsibilites of elementary and secondary schools and their professional staffs in light of current civil defense plans and programs. (1964) 32 pages.

Checklist of Safety and Safety Education in Your School. This comprehensive check list provides a convenient, systematic means for checking the adequacy of the school's physical plant and instructional program from the standpoint of safety and safety education. (1963 revised) 47 pages.

Who is Liable for Pupil Injuries? Basic principles regarding the liability of school systems and school employes. (1963 revised) 70 pages.

Accident Research for Better Safety Teaching. The first review of selected accident researches and discussion of their implications for teaching and learning in elementary, secondary, and higher education. (1964) 32 pages.

Safety: Journal of Administration, Instruction, Protection. The magazine is designed to serve the needs of safety education from kindergarten through college and university, including adult education. Published bimonthly in September, November, January, March, and May.

School transportation

Selection, Instruction, and Supervision of School Bus Drivers. Recommended Minimum Practices. This revised edition of standards and training programs for school bus drivers was developed by the 1959 National Conference on School Transportation. (1961) 24 pages.

Minimum Standards for School Buses. The minimum standards stated in this bulletin were determined by the 1959 National Conference on School Transportation. (1960) 71 pages.

For elementary schools

Bicycle Safety in Action. This bulletin contains suggestions on how to take advantage of the child's interest in bicycling to teach him safe habits and practices. (1964 revised) 40 pages.

Safety Guide for You . . . in the Intermediate Grades. For grades four, five, and six. Topics developed include safety in regard to school and community citizenship, bicycles, highways and railways, aviation, waterways, electricity, fire, and civil defense. (1962) 128 pages.

Safety Guides for You . . . in the Primary Grades. This bulletin is a detailed guide for teachers of kindergarten, first, second, and third grade pupils in planning safety education activities. The "why," "what," "how," and "where" of safety are explained for traffic, recreation, eating and drinking, clothing, home, fire, pets, and civil defense. (1961) 100 pages.

For secondary schools

Policies and Practices for Driver Education. These policies and practices related to programs for high school and college students, adults, and out-of-school youth, were developed by the 1963 National Conference on Driver Education. (1964) 96 pages.

Seven Steps to Traffic Safety. Includes a statement of the purpose, persons or groups to be involved, procedure for setting up a school safety committee, suggested activities, summary report of the activities engaged in, evaluation of the reports, and suggested printed and film materials to aid in developing a school program. (1962) 32 pages.

Publications of the National Safety Council
425 North Michigan Avenue
Chicago, Illinois 60611

School Safety. Written expressly for the very busy teacher. Published every other month during the school year (September, November, January, and March). Contains ready-to-use safety lesson material and articles for the teacher on new ideas, methods, developments in safety education. (Elementary School)

Traffic Safety Magazine. The magazine is concerned with motor vehicle and pedestrian safety. Editorial content deals with traffic safety methods, state and community programs, and new developments in traffic accident prevention. Four special issues: 32 page "Research Review" included in March, June, September, and December. (Driver Education)

Family Safety Magazine. A magazine concerned with the safety of family members, in their homes, at play and recreation, and while driving. Editorial content consists of short, nontechnical articles with many photographs. Published quarterly. (General)

National Directory of Safety Films, 1964 ed. Lists over a thousand films and film strips on all aspects of safety—traffic, home, farm, occupational, school, recreational, and sport. Each listing gives a description of the film (type, length, year produced), summarizes the content, gives source from which available, and tells whether it can be rented or must be purchased. (General)

Safety Education Data Sheets. Practical information on common accident hazards to school age children. They give the teacher information for teaching accident prevention. Ninety-four data sheets—from bicycles to safety in archery. (General)

Chapter xii

Preparation
for family living

The well and happy family is the basis of a stable and wholesome society as well as a key to individual happiness. Education is concerned not only with familial hygiene but also with the economic, social, cultural, and spiritual phases of family life. In a book on school health, we must confine our consideration to the health aspects of family living. In this area, sex education is of paramount importance. Educationally it presents many difficulties, and this chapter is designed to help teachers and others working with children to acquire an increased understanding of the sex education phase of family-life education.

New pressures and problems

Education for family living, especially for youth at adolescent and post-adolescent ages, is currently the subject of serious discussion and may change under the pressures of the population explosion.

It took a million or more years for the world population to grow to an estimated 250 million people at the time of Christ. By the year 1900, it had grown to 1½ billion. Since then, it has doubled. At the present rate of population increase, the number of people on earth will double again by the end of this century.

Think what that will mean in many parts of the world where the people cannot raise sufficient food at present. And those are the countries where population increase is greatest. Continued population increase at the present rate may mean, eventually, not merely increased poverty, but actual starvation. In less than 400 years, at the present rate of population increase, there will be 1,000 persons on earth for every person now living.

To date, Japan is the only country which has sharply lowered its birth rate. Intensive national effort there dropped the birth rate from 2 per cent annual population growth in 1947 to 1 per cent by 1961.

Recently the long term controversy over birth control has turned to positive activity. President Johnson said in his January 4, 1965, State of the Union message, "I will seek new ways to use our knowledge to help

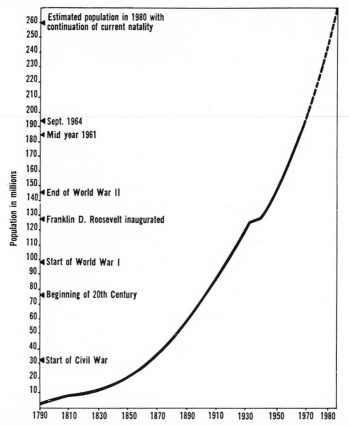

Fig. 41. Growth of United States population, 1790–1980. (From *Smith College Alumnae Quarterly*.)

deal with the explosion of world population and the growing scarcity of world resources."

The subject of birth control had previously been regarded as too sensitive for discussion and action by Congress. But the sponsoring of government action by the President broke down the wall of Congressional resistance and on June 2, 1965, Congress held its first hearing upon this subject. On June 7, 1965, the Supreme Court of the United States struck down the Connecticut birth control law which had forbidden the use of contraceptives.

In 1965, the Catholic Church, which had approved birth control only through abstinence during the period of female fecundity, appointed a commission on birth control. On May 21 of that year, the World Health Organization was for the first time authorized by its Assembly of Member States to include birth control in its official program by supplying "technical advice on the health aspects of human reproduction" to member states at their request.

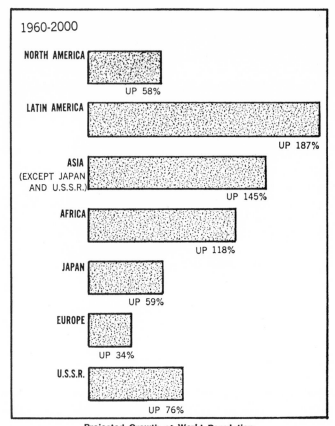

Projected Growth of World Population
From: United Nations

Fig. 42. Projected growth of world population, showing degree to which rates of population growth vary in different parts of the world. (From *Nursing Outlook.*)

These developments inevitably raised questions in regard to sex education in schools as well as outside. Everyone agrees that youth should develop consideration for other persons, a realization of the importance of conforming to the mores and ideals of his society, and a knowledge of how family life and parental obligation can be met in such a way as to bring satisfaction and achievement to both parents and children. There is not agreement as to how much youth should be told about sex relations, contraception, and birth control, or as to who should impart the information. Related to this problem are the currently increasing venereal disease rates among young people, the fact that an estimated quarter million babies are born out of wedlock each year, and many moral questions of individual behavior. Educational practices vary in different school systems and in different countries; but in general schools are being asked to take greater responsibility in sex education.

Fortunately there are good sources of information as to the facts and the developments in sex education, such as, for example, the Planned

Parenthood Federation of America, 515 Madison Avenue, New York, N. Y., and the Sex Information and Educational Council of the United States (SIECUS), 1790 Broadway, New York, N. Y. Information on current and projected programs of sex education in schools can be secured from the American Association for Health, Physical Education, and Recreation, 1201 Sixteenth Street, N.W., Washington, D. C. 20036. Sex education is a field to be entered into or expanded only by the well-prepared teacher working in harmony with the policy of the school system and with the support of the community.

The sex aspect of life is an integral part of the whole of living. Understanding develops from many diverse experiences and sex education assumes its proportionate place without over-emphasis when it is considered in the total context of personal and family life.

From infancy an individual is developing feelings about himself and others in his world—mother, father, brothers, and sisters. Growth and developmental changes occur continuously. A child is normally curious about his world and his relationship to the people in it. As he matures, strong innate drives arise which are often in conflict with the mores and standards of the group of which he is a part. If he is to live happily with himself and as a member of the group, he must learn to understand, accept, and deal adequately with the changes which are occurring within him, and to control and direct his sex drives in personally satisfying and socially acceptable ways.

Parental demand for sex education of their children is growing rapidly. A questionnaire to Los Angeles parents revealed that more than 97 per cent wanted such instruction given in high schools, 95 per cent in junior high schools, and 75 per cent in the elementary grades.

Venereal disease education

The venereal disease problem, like the problems of population explosion and birth control, raises serious questions as to what related health education the school can and should provide. Here, as in birth control, treatment of the subject in the health education curriculum varies from no treatment at all to frank and extensive discussion. Programs differ and no single plan of instruction can be used by all school systems. Let us examine the seriousness of the problem and consider some of the possibilities.

Venereal disease is on the increase, as we have pointed out in Chapter 10. During and immediately after World War II, intensive efforts of the government and the use of improved methods of treatment reduced the incidence of these diseases; but more recently the number of cases has increased rapidly, especially among teenagers, whose rate of syphilis more than doubled between 1956 and 1963. Over half of all reported cases of syphilis occur among persons under twenty-five years of age. Table 8 gives data on both syphilis and gonorrhea, showing their increasing incidence. We do not have accurate data on the number of cases because a large

Table 8. Venereal disease annual case rates per 100,000 population in the United States, 1956 and 1960 to 1964

	Primary and secondary syphilis			Gonorrhea		
	White	*Nonwhite*	*Total*	*White*	*Nonwhite*	*Total*
Ages 1-14						
1956	—	1.1	0.2	1.8	43.0	7.2
1960	—	1.8	0.3	2.1	50.1	8.7
1961	—	2.9	0.4	2.3	37.9	7.3
1962	—	3.0	0.5	1.7	36.3	6.7
1963	0.1	2.8	0.5	2.0	35.8	6.9
Ages 15-19						
1956	2.6	60.9	10.1	75.9	2653.0	407.8
1960	4.2	130.5	19.8	98.7	2642.2	412.7
1961	5.2	158.9	24.2	100.8	2465.0	392.7
1962	4.7	169.5	24.8	94.9	2245.7	358.0
1963	4.4	153.2	22.8	103.5	2185.7	361.9
All ages						
1956	1.6	22.5	3.9	30.7	991.6	135.9
1960	3.7	50.4	9.1	40.4	954.0	145.3
1961	4.1	63.6	11.0	43.2	930.1	145.8
1962	3.7	70.6	11.5	44.4	893.4	143.5
1963	3.8	72.7	11.9	47.8	910.6	149.2
1964*	3.6	75.8	12.2	51.3	956.5	159.6

Data are taken from *VD Fact Sheet—1964* published by the U. S. Public Health Service.

*Rates for "all ages" for 1964 are from the "VD Statistical Letter" of the U. S. Public Health Service, Issue No. 85, May 1965, and are estimated on the basis of cases reported during the October-December quarter of 1964, known military cases excluded.

percentage of cases treated by private physicians are not reported to health authorities. Our data do show the trends in the prevalence of the diseases.

To what extent the increase in venereal disease is caused by what appears to be a more liberal attitude on sexual promiscuity, prevalent in certain groups in our present day society, is difficult to determine. There is doubtless a decadence of sexual standards in some areas. To reverse this trend will require the cooperation of the home, the church, public health services, and schools. Since not all parents have the knowledge, the background, or the willingness to assume this responsibility, it would appear that the schools must take a stronger role in sex education.

"Venereal Disease Education,"[1] presenting the report of a special ad-

[1] A report of the Special Subcommittee of the Public Advisory Committee on Venereal Disease Control, U. S. Department of Health, Education, and Welfare, Public Health Service, Communicable Disease Center, Venereal Disease Branch, Atlanta, Georgia 30333. Public Health Service Publication No. 1190, available from U. S. Government Printing Office, Washington, D. C. 20402, price 20¢.

visory committee to the Public Health Service in 1964, makes the following general recommendations:

1. VD education per se should consist of the presentation of a body of information about syphilis and gonorrhea which may be expected to motivate the recipient as follows:
   a. To be sufficiently concerned about the disease to do what he can within the total framework of his own knowledge and behavior to avoid it;
   b. If exposed, to recognize the possibility of infection, know what to do about it, and do it;
   c. As a responsible member of the community, to demand community action to halt the spread.
2. VD education properly includes biological, pathological, historical, epidemiological, and sociological aspects of VD, broadly embracing causes, effects, prevention, transmission, recognition, treatment, and community responsibility for control.
3. VD education per se should be initiated not later than the 7th grade and continued at least through senior high school.
4. Whenever possible, the facts about VD and their implications should be taught routinely in existing classes under existing conditions without segregation of sexes or any other imposed conditions which would tend to place VD in a special category other than as one of a number of intolerable diseases.

Sex education

Life today is very different from what it was at the beginning of this century. Industrialization with the great increase of population in urban centers has brought about vast changes in family life. More women are working outside the home. Patterns of family life are more diverse. There is greater individual freedom and less supervision of the young. Many parents and young people have been confused by changing ideas and standards of conduct.

The child receives his sex education today from many sources and at an early age. Mass media of communication bring ideas to child and adult alike. Television, radio, motion pictures, picture magazines, and the newspapers constantly bombard the child with ideas relating to sex. He may see the birth of a baby pictured in a magazine, observe many forms of love-making on television and at the cinema, hear jokes about sex on the radio, and read about sex crimes in the newspaper. To counteract the impact of these experiences, the combined efforts of the home, school, and church are required in order to provide children and youth with scientific information, sound sex attitudes, and desirable standards of conduct.

Some basic principles of sex education

Sex education is not a separate subject or series of lectures. It is a broad program extending from infancy through and beyond high school days. Some excellent guiding principles are to be found in the following statement from a report of the Joint Committee of the AMA and NEA:[2]

---

[2]Joint Committee, National Education Association and American Medical Association: *Health Education,* rev. 1948, National Education Association, 1201 Sixteenth Street, N.W., Washington, D. C., 413 pp.

Sex education—good or bad—really begins at home, long before the child starts to school.

Sex education in schools should be integrated with the total health education program at all grade levels. It should not be singled out for separate or undue emphasis.

Example on the part of parents and teachers is far more effective than precept.

Sex education should be couched in terms easily understood by the child and should make use of examples within his experience.

Sex information should not be forced upon the uninterested child but should be adapted to his maturity level at each stage of growth.

Sex should be presented in a dignified vocabulary.

Sex should be taught positively by showing its nobility in terms of creative drive and family happiness rather than negatively through the enumeration of horrible examples of immorality.

Venereal diseases should be taught in conjunction with units on other diseases.

Sex anatomy and physiology should be considered as just another body system; due allowance must be made for modesty.

Reliable source materials for further study and information should be furnished; books should be left on open shelves.

Sex education should point toward fuller, better home and family living so that young people may be better prepared for marriage and adult life.

The medical profession's role in all such matters should be made clear.

The many relations of sex to all phases of normal, private, and public life must be discussed in an objective manner.

Except when topics peculiar to a single sex are being considered, sex instruction should be in mixed classes and groups and the materials and methods of instruction adapted to this situation.

The role of the parents

Ideally, the school should supplement and build upon a firm foundation relating to sex already laid in the home. Practically, it is faced with the problem that children come from varied backgrounds bringing with them very different attitudes toward sex. They often come with misconceptions and misinformation.

Some children come from homes where parents have not had the opportunity to acquire the scientific information they need or the vocabulary with which to express themselves comfortably. Those parents do not talk with their children because they do not know what to tell them. Silence is a cloak of protection. This forces normally curious children to get the information they desire in whatever ways they can.

Other children come from homes where parents want to discuss these matters with them but suffer from sexual repressions and taboos carried over from their own childhood. They feel embarrassed when their children ask them questions, and they find it difficult to try to answer them. This embarrasses the children, and they do not ask again.

Some children come from homes where parents have had unfortunate experiences and are themselves emotionally maladjusted and unstable. Their own attitudes are warped and unwholesome. Consequently, the attitudes of their children are likely to be biased and unsound. Some children come from homes where disturbed relationships between parents have profoundly confused them, or they come, with unrest and anxiety, from

Fig. 43. The well and happy family is the basis of a stable society and a key to individual happiness.

broken homes. More and more children, fortunately, are coming from homes where, happily, they have had wise sex guidance from early childhood.

Parents have a close and continuous relationship with the child that no other individual has. They are accessible when the child wants to ask questions. Family life also affords many natural opportunities to increase gradually a child's understanding of the normal place of sex in life. It is from his parents that he receives his earliest attitudes toward sex. They can help him develop standards of personal conduct and the strength of character to maintain them. They can help him to form values which will enable him to make wise choices. He will need these if he is to succeed in directing his own strong biological urges wisely and in meeting the conflicting ideas of his peer groups.

Parents have the responsibility of (1) letting their children know that they are loved, wanted, and accepted for themselves, (2) understanding the growth and developmental changes occurring in children, (3) acquiring scientific information and a vocabulary with which they can express themselves with ease in talking about sex, (4) learning how to answer questions relating to sex simply and directly, (5) establishing a continuing relationship with each child so that he feels free to ask any questions which are of concern to him as he matures, (6) directing youthful energy into wholesome, constructive channels, (7) building sound attitudes toward sex and high standards of conduct, (8) helping children become independent, responsible persons, and (9) showing by their lives day-by-day how the well-adjusted adult views the whole subject of sex and fits it into its proper place in life's general scheme. Young parents are assuming these responsibilities in increasing numbers. They are better prepared to do so than were earlier generations of parents.

Answering the questions of little children

Children of about 3 to 5 years are likely to ask parents or teachers, "Where did I come from?" or "Where did Mrs. Sealey's baby come from?" This has been such a common question that parents have developed such stock answers as, "The stork brought you," "The doctor brought you in his bag," or "The doctor got the baby at the hospital." Many announcement cards today have the picture of a flying stork carrying a baby.

In the past, the reactions of parents, when asked questions about sex, made the child feel that something was not quite right. Parents acted embarrassed, they scolded, they kept quiet or told untruths. A child is sensitive to change in the tone of the voice or facial expression. Hence, many children from their first questions to adults have become aware that there was something different about asking questions concerning sex. They were made to feel uncomfortable.

Adults need to realize that the first questions which children ask about sex are without emotion. They ask quesitons relating to sex in the same manner in which they ask, "Why are leaves green?" or "Why is the moon yellow?" The questions should be answered in a matter-of-fact way, simply and truthfully, without embarrassment. The child should not be put off. He should feel comfortable when asking the questions, and the parents or the teacher should feel comfortable when answering them.

When the child asks, "Where do babies come from?" he can be told simply, "You grew inside mother's body until you were big and strong enough to live in the world outside," or "Babies grow inside their mothers." He may ask more questions then or he may come back at another time. Sooner or later he will want to know, "How does the baby get out?" One can say, "You came through a passageway in mother's body provided for that purpose. It is the birth canal and the process of coming out of the mother's body is called 'being born.'" Or you can say, "There is a special opening for the baby to come through." Answer all his questions but do not force unasked-for information upon him. As he wants to know more, he will come back.

A special opportunity for the teacher of a primary grade is that of helping to adjust, reassure, and make happy the child when a new brother or sister arrives. The family lets him into the secret near the end of pregnancy when he can enter into preparation for the new baby. As he helps to get ready for the baby, he will look forward eagerly to its arrival. When the baby comes, the class can share his joy and help him to feel pride in being an older brother. The teacher can help the parents in making him feel loved and wanted during the time when so much attention is being paid to the new baby.

The responsibility of the school

The high divorce rate, unhappy marriages not ending in divorce, illegitimate births, criminal abortions, sexual maladjustments, venereal diseases, prostitution, and sex crimes are unwholesome conditions in society which testify to the failure of the home, the school, and the community in meeting the needs of children and youth. Sound sex education can help prevent some of these conditions and alleviate others. Schools cannot ignore their responsibility.

Teenage out-of-wedlock pregnancies have increased markedly in recent years, and are causing deep concern in the schools and other agencies of the community. This situation has very definite implications for the need to improve programs of family life and sex education. The U. S. Department of Health, Education, and Welfare reports that the teenage illegitimacy rate rose from 8.4 per thousand unmarried women in 1940 to 16 in 1961, that in 1961 there were 240,200 illegitimate children born in the United States, and of that number 41 per cent were born to parents under 20 years of age.

While poor socioeconomic conditions and inadequate housing undoubtedly are factors in the high rate of illegitimacy, births out of wedlock occur in all levels of society, among the educated and the uneducated. Faulty child-parent relationships, with adolescent rebellion and estrangement, are often precipitating factors. There is reason to believe that adequate sex education and counseling in junior and senior high school and neighborhood parent-education courses are of value in helping to meet this problem. Counseling of pregnant girls and a continuing school program through special classes are important educational services which schools should be prepared to offer.

In 1962 the Los Angeles City Schools initiated a pilot program for school age pregnant girls with the cooperation of the Welfare Planning Council, the City and County Health Departments, the County Probation Department, the Bureau of Public Assistance, adoption agencies, and maternity homes. The girls reported daily to a neighborhood health center for at least five hours of instruction. The project has demonstrated the feasibility of a multidisciplinary approach to a very difficult problem. The health center, through the services of its staff, makes available to these girls medical care, instruction in prenatal, postnatal, and infant care, and casework service by a professional social worker. The grades taught are ninth through twelfth. Each girl took the same required academic subjects and courses of study as in the regular school. The attendance was exceptionally good, with an average of 25 girls a day. Academic accomplishment was high, and most encouraging was the apparent emotional and social growth of the group. The cooperating agencies are deeply interested in the project and impressed with its achievements. As of October, 1963, 16 had graduated, 19 were still in school, 2 were in college, 9 dropped out, 6 had had a second baby, and 7 could not be located.

Valuable as sex education is in preventing venereal disease, illegitimacy, and broken youthful marriages, its most important role is a positive one. It helps children and youth to integrate sex into their lives in a responsible and constructive manner. Day by day boys and girls gain an understanding of those relationships which lead to successful adjustment to the opposite sex, lasting marriage, and a happy home life.

Teacher responsibility

In the past a speaker was often brought in to give a talk or a series of talks to girls and to boys separately. The school felt it had discharged its full responsibility in this area when this was done. Gradually both school administrators and teachers realized that there were many advantages in having the regular classroom teacher do this work. The teachers knew the pupils and their needs more intimately than an outside speaker. They could plan the learning experiences over a long period of time so that they were an integral part of a whole and did not, therefore, receive undue emphasis. The regular teacher had time to build a background of understanding and a classroom atmosphere conducive to free discussion of problems. Today, an occasional speaker may supplement classroom work, but the main responsibility belongs to the regular teacher.

The teacher, first of all, needs accurate and scientific knowledge of the facts relating to conception, prenatal growth, birth, postnatal growth, and development. Facts alone, however, are not enough. He needs, also, to be emotionally well adjusted, with wholesome attitudes toward sex and with a background of understanding of the normal place of sex in the life of the individual and in our culture. He should feel free of emotional strain when discussing matters relating to sex. He will find it necessary to acquire a scientific vocabulary so that he can discuss such matters with dignity and respect. The informed teacher will know beforehand how to express, with clarity and simplicity, answers to questions children ask. He will realize that he has an opportunity with each question to build wholesome attitudes, as well as understanding.

As a child matures, he will want to know the answers to many perplexing questions. A warm, comfortable, and unhurried manner will make the teacher an invaluable source of help. This often means taking time to show interest in a child so that he feels that the teacher is his personal friend and one whom he can trust. How the teacher imparts instruction and the degree of confidence which the pupil has in him are most important. A sensitive teacher with insight will observe growth and developmental changes occurring in each child and will try to help him meet these changes with as little disturbance as possible.

The teacher who presents sex education at the secondary school level should be emotionally mature and accepted by the pupils, the other teachers, and the community. He should know the standards of the community in which he is working and the backgrounds of his pupils. He will need to recognize and accept individual differences in children—their cultures, backgrounds, and creeds. He needs an understanding of sound teaching techniques as well as adequate scientific information.

The place of sex education in the curriculum

Before the child enters school, his major interests in sex have centered around the questions of why boys' bodies differ from girls' bodies and where babies come from. If he has not learned before he enters school, he will soon want to find out the roles mother and father play in reproduction. These facts should be given as he inquires about them. Bodily differences, the use of toilets, and certain words may have to be explained by the teacher. Questions arise as experiences relating to new puppies or kittens in the household, farm animals, or a new baby at home or in the neighborhood are shared at school. Sound attitudes and understanding are developed through the care and rearing of pets at school, a visit to the zoo or a farm, the planting of seeds, nature walks, animal stories, or the dramatizing of family situations. In the middle grades, the pupil may learn the development of pollen, ovule, and seeds in nature study, or from flowers, pictures, or movies.

Gradually the child learns that growing up means not only getting bigger but also changes in the external and internal parts of his body. In the upper elementary grades, the story of how boys and girls grow and develop and the marvelous story of human reproduction may be integrated in planned learning experiences. Girls and boys should learn about the changes at puberty before these changes occur.

At the junior high school level, boys and girls are eager to discuss such problems as differences in maturing, normal development, boy-girl friendships, grooming, dating, petting, drinking, and smoking. Units may be integrated in such areas as health education, physical education, home economics, and biology. Previously, we have quoted the recommendation of the Public Health Service that venereal disease education should be provided between grades 7 and 12.

Boys and girls learn to assume responsibility little by little. They do not acquire complete freedom all at once. Adult guidance and controls diminish gradually as young people prove that they can accept responsibility. Although the influence of their peers often supercedes the influence of parents or teachers, youth is susceptible to personal example and will follow the right leadership. The school can help by providing wholesome recreational activities and by developing an enthusiasm for strong, clean bodies, physical exercise, and play. Boys and girls need a place to meet under desirable circumstances.

At the senior high school level, greater maturity is reached and the selection of a mate, the engagement period, success in marriage, responsibilities of parenthood, and prenatal and infant care are topics of great interest. Normal family life, the social implications of conduct, and social responsibility take on added significance at this time. Health education, biology, and home economics are areas where such topics fall naturally. Learning experiences may be integrated into many of the established courses of the curriculum, depending upon the readiness and capability of the teacher. Care should be exercised to prevent overlapping and yet to provide these experiences for all boys and girls.

Sex instruction will necessarily be given to mixed groups in the elementary school. At the junior high school level, separate groupings may be desirable for discussion of some problems because of an inner, just-awakening sex consciousness and self-consciousness. Discussion will be franker, easier and more enjoyable if the other sex is not present. In the upper grades of the senior high school, boys and girls are at ease with each other and can consider topics in family-life education in mixed classes. They may consider in separate groups topics peculiar to their own sex.

Gaining community support

In some communities schools have successfully provided curricular experiences in sex education for pupils for a long time. In other communities, schools have not yet undertaken to meet these responsibilities. In some areas sex education is still a controversial issue. Many teachers hesitate to undertake this work because of lack of preparation and experience in it, or through fear of community reaction.

Some administrators in the early preparation for such a program have found it desirable to bring in a well-known speaker to discuss trends, philosophy, and substance of the program with parent groups. Films have been shown to increase understanding. The proposed school program has been discussed and parent approval gained before introducing learning experiences of this kind into the curriculum. Community advisory councils or sponsoring committees have been formed to help interpret the program to the public and give backing to the undertaking. Parents and community leaders, when informed, are generally ready for sex education in the schools. In the beginning, schools usually allow the child of any parent who objects to the program to be excused from it. Carefully selected and well-prepared teachers increase support and cooperation of the public in this program.

Suggestions to teachers concerning direct sex instruction in the upper grades

1. Secure the approval of the principal before undertaking this work.
2. Establish a warm, friendly, open-minded classroom climate free of embarrassment and self-consciousness, in which students feel free to discuss problems which are of concern to them.
3. Discuss matters relating to sex in a direct, unemotional, and unembarrassed manner. Talk in the same objective, matter-of-fact way as in dealing with other subjects.
4. Acquire an adequate scientific vocabulary.
5. Emphasize the normal aspects of sex.
6. Develop an appreciation for the human body.
7. Seek to build fine attitudes and understandings which will enable students to make wise choices.
8. Think through problems with students and let them draw their own conclusions.

9. Give appropriate facts because understanding helps to eliminate excessive curiosity.
10. Let students participate in planning the units.
11. Use a question box in which students may put questions anonymously, if they do not feel free enough to ask questions in class. Class discussion is better, but this is one technique of getting a class started on the way to free discussion.
12. Use films and other visual aids to help clarify ideas.
13. See that adequate and carefully selected books in this area are on an open shelf in the school library.

Informational material for different age levels

Space does not permit the inclusion here of the extensive factual material needed at different grade levels. Excellent material prepared for specific age groups now exists in a series of pamphlets[3] which contain the recommended facts for different ages. The tables of contents of these publications follow:

A story about you

(For children in grades 4, 5, and 6—an approximate age range of 9 to 12 years)
Chapter 1. Growing Fast and Slow
Chapter 2. How Your Life Began
(Living Things Make New Life, Egg Cells Give Life From the Mother, Sperm Cells Give Life From the Father, How the Sperm Cell Finds the Egg Cell, Where Did Life First Come From?)
Chapter 3. Growing From An Egg Into A Baby
(How the Baby Grows in the Uterus, How the Mother's Body Helps the Baby to Grow)
Chapter 4. The Baby Is Born
(The Mother Helps the Baby to be Born, When Animals Have Babies, Helping at Home When the New Baby Comes, Keeping a Record of Births)
Chapter 5. Boy or Girl?
Chapter 6. Growing From A Baby To A School Child
(Growing Taller, Growing Stronger, Growing and Learning Go Together, Your Use of Language Grows, Your Feelings Change and Grow Up, Your Friendships Will Change)
Chapter 7. What Comes Next?
(How Your Changes in Adolescence, How Girls Change in Adolescence, How Boys Change in Adolescence)

Finding yourself

(For boys and girls of approximately junior high school age—12 to 15 years old)
Chapter 1. Find Yourself Here
(Tom and Jack Grew Differently, Curves Come with Growing Up, Attention—Please, Ease in Dating Comes Slowly)
Chapter 2. More About The New Look
(Shooting Up, Filling Out, All Arms and Legs, Your Face and Complexion, Glands and Growth, Your Picture of Yourself)

---

[3]Prepared by the Joint Committee on Health Problems in Education of the National Education Association and the American Medical Association, 535 North Dearborn St., Chicago 10, Ill.

Chapter 3. Steps Toward Womanhood
(When Ovaries Produce Egg Cells, The Journey of the Egg Cell, Menstruation Begins, "Feeling Fine—Thank You!")
Chapter 4. Steps Toward Manhood
(The Complex Path of the Sperm Cell, A Step Toward Maturity)
Chapter 5. Looking Toward Parenthood
(When the Sperm Cell Finds an Egg Cell, How the Unborn Baby Grows, Helping the Baby to Be Born, The Baby's Heredity, Parents Influence the Child's Personality)
Chapter 6. Boy-Girl Friendships
(Sue and Louise, Ben and Art, Marie and Her Friends, "The Story of a Bad Boy," The Story of Anne Frank, Your Capacity for Friendship Grows, Making More Friends of the Other Sex, When Should Dating Begin? What About Going Steady? Some Problems, Managing Your Urges Through Better Living, Forming and Living Up to Your Ideals)

Approaching adulthood

(For young people of both sexes—about 16 to 20 years of age)
Chapter 1. Years of Decision
(Time for Romance, Your Decisions Are a Part of You, Knowledge Helps Us Make Wise Choices)
Chapter 2. Some Basic Facts About Men and Women
(About Human Reproduction, The Male Reproductive System, The Female Reproductive System, Men and Women as Persons)
Chapter 3. It's A Two-Sex World
(You Have Always Known the Other Sex, Dating Becomes More Serious, Petting Presents Its Problems, Premarital Relations)
Chapter 4. Choosing A Marriage Partner
(Chances Are You'll Marry, If You Don't Marry, Why People Marry, What About Differences, The Engagement Period, The Wedding)
Chapter 5. Making Marriage Work
(There Are Sex Adjustments, Money Matters—Too, Relationships With Others, You and Your Babies, A Look to the Future)

In addition the Committee issues *Facts Aren't Enough,* prepared for all "adults who have any responsibility for children and youth which may create a need for an understanding of sex education," and *Parents' Responsibility,* prepared for parents of young children.

Supplying the needed information at the secondary school level with its new interest in love and marriage is the province of the specially prepared teacher in health, biology, social studies, or other related field.

References

American Social Health Association: *Today's VD Control Program,* a joint statement by the Association of State and Territorial Health Officers, the American Venereal Disease Association, and the American Social Health Association, New York, 1965, the Association, 1790 Broadway, New York, N. Y. 10019, 75 pp., single copy 50 cents.
American Social Health Association, 1790 Broadway, New York, N. Y., will supply printed matter and information.
Birth Atlas, the Dickinson Models, photographed and reproduced in sixteen plates (22 by 17½ inches). Obtainable from the Maternity Center Association, New York, N. Y.

Corner, George W.: *Attaining Manhood,* New York, 1952, Harper & Brothers; also *Attaining Womanhood,* New York, 1952, Harper & Brothers.

De Schweinitz, Karl: *Growing Up,* rev. ed. New York, 1953, The Macmillan Company.

Dickerson, Roy E.: *Into Manhood,* New York, 1954, Association Press.

Freedman, Ronald, editor: *Population: The Vital Revolution,* Garden City, New York, 1964, Doubleday-Anchor Books.

Hardin, Garrett, editor: *Population Evolution and Birth Control,* San Francisco, 1964, W. H. Freeman and Company.

Hauser, Philip M., editor: *The Population Dilemma,* Englewood Cliffs, N. J., 1963, Prentice-Hall, Inc.

Landis, Paul H.: *Your Dating Days,* New York, 1954, McGraw-Hill Book Company, Inc.

National Education Association: *What Parents Should Know About Sex Education in the Schools,* A six-page pamphlet (stock no. 051-02066) available from Publications-Sales Section, NEA, 1201 Sixteenth Street, N. W., Washington, D. C. 20036, 35 copies for $1.00.

Peterson, James A.: *Education for Marriage,* New York, 1956, Charles Scribner's Sons.

Planned Parenthood Federation of America, 515 Madison Avenue, New York, N. Y., will supply materials and information.

Reproductions of the Dickinson sculptured models showing fertilization, fetal development, and birth in human beings. Obtainable from the Cleveland Health Museum, Cleveland, Ohio.

Sex Information and Educational Council of the United States (SIECUS), 1790 Broadway, New York, N. Y., will supply materials and information.

Strain, Frances B., and Eggert, Chester L.: *Framework for Famiy-life Education,* Washington, D. C., 1956, American Association for Health, Physical Education and Recreation.

U. S. Public Health Service: *The Eradication of Syphilis,* Washington, 1964, The Superintendent of Documents, Washington, D. C. 20402, 30 pp., price 25 cents.

U. S. Public Health Service: *Venereal Disease Education,* USPHS Publication No. 1190, Washington, 1964, U. S. Government Printing Office, price 20 cents.

U. S. Public Health Service: *VD Fact Sheet-1964,* PHS Publication No. 341, Washington, D. C., 1964, U. S. Government Printing Office, 26 pp.

Part five

Methods and materials in health education

Chapter xiii

The conceptual approach to
health teaching

So vast is the amount of knowledge today and so rapidly is new knowledge developing that the task of the teacher is becoming increasingly complex. Dynamic forces are bringing about changes at an incredible speed. The teacher is faced not only with the mounting store of knowledge but also with new developments in instructional technology and in school organization. Children in school today live in a world of nuclear fission and man's exploration of outer space as he races to the moon. Communication is so rapid that children either witness or hear about many of the events via television or radio at the time they are taking place. Pictures of the planet Mars have been transmitted through 134 million miles of space by a camera in an unmanned projectile obeying directions from earth. Such rapid changes are necessarily bringing about drastic curriculum reassessment.

Health problems and conditions are likewise changing. Some old health problems, such as typhoid fever and poliomyelitis, are largely conquered, yet they lurk in the background; others remain; new ones are created. Urbanization and mobility of the population, as well as industrialization and mechanization, are creating new problems. Quackery in new guises remains with us; accentuated or new problems such as air and water pollution, the aging population, radiation, and space travel confront us. The health problems of the world are brought to our door as man flies from continent to continent in a few short hours.

There is need to constantly enlarge the child's horizon from his local community to the world community with which he is now so intimately related. Just as he learns to solve his problems in his classroom and school, so will he be solving problems tomorrow in his family, business, profession, and community. He may be dealing with health problems on city commissions, in the state government, and, perhaps, even in the Congress of the United States or in the United Nations.

Teachers faced with keeping abreast of new developments are constantly searching for better ways of helping children to acquire more meaningful, essential, clear, and vital concepts, which will motivate them to become increasingly self-directive and responsible. They seek ways of helping children cope with the staggering amount of constantly expanding knowledge. They help children learn to make wise choices in an unsettled and rapidly changing society. They are concerned about the way children learn and change their thinking and actions as a result of participating in health education experiences.

Verbal versus conceptual learning

This situation has led to new planning for conceptual learning. Verbal learning—learning what the book or teacher says and repeating it back either in oral or written form to the teacher—does not necessarily produce understanding; and it does not often affect human motives. Today isolated learning experiences are being effectively organized to provide continuity and sequence for children in an integrated learning experience throughout a child's school career. Increasing emphasis is being given to conceptual learning because concepts do greatly affect an individual's behavior.

The formulation of a concept is the development of an idea or understanding of something. It may be the concept of a concrete article like a chair, in which case there is a rather clear mental image. It may be the concept of a principle ("Haste makes waste"). It may be the concept of an abstraction such as health itself.

When a child enters school, health is to him just "not being sick." As the years go by, he gains some understanding of the body, the effects of hygienic or unhygienic living, communicable diseases, and a variety of health problems. He contrasts his own illnesses with his feelings of vigorous health at other times; he observes other people in sickness, in health, in athletic competition, and in life occupations. He reads and discusses the meaning of health and has many other experiences in perceiving, thinking, choosing, testing, and evaluating as he progresses from perception to abstraction and generalization. He gradually gains a broad concept of health, involving physical, mental, and social well-being related to the individual, the family, and the community.

Each person makes his own concepts from his personal contact with actual objects, events, or circumstances in life through his sensory organs. Each impression plants a bit of meaning in the mind which is added cumulatively to all other related meanings that the mind already has acquired. Concepts form as an individual re-examines and reviews the meanings he has acquired through experiences. The processes of seeing, hearing, tasting, touching, and smelling enable a child to perceive his world. It is out of his accumulating perceptions that he constructs his concepts. There is no possible substitute for the mental images one acquires through his senses. A child, therefore, should have much direct contact with real things in the early grades.

Concepts affect behavior, while the process of memorizing isolated facts without conceptualization has little value in decision-making. The

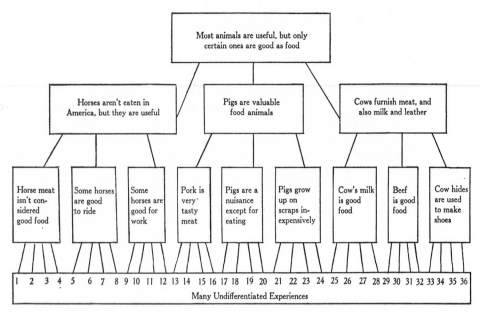

Fig. 44. Concept development from undifferentiated experiences to a generalized concept. In the 36 different experiences shown along the bottom of the figure, the child became partly familiar with many things. Among them were the following experiences which helped to produce the concepts shown above them. Numbers in the chart match those below. (From Woodruff, *Basic Concepts of Teaching*, San Francisco, 1961, Chandler Publishing Company.)

1. I had a pet horse.
2. I saw a man feed his cat horse meat.
3. My friends make fun of horse meat.
4. I read a ban on horse meat in the Bible.
5. I saw a man riding a horse.
6. I had a ride on a horse.
7. I rode a work horse, but it was not comfortable.
8. I heard people talk about good riding horses.
9. I saw a high-spirited horse wreck a cart.
10. I saw a strong horse pull a load.
11. A farmer's horse pulled our car.
12. I saw a picture of a horse pulling an ore car.
13. I tasted some bacon.
14. I had some baked ham.
15. I had some barbecued ribs.
16. I had some sausage.

17. I have never seen a pig work.
18. The pigs I saw were dirty.
19. I saw Mr. Black try to catch a pig and he couldn't.
20. Pig squeals hurt my ears.
21. I fed scraps to some pigs.
22. I saw pigs eating weeds.
23. We fed our pigs waste corn husks.
24. We bought a little feed for them.
25. I tasted some cream.
26. We made some butter.
27. We made some ice cream.
28. We ate some hot milk toast.
29. We had a roast.
30. I ate some liver.
31. I had a steak.
32. I saw an ad for beef.
33. I visited a shoe shop.
34. I tanned some hide.
35. I read a news item on leather.
36. My shoe label says "Top grain leather."

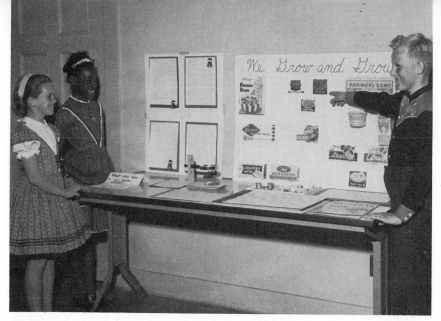

Fig. 45. Food concepts develop slowly from many experiences. (Courtesy Los Angeles City Schools.)

fact that a horse has four legs is a cold, though perhaps useful, item of information. The concept of a horse has warmth and related attitudes.

A single lesson or a unit of instruction can go far toward the development of a simple concept from undifferentiated experiences, as illustrated in Figure 44. More complex concepts develop slowly.

When a child must choose a line of action, he draws on his mental images, his past experiences, and his concepts to decide what he should do. He does the things his mental images show will bring about the results he wants. This involves thinking and choosing; thus, his concepts furnish the key to his actions.

Feelings are also associated with the formation or changing of concepts. Experiences out of which his concepts are formed are satisfying, neutral, or annoying. These feelings, based on their values to the self, gradually become well established as attitudes which affect the way he reacts toward things and the actions he takes.

For example, a child drinks milk, eats cereals, and tastes orange juice. He sees and experiences different substances that he takes into his body. Gradually, his specific accumulating concepts enable him to form the simple general concept, food. Other foods with pleasant flavors, such as candy and carbonated beverages, are introduced into his world. He learns that he must choose from the foods around him. If he becomes sick when eating a particular food, he may develop a dislike for that food because he thinks it was the cause of his illness. Thus his feelings become involved, and he develops a set or attitude against that food.

He learns that several foods are served together in a meal, and that meals in this country are usually served three times a day and are called breakfast, luncheon, and dinner. These he experiences firsthand. He learns that there are good combinations and poor combinations of food at each meal; again, many choices are open to him. He discovers the nutrients in foods and what each nutrient does for the body. He finds out that there are principles that guide him in wise selection of meals in order that his body may be well nourished. Later he discovers what happens to food in the body—the processes of digestion, absorption, and assimilation. His concepts are built up into larger and larger understandings until he arrives at the concept that "food becomes you"! Thus this natural, cumulative process serves as the guide in planning the health curriculum built up from bits of perceptual meaning into larger and larger understandings.

Planning for concept formation

The basic concepts, which subject-matter specialists in health education have selected to be included in the curriculum, should serve as guides for the teacher in selecting the learning experiences for the child. They lie in such areas as accidents, smoking, alcohol and drugs, mental health, venereal disease, the health of the family, dental health, medical economics, and consumer hygiene. Concepts themselves should not be taught as such, but the teacher plans the learning experiences so that the child forms the concepts for himself.

The subject matter is the object or event to be learned about. Teaching materials help in the vivid presentation of the object, action, or event to the students. The teacher uses varied procedures to help the student perceive the object or event, to mature his idea about it, or to develop his abilities.

Developing concepts

The early years are information-gathering years. Words are symbols of what the senses perceive. The wider the child's experiences with real, concrete things, the clearer perceptions he will have to construct valid mental images of his world. These concrete concepts facilitate learning at higher mental levels.

Putting these concrete concepts together so that they are in harmony with the real world outside the mind involves seeing how things are made (structure); how things act (function); and how things work together (relationships). It involves observing similarities and dissimilarities and organizing knowledge. It is thus that principles, abstract concepts, and generalizations are developed. They grow out of experiences and thinking with reference to perceptions, simple concepts, and relationships.

It is in searching for explanations of things which we perceive but do not understand, or imagine but cannot prove, that knowledge is extended. Man's insatiable curiosity about himself and his world has led him to discover, for example, more and more about how cells work—most recently DNA and RNA—and to explore outer space and reach for the moon and stars. These achievements have been made possible by mental processes of perceiving, conceptualizing, applying, analyzing, evaluating, synthesizing—that is, by critical and creative thinking.

How concepts, values, motivations, and goals affect behavior

Health education is concerned with affecting behavior—with helping the individual to make wise choices, learn the truth about those things which will promote his well-being, and protect himself from illness and injury in the world in which he lives. Verbalization of the isolated rules of health will no longer suffice. Helping a child develop concepts which guide his health behavior into desirable channels is a challenging task. The effective teacher inevitably must be concerned with the development of values and ideals, motivations and goals, if he is to influence health behavior.

The formation of values and ideals depends on having concepts in which the proposed way of living is seen as producing desirable results. Concepts, values, and the goals to which the child aspires affect his behavior. The teacher recognizes or creates a climate of readiness so that the child wants to learn. He helps the child to see what values certain actions relating to health have for him and how different actions affect him and others. He relates the desired action to the goals of the child and helps him to aspire to high goals. The goals of small children are immediate and concrete.

Health behavior is learned. A child tends to repeat that which is satisfying to him and tends not to repeat that which is annoying to him or in which he is not succeeding. The desired health behavior should, therefore, be possible for the child to achieve. He is frequently faced with choices conflicting with other goals where his values may be the deciding factor. He is likely to choose what he considers to be the best possible set of circumstances for the satisfaction of his strongest desires and feelings. Health choices provide the opportunity for developing a more self-disciplined, self-responsible, self-directing individual. They provide excellent experiences for developing character and the ability to think critically. Increasing emphasis upon the development of significant concepts will not change the scope of health instruction; but it will strengthen the beneficial influence of health education upon behavior.

Curriculum projects using the concept approach

Today's emphasis on concepts in planning health instruction is a logical development from research in this field dating back to the early part of the present century and from the greater use of the conceptual approach in curricula for the "new" mathematics, physics, and chemistry. Only recently, however, have significant attempts been made to identify important concepts in the field of health education which may serve to guide curriculum makers, teachers, and research workers in this field. Two notable efforts have been made to date:

(1) The Curriculum Commission, Health Education Division, American Association for Health, Physical Education, and Recreation (NEA), has been working for five years to formulate basic health concepts related to crucial health problems of the 1960's and 1970's. The members of the

Commission, who were health education specialists, have been working in conjunction with recognized authorities in each problem area under consideration. It was felt that these concepts should be the ones which every health-educated student should possess at the completion of his high school career. The concepts with supporting data are being published by the American Association for Health, Physical Education, and Recreation.

(2) The School Health Education Study, financed by the Bronfman Foundation of New York City and directed by Elena M. Sliepcevich, was designed to determine the nationwide status of health instruction practices in kindergarten through grade twelve and to develop experimental curriculum materials to be tested in tryout centers. The findings of the first phase of the Study were published in June, 1964, in a volume entitled, *School Health Education Study: A Summary Report.* The perspective of the second phase of the Study, with some broad concepts of a total school health education program, entitled *Health Education: A Conceptual Approach* has been developed. The experimental materials which were prepared have been tried out in selected schools during 1965. This creative approach to health education is currently being evaluated, and the results will be published.

Concepts on smoking for upper elementary grades

The following outline supports the concept that *cigarette-smoking is undesirable.* Examine the supporting concepts under the Roman numerals. Do they suggest learning experiences to you? Consider the supporting statements. Which do you think is a better learning procedure for children—to "tell" them the major concepts or, through discussion or other methods, to let them form these concepts for themselves? Observe that these are generalizations about related data. Children should be "pushed" in their thinking until they see these relationships and form these concepts for themselves. Which method of teaching do you think is more likely to prevent a child from smoking—learning facts or developing desirable concepts? What motivations would you use as appropriate for an upper elementary grade child? What experiences would you plan, as a teacher, to help the child discover these concepts for himself?

I. The tobacco plant is used by man in different forms.

    A. Originally, tobacco grew only in North and South America. Early explorers of these continents found the users of this plant snuffing it through a Y-shaped pipe called a "taboca," smoking a hollow reed or cane tube into which tobacco had been stuffed, or smoking rolled corn husks or other vegetable wrappers filled with crushed tobacco leaves.

    B. The explorers introduced the plant into Europe and along worldwide trading routes, where its use became a widespread habit.

    C. Besides being smoked, the plant was chewed or often snuffed up the nose in a powder form. Snuff boxes were commonly carried.

    D. Early white settlers in this country found the Indians smoking tobacco in their peace pipes. As a gesture of friendship, the pipe was passed from one person to another and smoked.

E. Today the dried leaves are shredded or rolled for smoking, pressed together in small hard masses for chewing, or made into a powder which is snuffed up the nose or placed under the lip on the gums.

F. The most widespread form in which tobacco is used today is in cigarettes; it is also smoked in cigars and pipes, chewed, and used as snuff.

II. Tobacco and tobacco smoke contain substances harmful to man.

A. Tobacco smoke contains a vast number of different chemical substances, some of which are harmful to man.

B. The body needs clean air, free from injurious substances. Our air tubes, branching out into smaller and smaller tubes like the limbs of a tree, are lined with cells having tiny, hair-like endings called cilia; these sweep minute foreign particles from the air in our lungs upward and out of the breathing tubes by wave-like movements; tobacco smoke slows down or may even stop the action of the cilia temporarily and may, eventually, permanently damage them; some of the foreign particles or substances in cigarette smoke remain in the body and injure it.

III. The extent of the injury which tobacco and tobacco smoke do to man depends upon how much of these harmful substances get into and remain in the body.

A. When a cigarette is smoked, only a little of these harmful substances gets into the body at one time.

B. The more one smokes and the longer one smokes, the more of these substances get into the body, and the more the body is harmed.

C. The effects are not seen and often are not detected for a long time; yet hidden damage is done little by little, year after year.

D. When one smokes tobacco for the first time, it may make him dizzy and nauseated because of its poisonous effects; the body learns to adjust to or tolerate these substances and the symptoms disappear with repeated use, yet hidden damage is being done because of the cumulative effects of the smoke.

E. After a while, these substances in cigarette smoke so irritate the air tubes that a chronic cough develops to get rid of substances that the cilia find it difficult to sweep out. Breathlessness also develops. Both are handicaps to athletes.

F. Endurance, the ability to hold out, is affected by the accumulation of these harmful substances; athletes need endurance.

G. When one of the substances in the smoke gets into the blood from the lungs, it causes the heart to beat a little faster and tiny blood vessels to contract, thus raising blood pressure.

IV. Little harmful effects day after day, although they are not seen and are not felt, may gradually cause big damages.

A. Chronic inflammation of the air passages may develop.

B. More smokers than nonsmokers develop lung cancer; risk of developing lung cancer increases with the length of time one has smoked and the number of cigarettes smoked per day.

C. The heart and blood vessels are affected.

V. Once one starts to smoke, it becomes a habit.

A. Repeated smoking creates a desire to continue smoking.

B. Smoking becomes a pattern of life.

C. A habit once established is difficult to break.

D. Some individuals start by smoking a few cigarettes a day and become chain smokers, smoking as many as three or four packs a day.

VI. Smoking may be costly and dangerous; it reduces the likelihood of winning in sports.

A. Smoking is an expensive habit.
 1. Smoking a pack a day costs a person approximately $100 per year.
 2. At the end of the year, $100 has gone up in smoke.
 3. One hundred dollars can be spent in more profitable ways which can bring great pleasure and lasting benefits.
B. Smoking is a fire hazard.
 1. A burning cigarette carelessly dropped in dry grass or dry twigs can start a forest fire.
 2. A person smoking in bed may drop off to sleep and set his house or a hotel on fire and endanger his own as well as other peoples' lives.
C. Smoking may interfere with winning in sports.
 1. Coaches do not want their players to smoke because it affects their breathing; it makes them short of breath.
 2. Good athletes find out and do those things that will enable them to perform well; they refrain from doing those things that will interfere with winning.
 3. Football and baseball players, swimmers, and other athletes desire to keep their bodies in good condition. Most athletes do not smoke.
 4. Competition in athletics and in life are keen today; the boy or girl who grows up strong and healthy is more likely to win in both.

References

American Educational Research Association: "Curriculum Planning and Development," *Review of Educational Research* (entire issue), June, 1963.

Association for Supervision and Curriculum Development: *Perceiving, Behaving, Becoming,* Washington, D. C., 1962, the Association.

Association for Supervision and Curriculum Development: *What Are the Sources of the Curriculum? A Symposium,* Washington, D. C., 1962, the Association.

Bloom, Benjamin S., editor: *Taxonomy of Educational Objectives, Handbook I: Cognitive Domain,* New York, 1956, David McKay Co., Inc.

Bruner, Jerome S. *The Process of Education.* Cambridge, Mass.: Harvard University Press, 1963.

Fleming, Robert S., editor: *Curriculum for Todays' Boys and Girls.* Columbus, Ohio, 1963, Charles E. Merrill Books, Inc.

Fraser, Dorothy H.: *Deciding What To Teach,* Project on Instruction, Washington, D. C., 1963, National Education Association.

Frazier, Alexander, editor: *New Insights and the Curriculum,* 1963 Yearbook. Washington, D. C., 1963, Association for Supervision and Curriculum Development.

Gilchrist, Robert S.: *Using Current Curriculum Developments: Report of the Commission,* Washington, D. C., 1963, Association for Supervision and Curriculum Development.

Goodland, John I.: *Some Propositions in Search of Schools,* Washington, D. C., 1962, Department of Elementary School Principals.

Goodland, John I.: *School Curriculum Reform in the United States,* New York, March, 1964, Fund for the Adancement of Education.

Johns, Edward B. "The Concept Approach in Health Education." *Journal of School Health,* May, 1965 pp. 196-207.

Johns, Edward B.: "Effective Health Teaching," *Journal of School Health,* March, 1964, pp. 123-31.

Kennedy, Wallace A., and Willcutt, Herman C.: *Motivation of School Children,* Tallahassee, Fla., 1963, Human Development Clinic.

Krathwohl, David R., Bloom, Benjamin S., and Masia, Bertram B.: *Taxonomy of Educational Objectives, Handbook II: Affective Domain,* New York, 1964, David McKay Co., Inc.

Miles, Matthew B., editor: *Innovation in Education,* New York, 1964, Bureau of Publications, Teachers College, Columbia University.

Miller, Richard I.: *Education in a Changing Society,* Project on Instruction, Washington, D. C., 1963, National Education Association.

National Education Association: *Schools for the Sixties,* a Report of the Project on Instruction, New York, 1963, McGraw-Hill Book Co., Inc.

Oberteuffer, Delbert: "Health and Education: An Appraisal," *Journal of School Health,* April, 1964, pp. 184-197.

Oberteuffer, Delbert: "Vital Ties Between Health and Education," *NEA Journal,* March, 1964.

President's Commission on National Goals: *Goals for Americans.* Englewood Cliffs, N. J., 1960, Prentice-Hall.

Russell, David H.: *Children's Thinking,* New York, 1965, Ginn and Co.

Russell, Robert D.: "Motivational Factors as Related to Behavioral Change," in *Synthesis of Research in Selected Areas of Health Instruction,* Washington, D. C., 1963, School Health Education Study, pp. 92–110.

Sliepcevich, Elena M.: *School Health Education Study: A Summary Report,* Washington, D. C., 1964, School Health Education Study.

Solleder, Marian K.: "The Selection of Fundamental Health Concepts for Various Grade Levels," in *Synthesis of Research in Selected Areas of Health Instruction,* Washington, D. C., 1963, School Health Education Study, pp. 111–14.

Trow, William Clark: *The Learning Process,* What Research Says to the Teacher, no. 6., Washington, D. C., December, 1954, Department of Classroom Teachers and American Educational Research Association.

Woodruff, Asahel D.: *Basic Concepts of Teaching,* San Francisco, 1961, Chandler Publishing Co.

Chapter xiv

Planning for health instruction

T he most important planning for health instruction is that which is done by the teacher for his own class. A planned general outline or course of study is helpful to him in this planning, and we may well give some consideration to its value, use, and preparation before we discuss teacher planning.

Developing a course of study

A curriculum is a charted course and flexible schedule for a voyage in education, set up by experts in subject matter, in school administration, and in educational methods for the various grade levels involved. The itinerary of this journey in education, be it attractive or unattractive, is not the voyage itself, nor does it determine how much the travelers learn from the voyage. The trip itself is a real life experience under the guidance of the teacher. The richness of the experience depends upon the guide more than upon the chart. Areas on both sides of the charted highway are profitably explored; but the chart is of value even though the route is not rigidly fixed.

Today no school system would admit that it is without a program in health education, although many have no course of study of their own. Some have none at all. Others use a state outline, which is modified in use to fit local conditions.

The local school system has many reasons for building its own course of study. As a learning experience for those who participate it is unexcelled; the teaching suggestions have local application; and the plans which the teachers themselves have made are more likely to be followed.

Any good course of study has certain definite values: (1) It makes clear to the teacher that the administrator in charge of the school system expects health education to be a part of the school program. (2) It presents a progressive plan by grades, showing the teacher what is expected at the grade level where he is at work, giving specific objectives, and avoiding the same program for an individual child in two or three successive grades. (3) It specifies the time allotment for health education. (4) It gives the teacher suggestions, methods and source materials for developing the instruction. (5) It suggests methods of measuring results. (6) It helps to ensure the completeness of the program as a whole.

In other words, through developing a curriculum by the cooperative efforts of its staff, the school administration says to the teacher, "You are expected to teach health and take the necessary time to do it. You can see what preceding grades have done and what your grade is expected to accomplish. Here are some suggestions as to method and some standards by which you can measure accomplishment."

A state or local course of study is usually prepared and periodically revised or rebuilt by a committee representing the various special skills and experiences which can make a contribution. The amount of experimentation or research varies widely. In different degrees all curriculum committees draw upon both experience and published material. Any teaching outline should be regarded as a tentative plan which will be adapted to classroom situations by individual teachers and revised from time to time.

The composition of the curriculum committee must provide knowledge as to what results of health education should be sought and what learning experiences can and should be provided to achieve these results. An examination of health curricula in this country and in several others reveals no fixed pattern of committee organization. The composition of the various committees has been determined by local needs, relationships, and available personnel. In a few cases, a very small working group has prepared the course of study. More commonly, where large school populations were involved, the committee has been large enough to include experts in many of the phases of health and education, such as school administration, public health, home visiting, educational psychology, school medical and dental services, school nursing, environmental health, nutrition, physical education, and curriculum construction. Classroom teachers in the elementary school and those who teach health in the secondary school are very important participants in curriculum construction. Where there is a supervisor of health education in the school system or a director of health education in the health department, such a specialist in health education is a key member of the committee. Several committees have drawn upon the department of public health for personnel, and some have included private citizens from professional or parent groups.

Much of the detailed work is done by subcommittees or on individual assignments for later committee checking and approval. Because the decision as to what material, methods, and procedures will be used in each grade can be made most effectively by experienced teachers at the respective grade levels, in addition to the central committee it is customary to have a subcommittee or grade committee of teachers for each grade of the elementary school.

The central committee agrees upon definitions and objectives. It decides what concepts, habits, and attitudes the school should seek to develop and what knowledge should be presented during the school life of the child. These decisions are based upon the expert knowledge represented on the committee and upon the health needs of the community. The committee also brings together an extensive assortment of desirable procedures and source materials.

The respective grade committees of teachers list the natural interests of children for the age in question and select incentives that may be used in encouraging the development of health practices. They select the activities and materials for the grade and send them back to the central committee, which organizes and unifies the material, adds the necessary items related to administration and the coordination of departments, and sees to it that the curriculum is put into usable form.

The course of study has special value in clarifying the cooperative relationships between the teachers, health specialists and others concerned with pupil health. In developing the statement of these cooperative relationships, the head of each department (medical service, nursing service, nutrition service, dental service, physical education, custodian service or school sanitation, and luncheon service) answers four fundamental questions:

1. What are the professional activities that you carry out?
2. In what way do these services contribute directly to the health education of the child?
3. What personal assistance and what help with pupils may the teacher expect from your department?
4. Just how can the teacher contribute to the success of your work?

With a knowledge of the health problems and requirements, together with an understanding of the potential and actual contributions of each member of the staff, it is possible to develop a program in which all activities related to health will contribute to health education, and health education will contribute to the success of these activities.

The United Nations Educational Scientific and Cultural Organization (UNESCO) and the World Health Organization (WHO) have produced a source book[1] to aid curriculum committees in the development of courses of study in health for the different educational levels. This book suggests that courses of study may well have two major sections. The first section, providing *orientation and background material for teachers*, discusses definitions, objectives, the scope of health education, considerations of growth and development, principles underlying health education, methods of teaching health, suggestions regarding source materials, and the relationships of both school personnel and school subjects in health education. The second is a section on *planning for health education*, which discusses the promotion of health education through healthful school living;

---

[1]*Planning for Health Education in Schools*, a work prepared for UNESCO and the World Health Organization by C. E. Turner. Copies are available in the U. S. A. through the UNESCO Publications Center, 317 East 34th Street, New York, N. Y.

school health services; health instruction; and school, home, and community relationships.

A preliminary draft of the manuscript was sent to ministries of education and ministries of health in the member states of these two United Nations agencies, and 94 countries sent comments and suggestions for the final draft. The book is in the nature of an annotated agenda which raises the questions to be considered by curriculum committees.

Bases for selecting subject matter and methods

The decision as to what will be taught in health at the various grade levels is based upon many factors, including the health status and needs of the community; the health problems of the child and the home; existing health customs and beliefs which reduce physical or mental health and efficiency; the present health interests and needs of the child; the orientation, information, and skills which are needed for future responsibilities; the extent to which health is taught in other subjects; and the contributions which health instruction can make to the general objectives of education.

Similarly, the choice of methods will be related to the methodology followed in general education; the maturity, interest, capacities, perceptions, and value systems of the children at the respective grade levels; the relative emphasis upon subject matter and health behavior at different ages; and the available resources in persons and materials.

The individual teacher is likely to use the teaching guide or the textbook as a general framework; but he usually prefers to make his own more specific plan for health instruction at the beginning of the year. He studies the health needs, present information, and health interests of his group by various means such as discussion, observation, questionnaires, health records, and reports. He decides upon a limited number of problems and the appropriate emphasis to be given to each in the development of a well-balanced program. His plan is flexible and subject to modification on the basis of pupil interests as the class participates in the more detailed planning of specific units of work.

Some guiding principles related to classroom methods

Health education is primarily concerned with behavior. In this respect it is like character education. We may appropriately consider some of the principles of educational psychology and philosophy which should guide the teacher's approach to health instruction.

1. *The same understanding of the child and of educational psychology is used in teaching for health as in other phases of education.* Teaching is the development of active learning on the part of the pupils or student. To be successful the teacher must understand the developmental status of the child, his degree of maturity, how he perceives situations, his value systems, his desires, and his antipathies.

2. *The child should think of health as a matter of conduct, not merely*

as a subject of instruction. Health behavior is more important than health knowledge. A program consisting merely of a recitation period in which only facts are considered would have but slight effect upon behavior. Hygiene and sanitation merely give us the guiding principles to healthful living. The procedure used in developing correct behavior utilizes the three steps which Strang has called "desire, insight, and practice" and which the Joint Committee lists as "need, knowledge, and utilization."

3. *Motivation bridges the gap between knowledge and action.* It is necessary so to motivate the child to want to do what is desirable that he will apply his new health knowledge.

4. *The nature of habits should be recognized in health education. Habits are acquired.* They are behavior patterns acquired by frequent repetition. Repeated practices become habitual. Keeping in mind that a bad habit, or the absence of a habit, is as much an acquired characteristic as is a desirable habit, the teacher seeks to promote correct behavior and to supplant undesirable actions with the preferred ones.

5. *The laws and ways of learning apply to health education.* The laws of readiness, exercise, and effect operate in the building of a habit. Learning is most effective when the learner is *ready* for it. If a child feels a need, or has developed an interest, then he wants to learn a response. He is ready. Readiness operates in setting the scene for habit building.

A response once made is not fixed. *Use* of that response or *exercise*, by the repeated calling forth of the same response to a given stimulus, helps to fix the stimulus-response bond. This bond is needed in fixing a single habit or in linking a chain of habits into a skill. Learning is experiencing. It comes through the continuous process of responding, reacting, and adjusting.

A response, however, is not likely to be repeated if its effect is unsatisfactory. Satisfaction of some sort must accompany a response if the habit is to be formed and maintained. The *satisfaction* may lie in the knowledge that one has done the best thing, or made the best choice, and not always in the act performed. Sometimes the correct response does not give the most immediate satisfaction. For example, a child may get immediate satisfaction from watching late TV programs, although he gets more lasting satisfaction from the ability to enjoy his daytime activities without unnatural fatigue due to loss of sleep.

It is possible to develop a *conditioned reaction* in health behavior as in other fields of conduct. By conditioned reaction we mean the continued use of a response pattern after the original stimulus is no longer operative. Many acts in such fields as personal cleanliness and food selection become almost automatic after a pattern has once been established.

It cannot be assumed that a habit once formed will persist uninterruptedly. We could not build a program upon the assumption that we could successfully teach ten habits in Grade I, ten other habits in Grade II, and eventually complete the list. It may, indeed, be more difficult to maintain the health practices at a higher grade level than it was to establish them at a lower grade level. Consequently, the *repetition* of certain elements of training is necessary, and for this reason the gradation of the program in such a way as to provide a *fresh approach* and *new material* at each grade level is particularly important.

Operation of the principle of *transfer* is also important. This principle emphasizes the effectiveness of transferring to real situations, as soon and as often as possible, those patterns of conduct discussed in the classroom as desirable—but which could not be put to immediate use. Finding ways to secure adherence to a regular bedtime hour is an example of the use of transfer.

Specificity is a principle of learning that requires the interpretation of abstract ideas into pictorial patterns that can be understood by young children. As educators we realize that youngsters do not generalize or associate ideas in the manner of adults. This is important in habit training, since we cannot assume carry-over of learned responses from a given situation to a similar one. Each problem must be treated separately and specifically, and abstract terms like "health," "growth," and "happiness" must be interpreted in terms the child can grasp.

6. *Emphasis is placed upon what to do, not upon what not to do. The teaching is positive, not negative.* If a patient comes to the physician's office with faulty digestion and is given a negative diet, he goes away in an unhappy frame of mind. Here are all the things he must not eat, and he is unable to think of anything he can eat. Practitioners in medicine and dietetics have found it wise to give positive diet lists—to tell people what to do.

If we can get a child to do the things we want him to do, we do not need to worry a great deal about preventing him from doing what we do not want him to do. In breaking a habit, the law of *disuse* is not entirely effective. Despite a lack of use an old response, once well established, will be called forth by the presentation of the old stimulus unless a new response has been learned. The substitution of a good new habit is the preferred way to break a bad habit. The old response must be unlearned by thoughtful substitution of a new, acceptable one.

7. *The distribution of objectives and emphases will vary in different classes, but the goals in health education should be clear and specific.* Not all groups of children have the same health problems. A capable teacher adapts his program to the particular group with which he is working. He discovers the present health practices of his pupils and acquaints himself with their physical conditions through personal conference, through a study of the cumulative health record of each child, and through conferences with nurse or physician. He then determines what things need attention and decides the sequence of the various items in the health education program.

Individual differences in the abilities of children, even of the same age and grade, and differences in the cultural, racial, and economic backgrounds make it necessary for teachers located in different areas of a city school system to adapt the suggested curriculum extensively. Often the same habit is of necessity taught in successive grades for emphasis, practice, or relearning where older pupils have become careless in simple matters. Every effort must be made to make such new teaching of an old habit interesting to the learner. A new, stimulating approach, an enlarged development substantiated by more factual science, vocabulary adaptation to the learner's level, and the like, make this teaching effective.

8. *Children are commended for success.* Their successes rather than their failures are emphasized. Commendation for success is more effective than blame for failure. When we weigh children, we do not criticize the youngster who failed to gain.

Each child will succeed in something. We ought to seek an opportunity to praise each child for something. A judicious, fair, and wise use of praise will go far toward developing the health behavior we desire in the group. Most children, and adults as well, blossom and develop under fair and honest appreciation of their efforts.

Success is a wonderful stimulus, and it is important in education to have the child succeed with as many undertakings as possible. Health behavior in such a field as cleanliness, for example, offers an opportunity for success to some children who have very little opportunity to succeed in the academic subjects. Not infrequently teachers have said that success in the health program has solved disciplinary problems with individual children and has encouraged some boy or girl to renewed effort and to a more cooperative and courageous attack upon all his school work.

Sometimes in starting a health program we have pointed out to children that this is something in which everybody can succeed. You remember the story of the foot race in *Alice in Wonderland* in which the tortoise and the other animals participated. "When do we start?" they asked. "Any time!" was the answer. "How far do we run?" "As far as you like." "Who wins?" "Oh, we all win." Health education is somewhat like that.

Commendation is a form of social approval. It should be strong, and for the right thing. Group approval sometimes works against the child. He responds to standards of conduct set by the group, even when such behavior is not for his own good. For example, a sixth grade boy may have to choose between a gang's approval of smoking and school approval of his good health habits. The stronger the hold on the lad by his teacher, nurse, or classmates, the more likely he is to follow their standards for healthful living. The right decision contributes to character education.

9. *Particular care is taken not to hold the child responsible for the improvement of conditions over which he has no control.* Thus, when establishing the clean-handkerchief habit, you define a handkerchief as any clean piece of cloth or as a paper tissue supplied at school. Then you can hold the child responsible for having a clean handkerchief because it is within his power to procure one. Nothing is more disheartening than being blamed for something one was powerless to prevent.

Even in this era, poor children may not have bathtubs, washbasins, and hot water available. Thus the checking of daily washing might seem unfair to such children. If the problem of washing and bathing is discussed and practical procedures worked out by the class as a whole, then those children can be assisted without embarrassment in establishing the proper practice.

Similarly, community conditions which may tend to defeat the class program cannot be laid at the feet of the child. The schools can and should join with other groups in clean-up campaigns and other activities for the improvement of community health. Children should be given responsibility, however, for only those things which they can do something about.

10. *The teacher helps the child to see that the ultimate reward of health practices will be found in growth, in improved physical accomplishment, and in other concrete evidences of health.* This removes the danger of rewarding children directly via stars, prizes, and other trophies for a good record of health habits. The reason for health habits ought not to be the winning of a specific reward at the end of a given period. If that is what is in the child's mind, then, when the reward is achieved, there is no longer any reason for continuing the habit. Furthermore, if a reward is the only value the child sees for doing the thing, there is a needless temptation for the child to falsify the record. Growth and accomplishment constitute a sufficient stimulus and a much better incentive.

11. *Interest in growth is one of the best single incentives toward the improvement of health behavior in children.* There may be some disagreement on this point, but our experience has led us to believe that there is no other one interest that so consistently and universally helps the elementary school child to want to do the things he should, in matters of diet, rest, and activity, as the interest in growing.

Every child wants to grow. Sick children do not grow rapidly; growth is roughly a sign of health. The failure to gain for a single month is not serious, but in general growth is more uniform when the child's habits are good than when they are poor. The teacher who weighs children every month and gets the children interested in watching their growth will find it easier to develop a health program because of the pupils' interest in growing.

12. *The tendency of children to imitate those they admire is a force that may be used in developing improved health behavior.* The example of the teacher is a constant force in shaping those habits that contribute to physical and mental health. Teacher leadership in following sound health habits is of definite value. It is the teacher's health behavior and not his health itself that helps children in this way. A robust teacher who disregards those principles of hygienic living that most persons need to follow is less likely to develop satisfactory health training with pupils than the frail teacher who protects, through hygienic living, the limited amount of health and strength he does possess.

In one of our schools we had to cope with the problem of eating candy at recess and at noon. Just across the street there was a candy shop. We

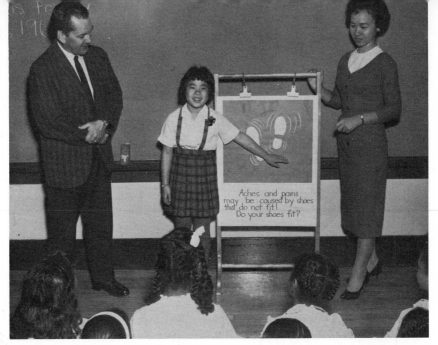

Fig. 46. A lesson about shoes and foot hygiene. (Courtesy Los Angeles City Schools.)

decided that the best way to attack the problem would be to see whether we could create in the older groups a public opinion against eating candy between meals. We asked the two upper grades in the school to make an investigation to find out whether it really is harmful. We gave them some references and some places to which they could write to secure information. They brought together such facts and authoritative statements as they could get and decided that candy between meals is injurious to health.

Then we used the tendency of children to adopt the ideas and imitate the practices of older children whom they admire. Individual pupils from the higher grades visited the lower grades and told the younger children about the study which they had made. They described how the project arose and what they had found out. The "minuteman" speeches of these older pupils, whom the youngsters wanted to imitate, had a powerful influence.

Hero worship develops during the later grades and the desire to imitate great men and women may be used to develop an interest in the health of the community and the nation through a study of health heroes. Emulation of the cleanliness practices of the school doctor and nurse as regards both their personal habits and their care of the medical office is still another application of the principle.

13. *Unhappy mental states are to be avoided.* In and of itself unhappiness is unhealthful. Moreover, pleasurable outcomes should be the result of the child's experiences in developing health habits. The avoidance of the injurious emotions of fear, anger, hate, and shame is most important. The studies of Pavlov, Cannon, and many subsequent investigators have shown the serious physical ill effects of these emotions in discontinuing the normal processes of peristalsis and the secretion of digestive juices and in modifying the activities of the circulatory and nervous systems. To

try to drive the child toward healthful living by fear would be absurd and destructive. All fears—fear of punishment, fear of being shamed before the class, fear of being peculiar, or inferior, or odd—develop anger and hatred toward the whole health program.

This does not mean, of course, that the child has to be immune to all the unhappy consequences that follow unhygienic and unsocial acts. He must realize that wrong habits impede growth and success in the classroom and on the playground. Health education makes clear the benefits of healthful living and the unfortunate results of unhygienic conduct. It must teach the common-sense recognition of facts regarding health and disease, but it seeks to avoid fear, shame, anger, and hate.

We find natural tendencies toward sympathy and toward cruelty in children. The attitude of children toward one another in matters of health should be one of sympathy. Not all children have the same native health, and we wish to develop reasonable sympathy for the crippled child or for children who are not robust, rather than to develop an antipathy toward them.

Some of the persons who have done most for the world have been of limited physical health. Elizabeth Barrett Browning, Robert Louis Stevenson, Charles Darwin, Helen Keller, Franklin D. Roosevelt, and many others either never had strong constitutions or had some permanent disability. Surely we think more highly of these individuals and their splendid contributions than of a perfect physical specimen of the human race who never did anything for anybody.

The teacher should help the child to think of health as a means of enriching life, not as an end in itself. There are many things in life that are more important than health. We sacrifice health and life itself in time of war, for the nation, our homes, and families. We are ready to sacrifice health in taking care of members of our own family when they are ill. Many qualities, such as honesty, integrity, and virtue, are placed before health in value.

We recognize that life is pleasanter and richer with health than without it, but we do not want to develop in school children the feeling that health is the most important thing in life and that other children are to be judged as friends or companions on the basis of their health alone. The possession of exceptional physical vigor may lead in the direction of less thoughtfulness for others, but it is not necessary that it should do so.

It means much to the child who is not strong to realize the important contribution he may be able to make in the world even without perfect health. Let us not make a critical, selfish snob of the child who is healthy or allow him to look down upon children who cannot do all the physical things he can do.

The richness of life is largely a matter of friendships, and the child, like the adult, likes to feel that he is an accepted member of the social group to which he belongs. In health activities we want general participation. We should see that no child is left out, that no child feels that he is inferior to the other members of the group or scorned by them.

14. *The gaining of knowledge and the development of a scientific attitude is an important objective in the higher grades.* Habit training alone is not sufficient. Pupils must be taught the health sciences commensurate with their understanding, and gain an ability to distinguish between fact and opinion. Such teaching will prevent dissatisfaction when the class is told that a given health practice is to be discarded because a recent laboratory finding makes this practice obsolete in the light of newer knowledge.

15. *Health education contributes to character education.* By the development of the initiative to adopt and follow certain desirable health practices, there is strengthened in the child a sense of self-mastery, responsibility for his own well-being and responsibility to his classmates, parents, teachers, and community. By avoiding unnecessary illness, by preventing the spread of communicable diseases, by cleaning up his back yard as part of a community project, a child not only practices good health habits but also builds character. Health education, further, should contribute to strengthening the moral qualities of loyalty, justice, truth, and consideration for the less fortunate. An honest health record is emphasized as more desirable than a perfect one. Loyalty and justice are strengthened by class activities.

The utilization of interests and incentives

The teacher has in mind the natural interests, tendencies, and incentives of his pupils when he plans for teaching health.

Health instruction is properly developed along with the expanding *curiosity* of the child. Information is given to the pupil, not when it happens to be convenient for the teacher, but when it meets the interests and needs of the child. It comes in answer to the curiosity he has developed.

At one time we were conducting an experiment in teaching the nature of bacteria. The group of junior high school boys sent a committee to the principal to ask that they might be allowed to omit basketball practice (for which they were excused from classes once a week) in order to come to the hygiene class, where some cultures of bacteria that they had been growing were to be examined. Curiosity lay at the root of this request.

Children like to *explore*. This interest may be utilized in health education with older children in making surveys of mosquito-breeding places, food surveys of stores, or surveys of some phases of cleanliness in the community, like the care of garbage or refuse.

Children like to be given *responsibility for doing worthwhile things*. They like to do things for the teacher, to help keep the classroom clean or to serve as monitors to watch the classroom temperature and maintain good ventilation.

The child likes to *make things*. He finds an opportunity in the health education program to make such things as graphs of his weight, scrapbooks, posters, and sand-table models. Anything representing the con-

Fig. 47. This simple pupil-made exhibit provided many learning experiences. (Courtesy Los Angeles City Schools.)

structive or creative activity of the child is sure to be examined in his home, whereas a scientific health pamphlet sent home by the teacher has very little chance of being read. The things that are made should have educational value, however. It sometimes happens that health posters are made mechanically, or by the selection of interesting colors, and are never considered from the standpoint of the health concepts portrayed.

Children like things that are their very own. They like to *collect things.* We should let children make or collect things that can be theirs, such as pictures, charts, records, and models. If something belongs to the child, it is important, and father and mother are quite likely to hear about it.

The child likes to *play.* Health can be made essentially a game.

Standards of acceptable *cleanliness* vary. Yet, in general, cleanliness is attractive although most children have a different idea of cleanliness from that of most adults. They also have a different standard of cleanliness as applied to themselves than as applied to other people. Most persons seem to tolerate in themselves conditions and actions in the physical, moral, and social realms that they condemn in others.

Women who go on vacations and leave their fathers, husbands, or brothers to keep house frequently find upon their return that the standard of cleanliness in the kitchen is one that would not be tolerated by the same men when the women of the house are doing the work. Similarly, in school John is much more charitable in deciding whether his own hands are clean than in deciding whether Henry's hands are clean. Our function in health education is to elevate the standard of cleanliness to a suitable level.

Because of the prime importance of motives for translating knowledge into behavior and because contemporary interests in keeping fit must be recognized in the curriculum, it is, perhaps, worthwhile to summarize here a list of certain incentives for motivating health behavior and some natural pupil interests upon which health teaching may be built. These have been evolved from the suggestions of a few hundred persons representing teacher groups and committees. By "incentive" we mean a desire that stimulates action; that is, a desire that motivates. A list of incentives follows:

Desire to grow
Desire for approval of one's social group (for social acceptance)
Desire to conform to custom, "style," or accepted procedures
Desire to earn recognition for worth-while accomplishment
Desire to imitate those one admires
Desire of adolescents to be attractive; interest in personal appearance; desire to be admired
Desire for good report in school work
Desire to participate in outdoor sports (skating, skiing, coasting, hiking, fishing, hunting, and camping)
Enjoyment in acquiring or improving skills
Desire to win in competition (competition between groups or with ones past record)
Desire for new experiences
Desire to do grown-up things
Desire to be helpful at home and at school
Desire to succeed in playground and gymnasium activities
Desire to earn membership and improved standing in Boy Scouts, Girl Scouts, and similar organizations
Desire to enter a specific occupation, such as medicine, nursing, engineering, or education
Desire to be a worthy citizen

All of these incentives reflect in different forms the basic human *desire for a feeling of personal worth.*

Wholly apart from these incentives that may be used in actually motivating the child, we find a group of natural interests that may frequently be used to advantage in health education. They provide an interesting approach, a point of departure for the discussion of health facts, and suggestions for teaching units. The child will not improve his health habits because he is interested in these things, but they do provide an opportunity for the association of interests. The groups of teachers previously mentioned have suggested that children are naturally interested in the following things:

Animals
Babies
Care of dolls, housekeeping duties
Cartoons
Class and school loyalty
Clubs
Collecting things
Community centers
Concerts
Cooking
Debates
Dramatization
Drawing and painting, poster making
Excursions
Exercise
Father's occupation
Folk dances
Free expression
Games and toys
Handling things—manipulation
Health magazines
Keeping a diary
Machinery
Making things
Motion pictures
Music
Nature
Other children

Parents, brothers, sisters
Parties
Perfect attendance
Physical activity
Pictures
Play, in and out of doors
Policemen, firemen, engineers
Possession or acquisition
Puppet shows
Radio
Reading
Safety council
Saving or thrift

School and building activities
School fund
School newspaper
School orchestra
Scrapbooks
Seasons
Sewing
Slides (pictures)
Stories
Styles
Writing original plays and stories
Writing poetry, slogans

Planning the lesson or unit of instruction

The planning of a selected unit of instruction, whether it be a lesson in health science in the secondary school or a long teaching unit in the elementary school providing correlation with other subjects and extending over some weeks, involves the determination of *objectives*, the provision of an interesting *approach*, the setting of educationally sound *contents and procedures*, the selection of helpful *materials of instruction*, and an *evaluation* of outcomes.

Major *objectives* in health education are directed toward health behavior; and behavior is determined—aside from the varying force of social pressures—primarily by one's concepts, habits, skills or performance abilities, and attitudes or feelings. Specific health education objectives, therefore, are characteristically either concepts to be developed (protein foods are needed in the diet), habits to be trained (eating slowly), skills to be acquired (applying a bandage or brushing the teeth properly), or attitudes to be formed (a feeling of friendliness toward younger children).

We have considered the development of *concepts* at some length in Chapter 13. *Habits*, strictly speaking, are learned motor acts which have become automatic reactions taking place when the associated stimulus is present. They develop over a period of time and become established by repetition. Health practices become habitual when they take place automatically in similar situations.

A *skill* is a learned power of doing a thing competently. In its restricted meaning, it is a neuromuscular coordination developed to a high degree by intensive practice, like applying a splint in first aid or like typing. A performance ability is an overt act in which a high degree of skill is not necessary and which is developed more casually, such as eating, dressing, or working on a committee. *Attitudes*, like habits or performance abilities, develop and change with time.

The objectives should be perfectly clear and preferably set down as short, concise statements. Each will be related directly to behavior or to the acquisition of needed factual information in the health field. All objectives should be specific, practical, and obtainable by the pupil group in question.

The *approach* should be a real and interesting introduction to the activity. It is the point of departure for the child upon a new adventure in learning. It is a link between the known and the unknown. It should stimulate curiosity and make the pupil ready and eager to undertake the activity. It should be applicable or pertinent for the particular class; that is, it should be related to the real needs, experiences, and interests of the pupils.

The *development of content and procedures* is the major task. The exact steps are often made clearer by separating the teacher activities from the pupil activities. The teacher and pupils determine the details of the problem and select the questions that the unit of work will try to answer. Specific experiences are selected as appropriate means of finding the answers to these questions.

Learning experiences should be (1) adapted to the abilities, skills, knowledge, and interests of the class, (2) dynamic in contributing to the development of good habits, (3) consistent with the objectives, (4) properly related to other subjects, (5) reasonably flexible, providing different kinds of activity for different children, (6) definite, (7) purposeful, (8) satisfying, and (9) rich in opportunities for pupil progress. The teacher will consider the inclusion of a variety of experiences—individual, group, audiovisual, and direct-action.

Selection of *materials of instruction* or other *resources* is made in advance by the teacher and built into the instructional plan.

Definite *outcomes* are to be sought and, where possible, *evaluated*. At the completion of each unit, information presented is reviewed and summarized. The value of the unit in terms of health behavior is considered. Objective tests may be used to review and measure the knowledge acquired. The outcomes should be recognized and understood by the pupil. The teacher will look for outcomes in all the fields of learning in which a contribution has been made.

The formation of a critical judgment concerning the value of a completed unit is of great value to the teacher in the development of professional skill. In reviewing a unit, the teacher checks the different activities to see how well they have met such standards as those suggested in the foregoing discussion. Did they develop and hold interest? Were they adjusted to the age level? Were they too hard or too easy? Were they intelligible, interesting, clear, and practicable? Did they contribute to health attitudes and practices? Were right interpretations developed? Did they produce right emotional reactions? Was the unit satisfactorily summarized?

One should keep in mind when developing a unit of work the need to:
1. Plan in sufficient detail.
2. Make provisions for the students to grow in ability, to work with materials, to work together effectively, to recognize and solve problems, and to become more self-reliant.
3. Make a tentative outline as to sequence of activities.
4. Acquire suitable materials for pupil use.

5. Become familiar with the many resources in the community that may be of service to the unit.

6. Use only recognized and authentic sources for factual material.

Outlines for units of study vary in terminology, but, as implied in the above discussion, the essential sections are:

    I. Objectives or expected outcomes (concepts to be developed, skills to be acquired, health practices to be encouraged, facts to be learned)

    II. Approach or introduction (a stimulating transition from existing knowledge and interests to the subject of the new unit)

    III. Class activities and procedures (methods, devices, and techniques, including suggested topics for class discussion, questions to be answered, possible dramatization or role playing, new words to learn, reading assignments, writing of reports, stories or letters, field trips, simple experiments, preparation of drawings or models, preparation of standards of behavior, quest for pictures or other illustrative material, and correlations with what is being learned in other subjects)

    IV. Source materials (books, pamphlets, and various audiovisual materials)

    V. Teacher information (background knowledge for the teacher, sometimes distributed through the unit, sometimes in a separate section of the unit, and sometimes left to the textbook)

    VI. Evaluation procedures

    VII. References (those for teachers and for students are usually listed separately)

Some educators prefer to present the above sections in sequence. Others set units in tabular form, with columns such as the following:

Title of the unit or lesson

Objectives	Class activities	Source materials	Teacher information	Evaluation procedures

A unit of instruction

The following guidance unit in health and science was developed by Mrs. Helen B. Johnson and cooperating teachers with boys and girls in third and fourth grades in the public schools of Denver, Colorado. It is used here by permission of the National Dairy Council. A copy of the illustrated pamphlet from which it is taken may be obtained from National Dairy Council, 111 North Canal Street, Chicago, Illinois 60606. If you live in a city where there is an affiliated Dairy Council unit, you may request a copy from the Dairy Council office serving your area. The pamphlet includes samples of check lists and survey forms.

Doing better at work and play

THE "HOW" OF "WHAT" WE DID

Third and fourth grade children are still more or less dependent upon adults. But they are beginning to seek the approval of their peers, and they are asking "Why?" They are curious and are easily satisfied with reasonable answers to their questions. They are interested in such things as their own likes and dislikes, the kinds of activities they engage in, the foods they like to eat, when they want to go to bed. They show their feelings about such things.

The method we used in developing the unit is an expansion of the problem-solving approach to learning. It is a method of working with children which enables them to identify their own problems, to explore ways of getting answers, to test possible solutions, to draw conclusions satisfying to themselves, and to plan further exploration to broaden their interests. The plan as reported in this booklet:

1. Suggests ways of discovering major areas to be explored.
2. Seeks to discover possible concepts which will meet individual needs and can be tested to the satisfaction of the children.
3. Attempts to broaden the scope of children's health interests to stimulate desire for further exploration.
4. Proposes ways of measuring growth in knowledge, behavior and attitudes.
5. Suggests use of information, learning experiences, and resource materials.

The project was an on-going activity throughout the year. But, sections may be used separately anytime. The identification of group and individual needs and concerns was made by the class in the fall. The planned learning experiences and activities with opportunities for practice were carried on during the winter months. The progress inventories, final evaluations, and culminating activities were arranged for late spring.

We found scheduled time allotments in English, reading, art, social studies, science, and physical education were adequate for strengthening basic skills and introducing subject matter in health. We used the services of others. The routine activities of the school nurse and other health services provided motivation for learning experiences. The school lunch program offered many opportunities for emphasizing the importance of proper eating habits and good manners. Parent participation, desirable for the successful culmination of activities involving home situations, was received enthusiastically.

Interests at the third and fourth grades varied. The third graders' greatest concerns were learning to like new foods, practicing good manners and getting along with others. Fourth graders showed more interest in the "how's." They were concerned about improving physical skills in sports activities, school grades, how the body works, how proper food and the right amount of sleep help to keep the body in good condition. They wanted to know about fear, anger, temper, overcoming undesirable habits and forming better ones.

OBJECTIVES

To develop understanding of some "why's," "what's," and "how's" in areas of health information

To extend and enrich health learnings acquired in previous grades

To develop appreciation for and cooperation with health routines established in the home

To strengthen attitudes of cooperation with school health and safety routines

To develop increased responsibility on the part of children for their own health and happiness

To broaden the scope of interests and to stimulate the desire for further learning

To develop understanding about the use of the problem-solving method for securing and evaluating information.

CONCEPTS DEVELOPED WITH THE CHILDREN

People are different; they have different abilities and different needs. Some are naturally tall; some are naturally short. Some children grow fast; some grow slowly.

To do better in work and play you need a healthy body. You need to do everything you can to keep yourself in the best physical condition.

Taking care of the body is more than keeping it clean and resting it. All parts of the body work together; every part needs special care.

Health practices are a continual process. If you do them irregularly, they do little good.

You don't have to be a "star" in everything; decide what you want to do better, then make a plan for practice and follow it.

Study habits and behavior can be improved if you make up your mind and follow your plan for practicing.

Thoughtfulness of others and good manners are good habits. They, too, can be improved with practice.

PLANNING APPROACH, DEFINING A BASIC GROUP PROBLEM

At the beginning of the school year it was easy to lead the class into discussions involving adjustments to school and situations in the classroom. We discussed individual and group problems along with current needs in the classroom, home, playground, and lunchroom. I observed, explored, and asked questions about the behavior I saw. We, the children and I, asked:

Why are things hard for some children and easy for others?

How does it happen that some children always seem to be the head of the class?

Why are certain children chosen to be leaders?

Why is it that some children seem to feel good most of the time and are able to do well what they like to do?

How can we help ourselves to improve our skills in things we wish we could do better?

The children prepared such questions as:

How can we improve our skills in gym?

How does a healthy body help us do better?

What can we do to keep our bodies in good condition?

What are some good rules for practicing skills?

The discussions created interest and suggested an idea for a class project:

How Can We Do Better in Work and Play?

DETERMINING BROAD AREAS TO BE EXPLORED

We studied those things which the children thought they could do better. Their ideas were written on the chalk board. Secretaries selected from the class recorded them. From this list we organized their ideas into:

1. Activities—physical education and out-of-school sports, outdoor play, skating, swimming, music, dancing, home activities, writing, spelling, arithmetic, reading, art
2. Food—kinds, amounts, eating habits
3. Sleep—hours, bedtime activities
4. Health routines—cleanliness, care of skin, hair, eyes, ears, first aid, safety, teeth, nails, immunizations, physical checkups, how the body works
5. Feelings—anger, fear, sulking, temper, friendliness, generosity, confidence.

IDENTIFYING INDIVIDUAL PROBLEMS

We made preliminary surveys to discover what the children had already learned, things they did with willingness and understanding, as well as indications of areas in which their knowledge had not brought about desirable behavior. The results suggested some understandings that should be strengthened and desirable behavior to be encouraged.

I compiled check lists, one for the child and one for the parent. The specific items were suggested by the surveys. Identical lists were used so that each child and his parents could react to the same items. The child could write a wish on each section of his check list if he wanted to. I explained that parents' answers would help the children decide what they needed to study.

We sent letters to the parents explaining the project and inviting them to a meeting. They were asked to respond to the parents' check list and to indicate major concerns they might have about their child's attitudes or behavior.

The functions and responsibilities of parents were discussed with the class, so that the children would develop an understanding of parents' concern for their well-being and development, especially in habits of eating, sleeping, and other health practices. From the analysis of both children's and parents' check lists, we were able to compile questions for study. Planning for activities and collecting materials began.

Typical questions that the children wanted answered

1. *Activities*
   How do athletes train for their sport?
   Can we improve in other kinds of skills in the same way?
   Why do some children try to do too many things?
   Why do some children dislike gym activities?
   Why is outdoor play so important?
2. *Food*
   Why is breakfast so important?
   What foods should we have every day?
   Why do some children dislike certain foods?
   What causes us to be hungry?
   Is learning to like all kinds of food important?
3. *Sleep*
   What are some signs that we do not get enough sleep?
   How can we help ourselves fall asleep quickly?
   Why do some children dislike to go to bed?
   What happens to our bodies when we are asleep?
4. *Health routines*
   a. *Muscles and bones*
      How do bones and muscles work?
      How does exercise help our muscles?
      How does food help our bones and muscles?
      How do our hands, arms, or legs know what we want to do?
   b. *Eyes, Ears*
      How do the eyes work? How is vision tested?
      Why do some people need to wear glasses?
      What should we do if something gets into the eye?
      Where do tears come from?
      How do ears work?
      How should we take care of our ears?
   c. *Teeth*
      Why do we have baby teeth and later get permanent teeth?
      Does food help us have good teeth?
      How should we care for our teeth?
      Why are teeth so important?
      Why should we have regular dental checkups?
   d. *Skin, Hair Nails*
      What does the skin do for us?
      What should we know about first aid for cuts and scratches?
      What makes the skin perspire?
      Why are baths so necessary?
      Why are fingernails so important?
      How can we keep hair in good condition?
   e. *Immunizations*
      Why do people need "shots"?
      Why should we not be afraid to get "shots"?
   f. *Physical Examinations*
      Why should we go to the doctor for checkups even if we are not sick?

Fig. 48. The food groups. (Courtesy National Food and Dairy Council.)

5. *Feelings*

Why do some children cry when they get hungry?

What makes us want to "fight"?

Why is "temper" such a big deal?

Why does doing what we don't want to do get us all upset?

Why are good manners so important?

Why do some children dislike to do chores?

PLANNING LEARNING EXPERIENCES AND ACTIVITIES

Interesting things to do and ways to find out what they wanted to know were discussed and planned with the children. As suggested activities we included:

Ask questions of resource people like the school nurse, the dental hygienist, and others

For the nurse—
Why is a good breakfast so important?
How can we learn to like different foods?
How can we tell how much sleep children should have?
How do you test eyes and ears?
How much should a child grow or gain in a year?
What should we learn about first aid?

For the dental hygienist—
How can we keep from getting cavities?
How do teeth grow?
What foods should we eat?
Why is brushing so important?
Why should we see the dentist regularly?

Read books and other materials, encyclopedias, and the like
See films
Study charts
Watch demonstrations
Plan experiments to find out what happens
Act out situations (role playing)
Make booklets to keep records of what we do
Draw pictures
Learn poems, or write some
Write stories, make reports
Watch for and bring in reports about special television or radio programs, newspaper and magazine articles
Plan a culminating activity to share learnings with parents and friends

GROUPING AND ACTIVITIES

At this point the children were ready to select an area for research and study. Each child wrote a simple statement of what he needed to work on, expressing a first and second choice. From these statements we organized the class into five groups of six or seven pupils. Textbooks, pamphlets, charts, and other materials were distributed so work could begin.

The groups were composed of pupils of varying abilities, but each member assumed the responsibility for one or more questions, or a special assignment. Special assignments included drawing illustrations, previewing and introducing films, inviting special guests, helping to plan dramatizations, reporting on television or radio programs of interest. The groups started research on their problems most enthusiastically. The scope of their interest and the concepts developed broadened amazingly as they worked.

Interested parents sent children's reference books from home, and watched for articles in newspapers and magazines. Among our parents were a doctor and a registered nurse. We invited them to take part in the investigations by some of the groups.

Progress reports were given as each group discovered new ideas, was ready to relate experiences described in the textbooks, wished to present dramatizations, or show films. Individual groups asked the class for suggestions and comments on the work completed. The reports and presentations were revised and additions made according to the comments given by the class.

During these procedures the children started and continued practice for self-improvement. Comparisons of achievement test scores, physical fitness records, and school grades provided the children with evidence of their progress. The Stanford Achievement Tests and physical fitness tests (pull-ups, toe touching, sit-ups, trunk lifter, push-up, standing broad jump, dash) are routinely given in the Denver Public Schools. Besides, I gave encouragement many times, in any situation where sincere effort and improvement were observed.

Conferences with individual pupils helped to clarify strengths and weaknesses in academic as well as health areas. Parent conferences presented opportunities to discuss parent concerns and to plan ways to encourage the child. The school nurse discussed with individual pupils such problems as weight control, rest and sleep, vision, hearing. The dental hygienist's routine visit made its contribution.

MEASURING PROGRESS

As the reports for the five areas being explored were completed, some sort of simple knowledge test was given. The purpose of these tests was to pinpoint weaknesses or gaps in understanding rather than to check knowledge as such. Evidence of measurable gain in knowledge was satisfying to the children.

Growth in attitudes and behavior was much more difficult to measure. Throughout the whole unit the children were closely observed for improved study habits, evidence of better attention, and desire to improve skills. Every opportunity was taken to point out ways in which improvement was being accomplished.

The children kept a daily record of health activities for one week, a record entitled, **Am I Improving?**
It covered:

1. Kinds of Activities I Have Practiced
2. What I Had to Eat
3. My Bed Times and Hours of Sleep
4. Health Habits I Have Practiced
5. Good Behavior and Good Manners I Have Practiced

Space was included for self-evaluation and a statement of what was needed for further improvement. Use of this record proved helpful in measuring the children's own progress and in setting up goals for further efforts.

EVALUATION

Record of accomplishment—Items for a final questionnaire were selected by the children. The questionnaire entitled, **How I Have Improved**, was used to record actual accomplishments. The children took these lists home to be checked and initialed. Parents were very cooperative and eager to help in this part of the activity.

We made a summary of areas of greatest improvement in the class. This report was given at the close of the culminating program.

Culmination—A culminating program, presented as a play, provided an opportunity to share with parents and friends some of the things the class had learned. The children chose the plan and worked by groups on the various parts. The planning itself proved to be an important motivation in making reports accurate, interesting, and meaningful.

Each group organized, rehearsed, and presented its part of the play. The children put together dramatizations, pantomine, stories, poems, and reports with a pleasing balance of fact, fantasy, and humor.

Finale—As a finale we asked three questions of the children:

1. In what part of the study did you learn the most?
2. In what part did you want to know more?
3. What would you want to leave out?

The responses to the first two questions were as individual as the pupils, but a typical answer to the third question was "Nothing. I liked it all."

Teacher reaction—The cooperating teachers said:

"The children and I enjoyed participating in this experimental unit. I feel we have gained from this experience."

"In my fourth grade, the parents expressed gratitude for the boost to the children's morale in taking greater responsibility for sleep habits, eating new foods and personal grooming."

"The project was an inspiration to me because of the exceptional parent cooperation and the attitudes of the children toward identifying and trying to solve their own problems."

RESOURCES AND REFERENCES FOR TEACHERS AND CHILDREN

Textbooks

Health, Happiness, Success Series. "Keeping Fit for Fun, 3" and "All Aboard for Health, 4." Lyons and Carnahan, Chicago. 1958. Teacher's editions available. Stories to present health facts and information. Specific concepts and goals stated. Exercises and activities to bridge the gap between learning and practice. Glossary, index, evaluation, resources for health and safety materials.

Macmillan Science—Life Series. "Science, Health, Safety, 3" Units 1, 3, 4, 5, 6. "Science, Health, Safety, 4." Units 2, 3, 5, 6. The Macmillan Company, New York. 1959. Teacher's editions available. Contains helps for children on using *scientific method.* Lists for check and review. Glossary, index, audio-visual resources.

The Basic Health and Safety Program. "From Eight to Nine, 3" and "Going on Ten, 4." Scott, Foresman and Company, Chicago. 1962. Teacher's editions available. Excellent illustrations and text to build background. Enrichment activities. Exercises for application of ideas. Special research for hard workers. Evaluation, glossary, index.
Illustrative charts to accompany texts: "Choosing a Good Breakfast," "Your Bones and How They Fit Together," "What Happens When We Sleep?"

The New Road to Health Series. "Habits for Health, 3" and "Building for Health, 4." Laidlaw Brothers, River Forest, Illinois. 1960. Teacher's editions available. Relates to interest and needs of third and fourth graders. Excellent illustrations. Suggests games, activities. Summaries, ideas for evaluation, indexes, resources, visual aids.

Individual titles

Leaf, Munro. *Health Can Be Fun.* J. B. Lippincott Company, Philadelphia. 1945.
Leaf, Munro. *Let's Do Better.* J. B. Lippincott Company, Philadelphia. 1945.
Nemir, Alma. *The School Health Program.* W. B. Saunders Company, Philadelphia. 1959.
Parker, Bertha and Dowing, Elizabeth. *You as a Machine.* Row, Peterson and Company, Evanston, Illinois. 1958.

Poetry

Arbuthnot, M. *Time for Poetry,* A Teachers' Anthology. "Miss T." "Poor Tired Tim." Scott, Foresman and Company, Chicago. 1951.
Huber, Marion Blanton. *Story and Verse for Children.* "Washing." The Macmillan Company, New York.

Materials from National Dairy Council

Food Models—full-color cardboard models of foods for daily meals, die cut.
How Your Body Uses Food—booklet developed for fifth through seventh grades to challenge interest in the body's use of foods for growth, energy and health. Provides background information for the teacher.

My Growth Record—tabular and graph forms for recording height and weight.

Ready for Breakfast—information on a basic breakfast pattern. Available in poster and miniature forms.

The Four Food Groups (A Food Chart for Intermediate Grades)—a full-color teaching poster to aid in effective discussion of the four food groups.

The Four Food Groups (Miniature and Activity Piece)—activity piece, for individual use, reproduces chart and provides space for menu planning.

Films

About the Human Body. 15 Min. Color, black and white. Sound. Churchill Films, 6671 Sunset Blvd., Los Angeles 28, California. Explores the function and uses of bones, ligaments, and muscles. Shows the working of the nervous, respiratory, digestive, and circulatory systems.

Care of the Skin. 11 Min. Black and white. Sound. Encyclopaedia Britannica Films, Inc., 1150 Wilmette Avenue, Wilmette, Illinois. Shows three children getting ready for bed. Shows proper way to wash hands and bathe. Illustrates common skin ailments. Shows through use of animated drawings, structure of skin and why soap is necessary for cleanliness.

Don't Get Angry. 12 Min. Color, black and white. Sound. Encyclopaedia Britannica Films, Inc., Wilmette, Illinois. Explains anger as a natural emotion which cannot be entirely avoided, but can be managed in a mature way. Reveals some physiological changes during periods of excitement; emphasizes control of anger in children and adults.

Eat for Health. 11 Min. Color, black and white. Sound. Encyclopaedia Britannica Films, Inc., Wilmette, Illinois. Introduces five fingers as a check-off device to learn to eat a balanced diet.

Exercise for Happy Living. 11 Min. Black and white. Sound. Encyclopaedia Britannica Films, Inc., Wilmette, Illinois. Presents role of exercise in building a strong body and healthy, happy personality. Shows a boy's disappointment at being a substitute on a team until he acquires good habits in exercise.

Exploring Your Growth. 11 Min. Color, black and white. Sound. Churchill Films, Los Angeles, California. Shows by animation how food is digested in the mouth, stomach, and intestines. Describes how digested food is carried by blood to the cells of the body. Points out that food allows cells to grow and divide, resulting in growth.

Eyes Bright. 10 Min. Color. Sound. Avis Films, P.O. Box 643, Burbank, California. Discusses care and protection of eyes, rest for eye muscles, habits of cleanliness, how to hold a book, watch television, safety on playground and home.

Hear Better, Healthy Ears. 11 Min. Color, black and white. Sound. Coronet Instructional Films, 65 E. South Water Street, Chicago, Illinois. Shows pleasure that comes through hearing well. Details structure of ear and process of receiving air vibrations, changing them to sound.

Nutritional Needs of Our Bodies. 11 Min. Color, black and white. Sound. Coronet Instructional Films, Chicago, Illinois. Shows need for a balanced diet, how body cells oxidize nutrients, and foods for energy, growth, replacement, and regulation.

Project: Teeth-Dental Health and Classroom Science. 14½ Min. Color. Sound. American Dental Association, 222 E. Superior Street, Chicago 11, Illinois. Motivates children to become interested in learning more about their teeth and mouths.

Rest That Builds Good Health. 11 Min. Color, black and white. Sound. Coronet Instructional Films, Chicago. Describes sleep as a type of rest; relaxation, change, exercise as others. Outlines how to develop good rest habits, what happens to our bodies while we sleep, proper amounts necessary for growth and well-being.

Save Those Teeth. 11 Min. Black and white. Sound. Encyclopaedia Britannica Films, Inc., Wilmette, Illinois. Emphasizes proper cleansing, how teeth are affected by excessive use of refined sugar, the use of sodium fluoride in the prevention of tooth decay.

Sleep for Health. 11 Min. Black and white. Sound. Encyclopaedia Britannica Films, Inc., Wilmette, Illinois. Presents importance of regular sleep habits, emphasizes child's own responsibility in formation of good habits.

Sneezes and Sniffles. (Health and Safety for You.) 10 Min. Black and white. Sound McGraw-Hill Text Films, 330 W. 42nd Street, New York 3, New York. Demonstrates how colds are spread by sneezing, coughing, and careless handling. Outlines precautions to prevent spreading colds.

Teeth Are to Keep. 11 Min. Color. Sound. Encyclopaedia Britannica Films, Inc., Wilmette, Illinois. Stresses elements of proper care of the teeth.

Uncle Jim's Dairy Farm. 12 Min. Color. Sound. National Dairy Council, Chicago, Illinois. Increases understanding of growth and development through a story of children and their summer on a farm.

Ways to Good Habits. 11 Min. Color, black and white. Sound. Coronet Instructional Films, Chicago, Illinois. Outlines steps in habit formation: (1) identifying problem, (2) getting help from others, (3) starting to practice, (4) not slipping back.

Filmstrips

An Adventure at Camp Habit. 29 Frames. Color. Eye Gate House, Inc., 146-01 Archer Avenue, Jamaica 35, New York. Depicts good habits which should be formed and bad ones which should be broken. Shows how good habits influence health.

Foods We Eat. 40 Frames. Color. Film Strip of the Month Clubs, Inc., 355 Lexington Ave., New York 17, New York (Museum Extension). Discusses relationship of food to growth. Shows purpose of different nutrients in the body, work of vitamins. Demonstrates simple food tests. Illustrates simple experiments with vitamins.

Happy, the Medicine Man. 29 Frames. Color. Eye Gate House, Inc., Jamaica, New York. Points out necessity of regular health checkups, seeking help from physicians when illnesses appear, importance of following treatment and advice.

You and Your Ears. 50 Frames. Color. Encyclopaedia Britannica Films, Inc., Wilmette, Illinois. Points out what sense of hearing does for us. Presents interesting drawings showing how we hear.

You and Your Eyes. 50 Frames. Color. Encyclopaedia Britannica Films, Inc., Wilmette, Illinois. Shows that the eye works like a camera. Describes how the eye functions.

References

American School Health Association: *Health Instruction—Suggestions for Teachers,* Kent, Ohio, 1964. This issue of the *Journal of School Health* for December, 1964, contains outlines of 22 suggested units of study for grades K to 3; 20 for grades 4-6; 6 for junior high schools; and 8 for senior high school, prepared by committees of the Association. A section on "Workable Ideas" will be found at the end of each committee report. Available from American School Health Association, 515 East Main Street, Kent, Ohio, 80 pp., price $1.25.

Berelson, B., and Steiner, G. A.: *Human Behavior,* New York, 1964, Harcourt, Brace and World, Inc.

Grout R. E.: *Health Teaching in Schools,* ed. 4, Philadelphia, 1963, W. B. Saunders Company.

Kilander, H. F.: *School Health Education,* New York, 1962, The Macmillan Company.

National Education Association and American Medical Association Joint Committee: *Health Education,* ed. 5, Washington, D. C., 1961, National Education Association.

National Education Association, Project on the Instructional Program of the Public Schools: *Deciding what to Teach; Education in a Changing Society; Planning and Organizing for Teaching,* 1964, NEA, 1201 Sixteenth Street, Washington, D. C. 20036.

National Education Association: *Schools for the Sixties,* a report of the Project on Instruction, New York, 1963, McGraw-Hill Book Company.

National Elementary Principals: *Health in the Elementary School,* Twenty-Ninth Yearbook, Washington, D. C., 1950, Department of Elementary School Principals, National Education Association.

Oberteuffer, Delbert: *School Health Education,* ed. 3, New York, 1960, Harper & Brothers.

Schneider, R. E.: *Methods and Materials of Health Education,* ed. 2, Philadelphia, 1964, W. B. Saunders Company.

Turner, C. E.: *Planning for Health Education in Schools,* 1966, UNESCO and WHO. Available through UNESCO Publications Center, 317 East 34th Street, New York, N. Y.

Willgoose, C. E.: *Health Education in the Elementary School,* ed. 2, Philadelphia, 1964, W. B. Saunders Company.

World Health Organization: *Teacher Preparation for Health Education,* report of a Joint WHO/UNESCO Expert Committee, Technical Report Series, no. 193, Geneva, 1960, 19 pp.

Chapter *XV*

Resources in health instruction

W hat teaching aids are available to the teacher, and what are the resource agencies and organizations to which he can turn for assistance?

Kinds and values of source materials

Experts on methods and techniques in education, meeting at UNESCO in Paris,[1] divided educational media into four classes or generations. The first generation of teaching aids consists of written materials, charts, maps, graphs, exhibits, chalkboards, models, demonstrations, dramatizations, and the like. All of these came before mass communication, and many of them have been used since the beginning of formal teaching. They require no machine or electronic device.

The second generation of media is represented by printed textbooks, workbooks, and texts. In contrast with handwritten books, manuscripts, and other items in group one, the media of the second generation are useful over broad areas. They provide a medium for carrying great teachers around the world and over periods of time. It was this group of media which made public education and world literacy possible.

Media of the third generation include photographs, slides, filmstrips, silent motion pictures, recordings on discs or tapes, radio, sound film, and television. These media distribute pictures and sounds over wide areas, making it possible for pupils and students to share great teachers, demonstrations, and dramatizations. These third-generation media appeared during the nineteenth and twentieth centuries as man learned to introduce a machine into the communication process.

Teaching aids of the fourth class include language laboratories, teaching machines, programmed self-instruction, and the teaching use of digital computers. The distinguishing characteristic of those media is that they depend upon communication between man and machine. The language laboratories allow the student to practice language skills and to hear his own efforts in comparison with the language of an expert. Programmed

---

[1]UNESCO: *New Methods and Techniques of Education,* Educational Studies and Documents No. 48, 1963. Available from UNESCO Publications Center, 31 East 34th St., New York 22, N. Y., 51 pages, $1.00

self-instruction appears in various forms and "automates" the tutorial process.

Schools today use many resources to make the teaching of health vital, interesting, and real. We turn to other members of the school health team or the personnel of the local health department for aid. We get help from experts in medicine, sanitation, safety, nutrition, and other fields, including the special interests of the various volunteer health agencies in our own communities. Four-H clubs, Future Farmers, Future Homemakers, and other youth groups bring their health interests into the discussions of health problems in the secondary school. Radio and television enrich the educational experience of millions of children.

From the state departments of public health, education, and agriculture, we get further assistance. Our Federal Government, certain professional societies, private agencies, trade associations, and business groups provide materials of wide variety. In addition to the textbook, we use pamphlets, anatomical and other models, chalkboard drawings, bulletin board displays, still pictures, charts, cartoons, flash cards, scrapbooks, slides, photographs, motion pictures, filmstrips, spot maps, posters, specimens, diagrams, graphs, tape recordings, and museum visits. We extend the pupil's visual experiences through field trips, dramatization, demonstrations, and exhibits. There is no longer any question of the value of audiovisual aids in school or outside. Those concerned with education in industry and in the Armed Forces have estimated that the learning process has been accelerated 25 per cent to 40 per cent by their use.

Let us review some of the more important kinds of source materials in terms of their nature, evaluation, and special contributions to the learning process.

The course of study in health. In a large percentage of schools, the teacher has at hand a teacher guide for health instruction, developed at the state or community level, which provides a general plan for health instruction. It suggests standards of achievement by the pupil in the acquisition of the health concepts, understandings, and knowledge which he is expected to acquire and in the health behavior he should develop. It relates health education to the general curriculum and presents a framework of health instruction of great assistance to the teacher in shaping a program to the needs of his class. (See also page 247.)

Textbooks. Excellent modern textbooks are now plentiful. State-adopted or state-approved texts give the teacher at each grade level suggestions as to both appropriate subject matter and useful methods. Many of these series of health texts provide either a teacher edition or a separate booklet of suggestions for the teacher in the use of each book. They present attractive and alluring possibilities of exploration and problem-solving in the health field.

The following items are characteristic of criteria used in the selection of textbooks:

1. *The underlying philosophy.* The source material selected should be based upon an educational philosophy that:
   (a) Recognizes health as related to all phases of human life—physical, mental, emotional, and social.
   (b) Considers health education as an integral part of a program of general education that seeks to improve the quality of daily living, not merely to prepare for adult life, to store information, or to provide mental discipline.
   (c) Acknowledges health as a means of enriching life, not as an end in itself.
   (d) Takes the positive rather than the negative attitude toward health in the presentation of material; for example, the first approach to the subject of bacteria should be that of biology or nature study, not that of pathology.
   (e) Recognizes that many pupil experiences outside class instruction, such as those in connection with health services and physical education, have an effect upon the health habits, attitudes, and knowledge of the child.
   (f) Recognizes that health behavior is the primary objective, since health attitudes and knowledge improve health only through their effect on behavior.
2. *The aims or objectives.* The aims should be to improve the health of the individual, the community, and the nation through the development of suitable habits, attitudes, and knowledge.
3. *Adaptation to age and grade level.* Materials should be adapted to the age, development, and interest of the group for which they are intended by:
   (a) Suitability of vocabulary and ideas.
   (b) Recognition of the changing needs of children.
   (c) Recognition of the broadening responsibilities of children.
   (d) Recognition of the child's gradually enlarging community.
   (e) The development of a fresh approach and some new topics in each grade, in addition to the necessary repetition.
4. *The development of self-guidance.* Provision for learning experiences of this sort may be secured through materials that:
   (a) Stimulate thought.
   (b) Contribute to the formation of attitudes of personal responsibility.
   (c) Develop ideas and activities that contribute to the solution of actual problems.
5. *The informational material.* The items of information presented should:
   (a) Reflect present-day knowledge with scientific accuracy.
   (b) Be presented in a psychologically sound manner.
   (c) Cover adequately the various phases of health subject matter.

6. *The skill used in the preparation of the material.* Elements of special value in the preparation of materials include:
   (a) Actual classroom experimentation.
   (b) A study or knowledge of the health needs of children.
   (c) The professional education and the health education experience of the writer or team of writers.

7. *Adaptation to teachers' needs.* Consideration for the needs and problems of the teacher should be provided through:
   (a) Respect for teacher judgment and initiative in the way material is presented.
   (b) The suggestion of many possible procedures and activities.
   (c) The suggestion of procedures for measuring accomplishment where possible.

8. *General style and make-up.* The literary and mechanical features of the material should be of good quality, in that:
   (a) Correct and readable English is used.
   (b) The bookmaking is satisfactory with respect to durability, quality of paper, and size and legibility of type. The following type sizes are commonly regarded as desirable for different ages:

AGE OF READER	POINT OF TYPE
Under 7 years	24
7- 8 years	18
8- 9 years	14
9-12 years	12
Over 12 years	10 or 11

   (c) The illustrations are of good quality and positive teaching value, not negative or gruesome. (It should be recognized that some illustrations are used for their motivating force in showing that certain procedures are pleasant or desirable, while other illustrations are informational in nature and demand careful study.)

Posters. Because posters for health teaching are widely available and because so many are made as pupil activities in health, the teacher is interested in their quality and their values. The poster presents an idea at a glance. It reminds; it calls attention; it suggests action very quickly; it arrests attention and presents a sound, true, timely, important, and appealing message.

A good poster is large enough to be read across the room. It has contrasting or striking colors, clear lettering, and wording which is immediately understood. Its message is easy to remember. It may be humorous, startling, or striking, suggesting a challenging topic for discussion.

When posters are made at school, they should provide learning experiences both in art and in health. The health message should be sound, and its presentation should be artistic. Classroom posters may be made not only by a drawing or a painting, but also with the use of magazine

Fig. 49. Posters are used to carry health ideas in every country.

pictures, wallpaper, tin foil, or newspaper cartoons. School posters presenting slogans for safety, good teeth, posture, and other health practices may be used on the school bulletin board or in the lunchroom as well as in the classroom.

Charts and graphs. Many types of charts are used to explain relationships. Some are purchased from supply houses; others are made by teacher or pupils. *Anatomical charts* showing basic structure of cells, tissues, organs and systems of organs are available for the use of older students. They enable the class to discuss body structure when structural relationships can be pointed out for all to see. Simple unlabeled anatomical diagrams provide an opportunity for the addition of labels during class discussion. *Organization charts* show the relationship of the different divisions of a health department or other agencies. The *flow chart* depicts the flow of materials, services, or functions by means of arrows from one visualization to another. *Tabular charts* are in constant use to present data in concise comparative form, as are *line graphs* (see page 219), *bar graphs* (see pages 42 and 43), and *pie charts* (see page 188).

Still pictures (pictures, photographs, filmstrips, and lantern slides). *Pictures* which carry a health message are available from magazines, advertising brochures, and folders of various kinds. When carefully selected on the basis of the concept they present and the soundness of its presentation, they provide excellent teaching material. They can be mounted on cardboard for class use or placed upon a bulletin board. Pictures can be classified under such headings as food, posture, safety, activity, and rest, thus facilitating their subsequent use. If the school has an opaque projector, pictures up to six inches square can be thrown upon the screen for class discussion.

The habit of taking *photographs* is so widespread that current activities and places of interest are constantly being photographed by teachers and

Fig. 50. The invaluable chalkboard is supplemented by charts and models. (Courtesy Los Angeles City Schools.)

older students. During field visits, sports, and classroom programs, the Polaroid camera, which produces a print immediately, has been used effectively in studies of public health procedures, body mechanics, first-aid techniques, and a variety of other pupil activities.

A special value of the *filmstrip* lies in its convenience. A strip of standard, safety 35 mm. film, three to six feet long, can carry twenty-four to forty-eight still pictures and can be projected from a lantern which is small, compact, light in weight, and extremely easy to operate. The film is easily moved forward one frame, or one picture, at a time.

The advantages of the filmstrip over the glass lantern slides are that the film does not crack, that it can be mailed from one point to another in its little tin box for a few cents, and that the time-consuming process of picking out and arranging and putting back lantern slides is avoided. Film-strips may be used in a semidarkened room while the teacher alternately uses chalkboard diagrams, posters, or other corollary materials to emphasize the lesson which the use of the filmstrip enhances.

A strip of twenty to fifty pictures is purchasable for a dollar or two, whereas glass lantern slides cost from twenty-five cents to a dollar each. The teacher can have a filmstrip made up by submitting the various pictures to some organization like the Society for Visual Education[2] to be transferred. The cost of the first strip is less than the cost of having lantern slides made. Subsequent prints of the filmstrip are much less expensive. Copyrighted pictures cannot be made into filmstrips and then sold; but the teacher may use such pictures in making a strip for his own use. Several ready-made filmstrips in the field of health are available to schools without charge from the official, voluntary, and commercial agencies listed elsewhere.

[2]1345 Diversey Parkway, Chicago 14, Ill.

Film slides (2 inches by 2 inches) may be made from pictures taken upon 35 mm. film. Such pictures may be taken in natural color, as well as in black and white. The individual pictures can be mounted in a paper mat between two glass covers. This inexpensive source of homemade lantern slides in black and white or in natural color offers real educational opportunities. The same small projector can show both filmstrips and film slides.

The modern 2 inch by 2 inch slides are more convenient to store and use than the old standard 3¼ by 4 inch lantern slides.

Inexpensive homemade *standard size lantern slides* can be quickly made by the teacher (or by pupils under his direction) for a particular lesson. Postural silhouettes, for example, can be cut from black paper and mounted between two glass slides, which will be bound with tape. A diagram from the textbook may be traced on a roughened glass slide, using several colored India inks or crayons to label various parts. A statistical table may be typed on cellophane, mounted between two glasses, and projected for discussion.

More time and planning must be allowed for the production of the smaller (2 inch by 2 inch) slide because the material must be photographed. Both types, of course, are available commercially for standard subjects.

Sound filmstrips (with accompanying voice recording) are also available. A bell signal on the record indicates when to change the picture. A 33⅓ r.p.m. turntable is necessary for the playback of the sound filmstrip.

Motion pictures. We seek certain unique contributions to classroom instruction from motion pictures. They present activities taking place, things in action. They bring events from other parts of the world to the classroom. They are often more instructional than field trips because they present only the things the student should see and do not confuse him with unimportant details. They are certainly more convenient and less expensive than field trips. Documentary films present complicated laboratory demonstrations that are too difficult, expensive, or dangerous to arrange for the lecture period. The "eye" of the camera can be at the most desirable place, and thus, when the picture is projected, the whole class sees the demonstration from a "close-up" view.

Slow motion analyzes rapid movement. Stop motion speeds up an activity, like the growth of bacteria, which is too slow to watch through the microscope. Animated diagrams show things the class cannot actually see, as in a picture of stomach contractions made from fluoroscopic studies. Diagrammatic films may even show processes that are not visible, as the exchange of gases or dissolved substances between the blood and the tissue cells.

Dramatic films motivate, as well as inform, and are to be evaluated upon their motivational and dramatic quality, as well as upon the clarity and photographic quality required of all motion pictures.

In *theatrical films,* we find (1) *feature pictures* like the "Life of Pasteur,"

(2) *news releases* dealing with current health problems or activities, and (3) *trailers* prepared by health agencies to present a message in one to four minutes to the typical theater audience.

In *nontheatrical films* produced by health agencies, we find (1) *dramatic films,* many of which are of theater quality; (2) *documentary films,* based on reality and showing real people in actual situations; (3) *community or local health movies,* usually photographed directly on 16 mm. film, reflecting a school or community health activity; and (4) *teaching films* prepared specifically for the presentation of material to support health instruction at a particular level and in a specific subject matter area, as in some phase of physiology (digestion, circulation, blood, breathing, skin, body mechanics), sanitation (bacteria, care of food, water supply, waste disposal), or hygiene (dental hygiene, home nursing, first aid, tuberculosis, immunization, etc.).

These factual films are prepared for classroom use with pupils who are seeking specific information. Their motivation of health behavior is accomplished by showing how and why things should be done, not by showing what happens to persons who do or do not follow hygienic practices. They are made with the same scientific accuracy as are medical films and may be used like laboratory material in helping students to develop powers of accurate, scientific observation.

The value of classroom films is enhanced by an accompanying *teacher's guide,* giving details concerning each scene and additional teaching material for the use of the instructor. In the silent movie, the film may be stopped at any time, leaving a still picture on the screen for class discussion. This means that each film represents a long series of still pictures as well as a motion picture. For example, a motion picture of the heart in action may be stopped on the screen to discuss structure. An animated diagram showing the movement of blood through the heart and the action of valves may be stopped on the screen while the students are asked to describe what has just taken place and what the next heart movement will be. Furthermore, films are valuable in developing vocabulary, because they leave the student in possession of definite knowledge that demands new words for expression. Like all visual material, films are adapted to wide differences in age level. The greater the pupil's knowledge the more he sees in a picture.

More and more schools today are making their own moving pictures on 8 mm. or 16 mm. film. A trip to a dairy farm can be filmed by the teacher with his own camera, and the film later can be built into class lessons.

A sound projector uses silent as well as sound films. A sound film cannot be run on a silent projector, however. Operation of the various types of visual aid projectors is usually taught in teachers' colleges. Teachers who do not possess this knowledge can obtain it by attending adult classes at local colleges or they may be given special instruction as a public service by a health or commercial agency. Health films are usually produced on cellulose acetate (safety) stock. Cellulose nitrate film is dangerously inflammable.

Screens are desirable but not always needed for classroom projection of films. A light-colored wall above the chalkboard serves as an adequate screen. A large white cloth on the wall is fairly satisfactory. An opaque class door panel frequently serves the purpose. Such opaque glass or blue linen draftsman's cloth in an old picture frame may be used as a translucent screen for rear projection, with the projector behind the screen. For such rear projection the film must be put into the machine with the film surfaces reversed.

There are numerous sources of information about films. In addition to all the commercial producers who publish source lists by subject matter, film lists are usually available from state and local offices of education, departments of visual aids, state and local health departments, the United States Office of Education, the United States Public Health Service, and from the voluntary health associations and noncommercial trade groups.

The film lists mentioned here may be helpful to the teacher:

1. *Directory of U. S. Government Films* (free), United States Office of Education, Washington, D. C.
2. *Lists of Films and Slides* (free), United States Departments of Agriculture, Interior, Labor, Navy, and the Bureau of Mines (many are not on health, of course).
3. *Educational Film Guide,* H. W. Wilson Company, 950 University Ave., New York, N. Y. This is a most complete list of educational films in all subjects and is kept up to date, quarterly.
4. *Encyclopedia Britannica Films,* 20 N. Wacker Drive, Chicago, Ill.
5. *Educator's Guide to Free Films* (annual edition), containing over 2,500 titles, is purchasable from Educators Progress Service, Randolph, Wis. This book also contains a discussion on the use of free films in the classroom and carries an availability index.
6. *Films on Health and Welfare,* National Film Board of Canada, 1270 Avenue of the Americas, New York N. Y.

(See also page 310 for a discussion on methods of using films.)

Models. Anatomical models give a better understanding of actual size and structure than word descriptions or drawings. Like charts, they are used in health teaching to show relationships of health significance. Models, for example, give the student a clear understanding of the eustachian tube as the avenue of middle ear infection, the delicacy of the middle ear and inner ear, and innumerable other structures in their relationship to health and disease. Many models are made so that they can be taken apart and reassembled.

Perhaps the most famous model is the transparent woman which is to be seen in many health museums and which has been used by the American Medical Association as part of its health education program. This model is nearly life-size and is made of plastic. It is equipped with an electric lighting system which illuminates one system of organs after another as a voice recording describes the model.

An infant-size, washable doll and its clothing give reality to the teaching of infant care. Pupils at appropriate grade levels can make models of gardens or water filters.

Exhibits. Exhibits may be made by the teacher, set up by the pupils, or they may be borrowed, rented, or purchased from health agencies or other sources in the community. They provide an opportunity for students to construct models, collect specimens, or create materials. They utilize visual learning and often bring the community into the school.

School-made exhibits deserve careful planning, with the children participating. Materials are carefully chosen; space needs and lighting are considered. Design, color, and lettering are used to bring out the central theme effctively. It may be desirable to set up the exhibit in the classroom if it is going to be used for work periods and with discussion groups. An exhibit that is large and carefully prepared may be made available to the other classes in the school building and shown to visitors, perhaps with pupil explanation. There are key spots in the building where exhibits may be effectively displayed. For example, an exhibit on foods and nutrition may be located in the lunchroom, while exhibits in other fields, such as school safety or first aid, may be presented in a corridor or in the school auditorium at the time of a parent-teacher meeting in the building.

Objects and specimens. Many real objects can be brought to class to add to the reality of seeing, touching, or handling in the study of an object. Primary school children become acquainted with individual fruits and vegetables at a fruit and vegetable party. A real meal is set at school. Different kinds of cloth can be seen and felt, as can various items of clothing. Pupils learn to read the thermometer as they study temperature. Different kinds of plants are brought to school. Sometimes pets are kept. Older students secure bacterial cultures and grow common bacteria. They examine specimens of body fluid.

Maps. Outline maps or maps showing limited geographic detail may be used to demonstrate many health situations. A spot map of the neighborhood or state can be made to show the distribution of disease in time of epidemic. A neighborhood map shows the exact location of an accident. State or national maps can be made to show areas of food production, concentrations of population, or which states have specific laws or regulations.

Flash cards. These are usually made on 13″ by 22″ cardboard and consist of words or pictures which can be flashed by hand for quick identification or for memory drills. They have been used in health education for drill in the study of word meanings and for strengthening the immediate recognition of foods with different nutritional values as well as for study of harmful insects, poison ivy, and other poisonous plants. They can help to distinguish quickly the differences between harmless and poisonous snakes or poisonous and edible mushrooms in stiuations where this knowledge is important.

Flip charts. The flip chart is a device made of large sheets of heavy paper, bound together at the top and mounted upon an easel, which allows the sheets to be turned readily. It may be made by pupils as they study a topic to show, for example, a series of safety situations, community health activities, different food groups, or other relationships.

Cartoons. Cartoons bearing upon health may be brought to class by teacher or pupils to give a humorous but challenging interest to a health topic. They are especially enjoyed by pupils of the intermediate grades. Constructive discussion is developed to bring out the facts in the situation and to make a contribution to education, not merely to entertainment.

Chalkboards, bulletin boards, flannelboards, and magnetic boards. Chalkboards, colored for effective contrast with chalk and sufficiently abrasive to take chalk well, yet sufficiently smooth and impermeable to clean easily, provide the most used medium in presenting visual impressions. They are used not only for word lists, but also for diagrams, charts, graphs, and sketches. There are usually chalkboards at the front and at one side of the room, but smaller chalkboards can serve as the center of a teaching nook or corner for small group instruction.

The general purpose classroom is also equipped with a *bulletin board* or *tack board* made of pressed fibers, soft wood, or self-healing cork. Plastic wall coverings are sometimes used to provide a washable bulletin board surface. The bulletin board in the classroom is a suitable place for many of the kinds of visual materials which we have mentioned. Selected and interesting materials may be placed there by pupils and teacher for their current interest, or the bulletin board may be devoted to an extensive series of clippings, pictures, charts, maps, and graphs related to a unit of study in health in which the children are engaged. Bulletin boards in corridors, cafeterias, libraries, and other rooms may be used to carry health messages. Those in the health service suite or the gymnasium more commonly carry bulletins of health advice or health schedules, in contrast to the displays which are provided and serviced frequently on the bulletin boards of classrooms and corridors.

A *flannelboard* is made by covering a sheet of masonite or similar board with flannel cloth. Cut-out flannel figures or pictures mounted on a card with a sandpaper back will stick to the surface of the flannel. The ease with which it can be put up and taken down makes the flannelboard an interesting device for the presentation of health ideas, either directly or in connection with class discussion. Other materials which can be attached to a flannel or felt surface include blotters, corduroy, velvet, and cotton. The flannel board is useful at all levels of instruction and is particularly valuable in illustrating a series of events or activities in a discussion period. Pupils may go to the flannelboard and change the illustrations as needed.

Flannelboards with suitable models provide a good method for presenting and discussing balanced meals, the basic food groups, the production and distribution of milk, seasonal clothing needs, the units of anatomical structure, the health facilities of the community, and the routes through which communicable disease is transmitted.

Magnetic boards are similar in purpose and use to flannelboards. They are metal sets to which either magnetic pieces or materials attached to magnets will adhere. Some magnetic boards are covered with a thin layer of oilcloth or other material which will not hinder the use of the magnet.

Workbooks and scrapbooks. Workbooks have been successfully used in the development of units of instruction and in the solving of health problems both in the elementary schools and in the secondary schools, in relation to both personal and community health.

Many classes in the elementary school have had a successful experience in keeping a class *scrapbook* in which health activities have been recorded. These loose-leaf scrapbooks have been used as exchange material among teachers of the same grade. Each scrapbook carries the name of the class and teacher who produced it.

Radio and television. In addition to station-sponsored and commercial health broadcasts, there are *radio* programs of direct instruction and many sustaining programs sponsored by health departments and medical associations. With good planning and careful integration, selected *radio broadcasts* in health can be used as teaching lessons. Both school and home listening are receiving increasing attention today.

F-M (frequency modulation) stations have become more numerous. Many boards of education operate their own F-M stations. Teachers will increasingly be concerned with the production of such programs. Where *public address systems* reach into individual classrooms, radio broadcasts can be carried to pupils in their homerooms, just as special health announcements and health programs originating within the school are carried over such a system.

Some radio stations (including A-M [amplitude modulation] networks) have experimented with programs for classroom use. A printed schedule of radio programs, with teacher guides, is available from such producers. The teacher must prepare the class for effective learning. Objectives must be set up, appropriate visual aids should be selected and used, and good reference material should be available for immediate follow-up. A listening atmosphere, quiet and uninterrupted, must be provided so that pupils can give their undivided attention to the program. Since radio broadcasts and radio advertising vary widely in reliability, critical listening habits should be developed. Appropriate follow-up by discussion and reference reading is usually desirable.

The Federal Radio Education Committee, United States Office of Education, Washington 25, D. C., will assist teachers and administrators who desire to make better use of radio as a tool of education. In addition to publishing a quarterly bulletin (free), this committee has such monographs as (1) *Central Sound Systems for Schools,* (2) *Sound Recording Equipment for Schools,* and (3) *Broadcast Receivers and Phonographs for Classroom Use.* This office, too, will direct teachers to other sources of classroom aids, notably to the networks which plan regular series of educational broadcasts for school listening.

Television has many relationships to education similar to those of radio, and it adds the powerful force of visualization. Commercial television stations have many programs dealing with health, and there are an in-creasing number of stations devoted entirely to education. It is a thrilling medium; but we should be critical of television, as we are of other resource aids, and use it only where it will effectively meet the educational need.

A unique exploratory project has been the development of the Mid-west Program of Airborne Television Instruction, which uses a circling, high-altitude airplane and serves some half million children in an area of 125,000 square miles. The airplane receives and relays broadcasts from ground stations and supplies 72 half-hour broadcasts during a six-hour school day by sending six separate programs simultaneously.

Schools are using television in education for presenting (1) a health authority to discuss a special topic for secondary school groups, (2) care-fully planned demonstrations too elaborate for the average classroom, (3) school projects presented by a teacher and pupils, (4) student panel dis-cussion, (5) on-the-scene telecasts of the work of official and voluntary health agencies, and (6) educational films. Supplementary materials for teacher and class use are often available. An extensive *Radio and Tele-vision Bibliography* can be obtained.[3]

Recordings. In addition to direct radio or television listenership, it is possible for teachers to use electrical transcriptions of special programs for effective health teaching. Such recordings have certain advantages. They are permanent. They can be used at the teacher's convenience and when the class is best prepared for the material they present. In addition, transcriptions are relatively inexpensive and can be made available to several classes of the same grade, allowing classroom groups to remain in their natural units while using this teaching aid, just as they do for most others.

Transcriptions may be made on discs or upon magnetic tapes. Tape recorders are widely used because of their flexibility and quality. The re-cording on the magnetic tape may be retained indefinitely, or it may be erased for a new recording. It is possible to cut and splice such a tape.

Tape recordings may be purchased from record libraries, produced within the school as a simulated broadcast by pupils, or recorded from commercial programs which come in over the air.

The health museum. The health museum is an excellent resource for health education. Health museums and special health exhibits in general museums are becoming more numerous. In a few places, traveling health exhibits may be brought to the individual schools. A field trip to special exhibits is of value, assuming of course that the exhibits are well arranged, adapted to the age levels of the pupils, and related to the program of study. Pupils need to be prepared in advance for the exhibits that they

[3]Prepared by the Office of Education, this bibliography gives a very complete list of the important articles in the literature, a list of the many periodicals concerned with radio and television education, and a list of the sources of general information in this field. It is available from the United States Government Printing Office, Washington 25, D. C., price 25 cents.

are to study. The museum lesson should have definite scope and objectives. It should not consist of superficial observation of whatever exhibits may be found upon arrival. Discussion and review of the museum trip are especially important.

The *Cleveland Health Museum*[4] is a source for the purchase, rental, or loan of exhibits. Teachers will find that their local art museums, museums of natural history, science museums, or children's museums may have loan exhibits or will arrange field trips on topics in the health course.

Programmed self-instruction. The current interest in programmed self-instruction began in 1954. For some time, this method of teaching was written about under the name of "teaching machines," a title which tickled the fancy of sensational writers. The emphasis is actually upon the programming of self-instruction, and most programs have been produced as printed booklets or duplicated sheets of paper.

The underlying principle is that the student learns by being active and through the responses he practices. His learning and his motivation are better if he is told immediately whether his responses have been correct.

Making an effective program is arduous and probably takes longer than writing a textbook. It involves the work of both subject-matter specialists and psychologists in developing, trying, revising, and testing the educational instrument. It has been shown in several areas of knowledge that the pupil can learn from a properly developed self-instruction

[4]8911 Euclid Ave., Cleveland 6, Ohio.

Fig. 51. The museum is a valuable resource in health education. In this picture the students are sitting on camp stools in order to group themselves conveniently around the man who is demonstrating models. (Courtesy Cleveland Health Museum.)

program. He can work at his own rate and learn without constant supervision.

Experts in programmed self-instruction feel that comparatively little is yet known as to what subjects or skills can be effectively programmed. Programmed instruction has not been developed in the field of health. If and when it is developed, it will educate in the field of knowledge and skills. It will not be expected to be highly motivational in the development of health behavior.

How to secure resource materials

Every teacher wants to know, from time to time, how to use outside resources to strengthen instruction at a specific grade level and on a particular topic. The most useful and direct assistance would be advice from someone who is already familiar with good and suitable sources of aid. A list of scores of films, pamphlets, posters, and exhibits in a book like this would help very little. The teacher would not know the quality of these as-yet-unseen individual items for his special use. He would usually be without facilities for securing the materials directly. Once the list became a few months old, he would never know whether an item he had selected might have been discontinued after the particular list was prepared.

The way to tap available resources most easily, quickly, and effectively is to turn to possible sources of aid in the order of their availability. The more important of these sources are listed below somewhat in the sequence in which they would be sought.

1. *The health library or the "instructional materials center" of the school system.* Many school systems provide for teacher use a central, completely equipped library on health, maintained at the central office, at a public library, or at some other central location. Here the teacher finds a complete collection of textbooks, reference books, and important pieces of printed source material from various agencies.

Provision is commonly made also for a small working health library in each school building. This small library contains selected reference books for the teacher and provides at least one reference in each important field, such as physiology, nutrition, personal and community health, mental hygiene, and health education methods. It also contains samples of some of the best available printed source material.

If the teacher is in a large school system, he may have access to a variety of audiovisual materials from a "materials center." Materials from health libraries or materials centers are immediately available to the teacher upon his own direct request.

2. *The health coordinator or health chairman for the school.* Many high schools have health coordinators who can devote part or all of their time to the promotion of health education and school health. Many elementary schools have a health chairman or coordinator who has special responsibilities for health education. While source materials represent only

one of their interests, they can usually be of direct assistance to an individual teacher.

3. *The director of health education or the director of health and physical education for the school system.* If such a person is employed, he will almost certainly know how to secure the needed source materials.

4. *Other members of the school health team.* Doctors, nurses, nutritionists, physical educators, dentists, and dental hygienists may help directly with topics in their areas or refer the teacher to useful materials.

5. *Director of public health education in the local health department.* In some communities, this person works directly with schools under a cooperative arrangement between the school system and the health department. Even if he does not, assistance in securing suitable health education materials is doubtless within the scope of his professional activities.

6. *Other branches of the local government.* Police departments and fire departments are interested in safety and may be able to help in that area. Agricultural extension services may be able to help with nutritional or other problems.

7. *Local chapters of voluntary health agencies and associations.* National organizations concerned with poliomyelitis, tuberculosis, heart disease, cancer, safety, Red Cross activities, and other health problems have local chapters or associations in many counties and cities. There are also local societies or chapters of medical, dental, and other professional groups. They can make available the needed materials more readily than their national offices can in most cases. Some national agencies refer back to their state or local offices specific requests for materials.

8. *State director of health education or director of health and physical education in the state department of education.* His office may be able to provide source materials and a list of sources of materials.

9. *Director of public health education in the state department of public health.* State health departments often prepare and distribute lists of sources of material, in addition to their own pamphlets in the broad field of public health.

10. *Other state departments.* The department of agriculture has a program in health and nutrition. Some states have a department of mental diseases, while others have a division of mental health in the state health department. The registrar of motor vehicles or some other state department is usually concerned with highway safety.

11. *State offices of voluntary health and safety agencies.* A safety council exists at the state level in most states. Some, but not all, of the voluntary health agencies have state offices. If there is not a local chapter of the agency from which you desire help, it is better to write to the state office than to the national office for assistance.

12. *National agencies.* A wealth of material is available from a variety of national sources, which we shall mention in the following section.

Sources of health education materials

Textbooks. There follows a list of publishers of health *textbooks* with the titles of their respective series and an indication of the grades for which separate books have been prepared:

American Book Co., New York, N. Y., The ABC Health Series, Grades 1 to 8.

Benefic Press, Chicago, Ill., The Health Action Series, Grades 1 to 8.

The Bobbs-Merrill Co., Inc., Indianapolis, Ind., Health for Young America Series, Grades 1 to 8.

The Economy Co., Indianapolis, Ind., Child's Health and Physical Development Series, Grades 1 to 8.

Ginn and Co., Boston, Mass., Health for Better Living Series, Grades 1 to 8.

D. C. Heath and Co., Boston, Mass., The Health Elementary Science Series, Grades 1 to 6.

Laidlaw Brothers, River Forest, Ill., The New Road to Health Series, Grades 1 to 8.

Lyons and Carnahan, Chicago, Ill., The Health, Happiness, Success Series, Grades 1 to 8.

The MacMillan Co., New York, N. Y., The MacMillan Science-Life Series, Grades 1 to 8.

McCormick-Mathers Publishing Co., Inc., Wichita, Kan., Living Today Series, Grades 1 to 6.

Scott, Foresman and Co., New York, N. Y., Curriculum Foundation Series, Grades 1 to 8.

The L. S. Singer Co., Syracuse, N. Y., Singer Science Series, Grades 1 to 8.

John C. Winston Co., Philadelphia, Penn., Winston Health Series Revised, Grades 1 to 6.

Supplementary materials. Agencies supplying *supplementary health education materials* may be divided into three groups: (1) governmental agencies, (2) societies, associations, and private agencies of a professional nature, and (3) commercial or semicommercial agencies. The nature of these agencies and the types of source material available from them will be briefly described.

1. *Governmental agencies.* Governmental agencies are international, federal, state, or local. The chief international governmental agency in the field of health is the *World Health Organization.*[5] The organization issues reports, pamphlets, and a monthly publication called *World Health.*[6]

The Federal Government promotes health education through several of its departments.

The agency most directly concerned with health education in schools is the *Office of Education* in the Department of Health, Education, and Welfare. This office publishes reports, monographs, bibliographies, and special studies upon various phases of school health including health education. It contributes material through *American Education,* the official journal of the Office of Education, dealing with general school problems.

---

[5]Regional office for the Americas is located at 1501 New Hampshire Ave., N.W., Washington 6, D. C.

[6]Its committee reports and other publications are sold, in the United States, by Columbia University Press, International Documents Service, 2960 Broadway, New York 27, N. Y.

The most important single health agency in the Federal Government is the *United States Public Health Service,* in the Department of Health, Education, and Welfare. It is under the direction of the Surgeon General. Its work includes cooperation with state and local health agencies, at their request, for the purpose of developing public health activities. It also includes scientific research, supervision of quarantine and medical examination of immigrants, the control of biologic products, and the operation of hospitals for the care of beneficiaries designated by Acts of the Congress. It collects and disseminates materials concerning the prevalence of disease, but its specific health education activities are concerned with the general public more than with health education in the schools. Its monthly publication is *Public Health Reports.* A list of many publications relating to problems of sanitation and disease control, as well as bibliography of health education, folders, supplements, posters, motion picture, and radio transcriptions may be secured from the Surgeon General, United States Public Health Service, Washington, D. C.

Other federal activities in the field of public health are to be found in the work of the *Children's Bureau,* in the Department of Health, Education, and Welfare. It studies the health of children and issues printed matter dealing with prenatal, infant, and child care, juvenile delinquency, and other phases of child welfare. It furnishes reports and statistics on child health, child labor, services for crippled children, and laws for the protection of children.

The *Bureau of Human Nutrition and Home Economics* in the Department of Agriculture carries on research concerning foods, clothing, and home-making, issuing educational bulletins in these fields. The *Office of Information* of the Department of Agriculture issues lists of educational films, pamphlets, leaflets, and posters. Some of this material contributes to the course of study in health.

The *Congressional Library,* General Information Bureau, now handles all government motion picture films.

Practically every *state department of education* and every *state department of health* prepares useful materials in the field of health education and will send a list of available publications to teachers. In most states a regular bulletin of the state department of health, as well as special bulletins, may be secured upon request.

The annual reports of the *local health department* provide interesting material for upper grade study. The local health departments of large cities, especially those where a staff of qualified health educators is employed, issue special bulletins and other pieces of health education material.

The teacher, of course, receives a large part of his source materials directly from the *local school system* in which he is working. These include textbooks and usually a course of study. If supervision for the health education program is provided, materials from many other sources are made available.

2. *Societies, associations, and private agencies.* The one international nongovernmental organization devoted entirely to health education is the International Union for Health Education. It publishes the *International Journal of Health Education* in French and English. This journal presents material on both school health education and public health education from all over the world. It has stimulating reference material for teachers in training and in service. A college, school, or individual teacher may subscribe to this quarterly magazine at three dollars per year. Address of the *Journal* is 3 rue Viollier, Geneva, Switzerland.

There are several *national professional groups or associations* that are interested in health education and are in a position to supply informational material with respect to certain topics. The material may be in the form of bibliographies, teaching units, study charts, posters, maps, leaflets, monographs, plays, films, filmstrips, transcriptions, radio scripts, or models. The more important of these agencies are listed here in alphabetic order.

Many of the following associations have affiliated state or local offices. The telephone directory or an inquiry at your state health department should help you locate such offices, where they exist. It is helpful for teachers to visit local offices to become acquainted with the health education staff, and with the materials available. By following this procedure, the teacher can benefit most from the services of each agency and keep abreast of new materials as these are produced. Greater coordination of school and community health programs can be effected in this way.

The staffs of the local offices are usually most happy to visit the schools, to advise parent-teacher associations and school health committees, to speak to classes or assemblies, and to assist in many other practicable ways. The list of such agencies follows:

The *Adult Education Association*, 743 N. Wabash Ave., Chicago 11, Ill., has two monthly publications, *Adult Leadership* and *Adult Education.* It has reprints, research reports, and lists of references.

Alcoholics Anonymous, P.O. Box 459, New York 17, N. Y., has pamphlets and reports.

Allergy Foundation of America, 801 2nd Ave., New York 17, N. Y., has research findings and reports.

Allied Youth, Inc., 1346 Conneticut Ave., N.W., Washington 6, D. C., publishes a monthly magazine, called *Allied Youth,* and other material concerned with temperance for teenagers.

American Academy of Pediatrics, 1801 Hinman Avenue, Evanston, Ill. Research findings and committee reports.

The *American Association for Health, Physical Education, and Recreation* is a department of the *National Education Association* with headquarters at 1201 16th St., N.W., Washington 6, D. C. It publishes the *American Journal of Health, Physical Education, and Recreation* and the *Research Quarterly.* It issues committee reports and special publications.

The *American Automobile Association*, 1712 G St., N.W., Washington, D. C., supplies safety education material including lesson units on traffic safety, with teachers' manual, posters, safety patrol pledge and equipment, and radio broadcasts for school use.

The *American Cancer Society*, 521 W. 57th St., New York, N. Y., prepares statistical material, news releases, radio broadcasts, pamphlets, slides, filmstrips, motion pictures, and other educational materials.

The *American Dental Association,* 211 E. Chicago Ave., Chicago, Ill., 60611, maintains a Department of Dental Health Education from which pamphlets, posters, charts, teaching outlines, and other materials may be obtained. A list of the available educational material will be supplied upon request.

American Diabetes Association, 1 E. 45th Street, New York 17, N. Y. Pamphlets and lists of material on diabetes.

The *American Dietetics Association,* 620 N. Michigan Ave., Chicago, Ill., is particularly concerned with problems of nutrition. It publishes the *Journal of the American Dietetics Association,* pamphlets, and lists of material.

The *American Foundation for the Blind,* 15 W. 16th St., New York 11, N. Y., has free book lists, and leaflets for boys and girls as well as adult material.

American Genetic Association, 1507 M Street, N.W., Washington 5, D. C., has informational materials on heredity and health.

The *American Hearing Society,* 919 18th St., N.W., Washington 6, D. C., has done much to promote better methods for detecting hard-of-hearing children and has prepared leaflets, posters, and exhibits.

The *American Heart Association,* 44 E. 23rd St., New York 10, N. Y., edits *Circulation* and issues special bulletins, pamphlets, leaflets, and films concerning the care and prevention of heart disease and rheumatic fever in children.

The *American Home Economics Association,* 1600 20th St., N.W., Washington 9, D. C., is interested in the problem of nutrition. It publishes the *Journal of Home Economics,* program outlines, reports, and bibliographies.

American Hospital Association, 840 North Lake Shore Drive, Chicago 11, Ill., has pamphlets and reports on hospital management and hospital care.

The *American Institute of Family Relations,* 5287 Sunset Blvd., Los Angeles 27, Calif., publishes the magazine *Family Life* and other materials in family-life and sex education.

The *American Medical Association,* 535 N. Dearborn St., Chicago 10, Ill., makes a distinct contribution to popular health education through its magazine *Today's Health,* which gives special consideration to school health problems. The magazine will supply detailed information concerning its special subscription plan for schools, in connection with which it furnishes classroom discussion topics with each issue. The Association issues information concerning patent medicines, cosmetics, and proprietary foods. It issues reprints, pamphlets, films, posters, radio scripts, and source lists on topics in many fields. It maintains a Department of Community Health and Health Education and publishes a bulletin on *Health Education for Schools and Colleges.*

The *American National Red Cross,* 17th and D Sts., Washington 13, D. C., has long been recognized as one of the most important nongovernmental health agencies. In many countries of the world the Junior Red Cross has been important in the promotion of health education in schools, and it has launched a broadened program of health education in 1964. In America the school work of the Junior Red Cross has given special attention to citizenship and international goodwill, although it has also contributed to health education. The Red Cross publishes textbooks, study outlines, pamphlets, posters, films, filmstrips, and radio scripts on first aid, home nursing, accident prevention, and water safety.

The *American Nurses Association,* 2 Park Ave., New York 16, N. Y., publishes the *American Journal of Nursing.* Upon request it will send a list of pamphlets and other publications in the nursing field.

The *American Public Health Association,* 1790 Broadway, New York 19, N. Y., is the professional organization in public health for North America. Its various sections provide a place for every kind of public health worker. The Public Health Education

Section includes individuals concerned with health education in schools and colleges but it is more concerned with public health education from health departments or other agencies. The School Health Section considers all phases of school health, especially the school health services. The Association publishes the *American Journal of Public Health*.

The *American School Health Association,* Secretary's Office, Kent State University, Kent, Ohio, publishes the *Journal of School Health*. It has committees working upon many phases of school health and health education.

The *American Social Health Association,* 1790 Broadway, New York 19, N. Y., with branches in many states, is a valuable source of material and advice regarding the teaching of sex hygiene and other phases of social hygiene.

The *Association for Childhood Education,* 1200 15th St., Washington 5, D. C., has reference lists for adults. It publishes *Childhood Education* and booklets for boys and girls.

The *Association for Family Living,* 32 W. Randolph, Chicago 1, Ill., publishes material on child development and family-life and sex education.

Association of Casualty and Surety Companies, 60 John Street, New York 30, N. Y., issues safety education materials.

The *Better Vision Institute, Inc.,* 630 Fifth Ave., New York 20, N. Y., has motion pictures, pamphlets, and filmstrips on vision.

The *Bicycle Institute of America, Inc.,* 122 E. 42nd St., New York, N. Y., has free material on bicycle safety for various school levels.

The *Boy Scouts of America,* New Brunswick, N. J., has a health and safety service with printed and visual materials in the safety field.

The *Child Study Association of America,* 132 E. 74th St., New York, N. Y., is interested in parent education and will supply at list of available publications upon request. It publishes *Child Study.*

The *Cleveland Health Museum,* 8911 Euclid Ave., Cleveland 6, Ohio, sells and rents exhibits and produces other educational materials. It produces a quarterly bulletin called *Tone.*

Columbia University Press, 2960 Broadway, New York 27, N. Y., is the national distributor for WHO and UNESCO publications.

The *Health Information Foundation,* The University of Chicago, Chicago 37, Ill., carries out studies in health and medical care and issues educational materials.

Hogg Foundation for Mental Health, University of Texas, Austin, Texas, issues educational materials on mental health.

The *Human Betterment Association of America, Inc.,* 32 W. 58th St., New York, N. Y., will furnish material on eugenics.

The *Maternity Center Association, Inc.,* 48 E. 92nd St., New York, N. Y., issues a *Birth Atlas* in printed and filmstrip form and other printed and visual material dealing with maternal health.

Mental Health Materials Center, 104 East 25th Street, New York 10, N. Y., issues materials on family life, human relations, and mental health.

Muscular Dystrophy Association of America, 1790 Broadway, New York 19, N. Y., issues educational materials concerning the disease and current research.

The *National Association for Mental Health,* 10 Columbus Circle, New York 19, N. Y., publishes a quarterly, *Mental Hygiene,* and monthly bulletins. From time to time, it issues reports of research or experiments. There are mental hygiene societies in many states.

The *National Board of Fire Underwriters,* 85 John St., New York 38, N. Y., distributes printed and visual materials on fire prevention through its Public Relations Department.

National Canners Association Home Economics Division, 1739 H Street, N.W., Washington, D. C., issues educational material on food and nutrition.

The *National Commission on Safety Education* of the National Education Association, 1201 16th St., N.W., Washington 6, D. C., has extensive materials on safety education in all of its phases, at all levels of education. A complete list of publications will be supplied upon request.

The *National Congress of Parents and Teachers,* 700 North Rush St., Chicago, Ill., assists the parent-teacher movement through pamphlets, reprints, and leaflets dealing with the summer roundup and various phases of child hygiene. It publishes the *National Parent-Teachers' Magazine.*

The *National Council on Alcoholism,* 2 E. 103rd St., New York, N. Y., has books and pamphlets dealing with alcoholism.

The *National Education Association,* 1201 16th St., N.W., Washington 6, D. C., is the professional organization of the educators of the United States. Its many departments concerned with general education naturally give some attention to health. The department primarily concerned with school health is the American Association for Health, Physical Education, and Recreation. The National Education Association has long maintained a Joint Committee with the American Medical Association, which has issued valuable reports upon a variety of school health problems. Several departments have yearbooks on health.

The *National Epilepsy League, Inc.,* 208 N. Wells St., Chicago 6, Ill., issues pamphlets and other materials for use at and above the junior high school level.

The *National Foot Health Council,* P. O. Box 57, Rockland, Mass., publishes data on foot troubles in children and on posture.

The *National Foundation,* 800 Second Ave., New York 17, N. Y., has free educational material dealing with poliomyelitis, birth defects, and arthritis. It has teaching units and pamphlets for free distribution. It has filmstrips and motion pictures for free loan or for sale at cost.

The *National Health Council,* 1790 Broadway, New York, N. Y., is a council of voluntary health agencies. It publishes materials concerning their activities and recruitment for the public health profession.

The *National Multiple Sclerosis Society,* 257 Park Ave., New York 17, N. Y., publishes material on the disease.

The *National Safety Council,* 425 N. Michigan Ave., Chicago 11, Ill., publishes *Safety Education* and will furnish upon request an extensive list of available pamphlets and posters. It is a source of accident statistics.

The *National Society for Crippled Children and Adults,* 2023 W. Ogden Ave., Chicago 12, Ill., issues visual and printed material, and it publishes the magazine, *The Crippled Child.*

The *National Society for the Prevention of Blindness,* 16 E. 40th St., New York 16, N. Y., carries on studies and publishes informational material in the field of vision, sight-saving, and school lighting.

The *National Tuberculosis Association,* 1790 Broadway, New York 19, N. Y., has a division of Health Education, which contributes to health education through the publication of health education materials and through field workers. State and local chapters of the National Tuberculosis Association also contribute to health education through published materials and field workers. A list of publications is available from the state and local associations.

The *National Woman's Christian Temperance Union,* 1730 Chicago Ave., Evanston, Ill., prepares printed material dealing with various phases of the temperance movement.

Planned Parenthood Federation of America, Inc., 515 Madison Avenue, New York, N. Y. 10022, provides information and educational material on family planning, birth control, and world population.

The *Public Affairs Committee, Inc.,* 22 E. 38th St., New York 16, N. Y., issues excellent booklets on health subjects, which can be purchased at book stores or directly.

The *Quarterly Journal of Studies on Alcohol,* 52 Hillhouse Ave., Yale Station, New Haven, Conn., has pamphlets for the senior high school and college level.

Rutgers Center on Alcohol Studies, Box 466, Rutgers State University, New Brunswick, New Jersey, issues educational material on alcohol and alcoholism.

SIECUS (Sex Information and Education Council of the United States), 1790 Broadway, New York, N. Y. 10019, has the services of a group of professionals in family life, marriage counseling, sociology, psychiatry, religion, preventive medicine, and education at all levels. It supplies reading lists, reprints, and suggestions for health education.

Society for Visual Education, Inc., 1345 Diversey Parkway, Chicago 14, Ill., prepares and distributes filmstrips and other educational materials.

United Cerebral Palsy Association, 321 West 44th Street, New York 36, N. Y., issues pamphlets and visual materials.

World Health Organization Regional Office for the Americas, 1501 New Hampshire Avenue, N.W., Washington 6, D. C., distributes *World Health* and other printed material from WHO.

3. *Commercial and semicommercial agencies.* Excellent source material in health education has been produced by commercial or semicommercial organizations of high standing. There are, however, less scrupulous companies that issue pernicious advertising material in the health field. Malicious and misleading advertising is one of the public health dangers with which we are confronted. Indeed, the health education program ought to accept the responsibility of teaching children to judge such advertising with discrimination.

Health advertising is used to sell some products that have no health value; other products that do have health value are promoted as though they were the *only* products possessing these desirable substances or qualities. In any case, the public school must not lend itself to the promotion of any particular brand of goods in preference to competing brands of similar value.

While it would be unwise to use material from commercial groups without discrimination, it would be equally unfortunate to refuse materials which are splendid from the standpoint of scientific accuracy, pedagogical quality, printing, and general attractiveness, provided they do not contain objectionable advertising.

We may distinguish three types of agencies among the business groups: (1) life insurance companies, (2) trade associations, and (3) manufacturing or distributing concerns. The first two groups are sometimes called semicommercial agencies, because they are not interested in the promotion of any particular brand of a product.

Life insurance companies are interested in the promotion of health. School children are not purchasers of life insurance, and the health education materials produced by such companies do not contain sales propaganda. All life insurance companies profit by the prolongation of life, but so do the public and the individual.

Among the life insurance companies the *Metropolitan Life Insurance Company,* 1 Madison Avenue, New York, N. Y., was the first to develop an extensive health education program. Both pamphlets and films are available. In addition, posters, filmstrips, graphs, and charts are released on given subjects. The well-known "Health Heroes" series of pamphlets with accompanying filmstrips is distributed free. A sound filmstrip and pamphlet in color on "What Teachers See" illustrate common departures from normal health.

Excellent educational materials are now available from many other companies:

Aetna Life Insurance and Affiliated Companies, Education Department, 151 Farmington Ave., Hartford 15, Conn. (Health and safety pamphlets and films for all school levels and lay groups.)

Employers Mutual of Wausau, 115 W. Wausau Ave., Wausau, Wis. (Pamphlets on health and safety for intermediate grades and higher levels.)

Equitable Life Assurance Society of the United States, 393 Seventh Ave., New York, N. Y. (Free booklets and posters on the living interests of people. "Health Careers" publications supported in the public interest by the Equitable are distributed by the National Health Council.)

John Hancock Mutual Life Insurance Company, 200 Berkeley St., Boston 17, Mass. (Printed and visual material for adult and child levels.)

Liberty Mutual Insurance Company, 175 Berkeley St., Boston 17, Mass. (Safety and health materials for senior high school and college level.)

Prudential Insurance Company of America, Newark, N. J. (Health pamphlets.)

Trade associations are supported by groups of companies doing business in the same field. They seek to extend the use of the type of product in question, but they do not promote the sale of any particular brand. Trade associations with health interests include:

The *American Institute of Baking,* 400 E. Ontario St., Chicago, Ill.

The *California Fruit Growers Exchange,* Educational Division, Box 5030, Metropolitan Station, Los Angeles 5, Calif.

Cereal Institute, Inc., 135 S. La Salle St., Chicago 3, Ill.

The *Florida Citrus Fruit Commission,* Lakeland, Fla.

The *National Dairy Council,* 111 N. Canal St., Chicago, Ill.

The *National Livestock and Meat Board,* Dept. of Nutrition, 407 S. Dearborn St., Chicago 5, Ill.

The *Paper Cup and Container Institute,* Public Health Committee, 250 Park Ave., New York 17, N. Y.

The *Wheat Flour Institute,* 309 Jackson Blvd., Chicago, Ill.

These organizations have produced an extensive amount of source material and will supply a list of available pamphlets, monographs, booklets, and visual material upon request.

It is easier to use material from a trade association than from *manufacturing or distributing concerns,* because no specific product is mentioned. Nevertheless, several manufacturing companies supply material that is attractive, scientifically accurate, and pedagogically sound. In fact, the only indication that some material comes from a commercial group and not from a professional or governmental source is the statement that the booklet is a publication of a particular industrial concern.

Many school systems have a fixed policy against using advertising material, and a teacher should secure the approval of the director of health education, the principal, or the superintendent before using it. We have not attempted to list here the many companies that publish and distribute free materials to schools.

The following *principles* were set up by one city school department in order to permit the classroom use of suitable material and yet safeguard the school from undersirable advertising:

1. Upon their own request, teachers will be allowed to use source material from commercial agencies, provided this material has been approved by the school department. Approved source material may, from time to time, be called to the attention of the teachers, but no source material from commercial agencies will be sent out from the school department to teachers for classroom use. The teacher will request this material or request permission to secure it.

2. No source material shall be approved that relates to a product the use of which is questionable or injurious to health.

3. No material shall be approved that is unscientific in statement or emphasis or that is educationally unsound in its approach or presentation.

4. No material shall be used that advertises any particular brand of goods. The name of the company through whose compliments the material is distributed may appear on the material, and such appearance shall not cause the material to be disapproved unless the name of the company is so prominent on or in the material as to give it an advertising flavor.

5. The superintendent shall determine by whom these standards are to be applied when material is to be passed upon. It is desirable that materials be recommended for special grade levels.

References

Significant reference materials are listed in the body of the chapter.

Chapter xvi

Teaching health in the grades

In building sound health attitudes, habits, and knowledge in the elementary school, we accept the principle that much can be done by providing healthful school living for the child through a safe and wholesome environment and a hygienic schedule of work and play. We expect, also, to make use of incidental teaching in health services and other situations with health implications. But we realize that these steps are not enough. In addition, we plan definite instruction both directly and in correlation with other school subjects. We also plan definite procedures to develop and strengthen various phases of health behavior.

The promotion of health practices

It is obviously desirable to develop a complete program of hygienic living as early as possible in the life of the child and to maintain and strengthen such practices throughout the later years of school life. The education of the child involves transferring to him the responsibility for health behavior and equipping him with such attitudes and knowledge as will ensure hygienic living now, in later childhood, and in adult life.

In practice the school must begin, in the kindergarten and first grade, with a limited number of the most important health procedures. Some elements of health behavior do not demand consideration until later. There are less important habits that might properly be emphasized in the lower grades but that are ruled out because only a limited number of practices can be considered to advantage with these little children. Habits should receive different degrees of emphasis in succeeding grades, according to (1) their importance in health maintenance and (2) the pupil needs.

We must not expect accomplishment on the part of the child in matters over which he has no control. This suggests a grading of health practices according to what the child is able to do on his own responsibility. We can gradually extend the list of practices from grade to grade as the child becomes capable of increased responsibility concerning the details of health behavior.

The majority of habits must be considered throughout the later grades, for only a few are so thoroughly established by younger children as to

Fig. 52. The kindergarten learns safety practices.

(H. Armstrong Roberts)

need no further attention. While specific new knowledge and skills can be acquired in a brief space of time, habits develop slowly and need re-emphasis. Thus a habit may need emphasis in every grade, while a unit of instruction on the subject may be taught in only one or two grades.

There follows a list of the health habits commonly found in courses of study for these grades.

Cleanliness

Uses individual towel and washcloth.
Takes a cleansing bath regularly.
Rinses and dries skin thoroughly to prevent chapping.
Bathes face, neck, ears daily with soap and water.
Washes hands before handling food and after going to toilet.

Hands and nails

Keep hands away from mouth, nose, ears, and eyes.
Keeps fingernails short and clean.
*Cuts toenails straight across.

Teeth

Brushes teeth and gums properly at least twice a day (always before retiring).
Keeps toothbrush clean, marked, and in a definite place in the sunlight.
Visits the dentist as often as he directs.

Nose and mouth

Uses own clean handkerchief or paper tissues every day.
Covers mouth and nose with handkerchief or tissues when sneezing and coughing.
Breathes through the nose with mouth closed.
Stays away from those with colds and sore throats.
Blows nose gently without closing nostrils.

---

*For emphasis in upper rather than lower grades.

Hair

Keeps the hair clean and combs and brushes it daily.
Keeps comb and brush clean.

Elimination

Evacuates bowels at regular time each day, preferably after breakfast.

Clothing

*Wears clothing suitable for the weather.
Helps keep clothing as clean as possible.
Removes all outside wraps when indoors.
Removes wet clothing at once if possible.

Food habits

Has a good breakfast.
Avoids excess of doughnuts, pies, cakes, and pastries.
Eats some fruit every day.
Eats meat, fish, or eggs daily.
Eats two kinds of vegetables besides potato each day, one leafy or raw.
Eats some food that requires chewing every day and chews food thoroughly.
Drinks 3 glasses of milk daily.
Eats candy only at the end of a meal if at all.
Uses some whole-grain cereal or some whole-grain bread daily.
Drinks plenty of water between meals.

Table manners

Eats slowly.
Uses knife, fork, and spoon correctly.
Keeps elbows off the table.
Chews food quietly with mouth closed.
Talks only when the mouth is empty.
Does not interrupt when grown-ups are talking.
Drinks when there is no food in the mouth.
Puts knife and fork across the plate at the end of the meal.
Uses napkin in the lap.
Says "excuse me" when leaving the table.

Play and exercise

Has a daily program of play and exercise adapted to strength, physical needs, and
  abilities.

Sleep

Goes to bed in time to get sufficient hours of sleep.
Sleeps with low pillow or none at all.
*Doesn't usually sacrifice sleep for movies, radio, television, etc.

Communicable disease control

Uses drinking fountains properly.
*Reports signs of cold to parents and makes effort to check it early.
*Keeps away from those who have "catching" diseases.
*Obeys health regulations established by the Health Department.
*Keeps mouth away from mouthpiece when telephoning.

---

*For emphasis in upper rather than lower grades.

Sanitation

Helps keep school and grounds clean.
*Helps keep home free from insects and rodents.
*Keeps own room clean at home.
Helps in general care of the home.
Avoids littering public parks, lawns, and streets.
*Drinks water only from sources that are known to be safe.

Harmful substances

*Drinks no alcoholic beverage.
*Uses no tobacco.
Avoids tea and coffee.

Growth and health

Cooperates in having physical defects corrected.

Mental and emotional health

Concentrates on the task one is doing.
Meets difficulties and disappointments squarely.
Is habitually cheerful, calm, and poised.
Controls self in anger, fear, or other strong emotions.
Is friendly with companions.
Is courteous, considerate, and sympathetic towards others.
Is obedient and respectful to those in authority.

Safety

Goes up and down stairs one step at a time.
Uses scissors, needles, pins, etc., properly.
*Keeps poison out of reach of younger children.
*Keeps matches in a metal or earthen container.
Avoids fallen wires and electric cables.
Avoids coasting down dangerous hills and streets and hills not properly protected.
Does not slide or skate on thin ice.
Paddles and wades only in safe supervised places.
Learns how to swim.
Recognizes poison ivy and other common poisonous plants and avoids them.
Does not tease animals.
Does not play or loiter around railroad tracks or bridges.
Avoids hitch-hiking and stealing rides.
Crosses street in a safe way—paying attention to traffic officer, traffic lights, and
   crosswalks.
Does not play in streets.

Health instruction

It is true that health behavior may be developed in little children in
the absence of scientific knowledge; however, reliable factual information
is needed by pupils when they leave school, to help them continue healthful living and make necessary adaptations under the changing conditions
of adult life. Experience has shown that instruction in the basic health
facts commands the interest of the child, stimulating the enjoyment of
positive health rather than the development of introspection and worry.

---

*For emphasis in upper rather than lower grades.

Two important characteristics of good health teaching are its adaptation to pupil needs and the utilization of community resources. The teacher learns the habits and attitudes of his pupils relating to diet, exercise, sleep, and the other basic phases of healthful living. He seeks solutions to health problems through the development of pupil interests and through the mobilization of resources in school, home, and community. His approach is not by topics but by needs, using a variety of teaching methods.

Gradation. The desirability of having a definite time allotment for health is now generally accepted. A planned program of health instruction with sufficient but not undue repetition and with a fresh approach in each grade is to be expected. In the first three grades the child is held responsible for very little specific knowledge in regard to health. The number of facts taught will increase from grade to grade as the child's natural curiosity demands more information and as his capacity for understanding becomes greater. It is especially desirable from the third grade on that a fresh approach through new subject matter should be made at each grade level.

There is no one perfect plan. The general plan suggested here reflects a merging of the thinking of curriculum committees in several communities (Malden, Cleveland, Boston, Brockton, and others) with which the writers have worked. It does not follow exactly the plan of any one of these communities but is presented to illustrate one possible and satisfactory framework.

In **Grades I and II** there is no particular problem of a fresh approach, because all the health work is new to the child. The program is informal and centers about health training by means of special projects and devices, correlations, and simple teaching units. Health readers are useful. Emphasis is placed upon the *most important health practices.*

The children in these grades will not be held responsible for reproducing specific information. In general it is desirable that they should learn:

1. Some habits that help them to grow (such as long hours of sleep, outdoor exercise, drinking milk, having a good breakfast).
2. How to wash the face, neck, and ears properly.
3. How to wash the hands and clean the fingernails properly.
4. How to brush the teeth properly.
5. That the sixth-year molar is the first of their permanent teeth and must be well cared for.
6. How to care for the toothbrush.
7. That they should go to the dentist regularly.
8. How to blow the nose properly.
9. How to cross the street safely.
10. That they may expect to gain about one-quarter to one-half pound a month.

In **Grade III** the activity and training program continues as the primary feature. The pupil is held responsible for only a little health knowledge. A reading book is used to lead the child to desire health practices and to furnish a framework upon which the health education program can be built. Emphasis may be upon *healthful living and growth.*

In addition to the foregoing items the children, by the end of the third grade, may be expected to know:

1. That growing regularly is a sign of health.
2. That there is a relationship between health habits and the way one feels (for example, the relation between loss of sleep or rest and feeling tired and restless).
3. Some of the most important health practices.
4. That there are a few plants, like poison ivy and poison oak, that are harmful.
5. That some kinds of sickness are "catching" and can be avoided by keeping clean and by staying away from people who have such sicknesses.
6. That our bodies are made from the food we eat.
7. That food is fuel for the body.
8. What constitutes a good breakfast.
9. That milk is one of the best single foods.
10. That eggs are good food for growth.
11. That fruits and vegetables promote health and good digestion.
12. How to read the thermometer.
13. That fresh air is healthful.
14. That becoming chilled may make a cold worse.
15. How to adjust clothes to weather conditions.

In **Grade IV** the child is more mature; he can be expected to take more responsibility for his daily regimen. Consequently there is an appreciable increase in the number of details of health behavior brought to his atten-

Fig. 53. Concepts regarding food are being developed. (Courtesy Los Angeles City Schools.)

tion. The approach also is changed. The emphasis is upon the *"how"* of health behavior, and this *"how"* is usually answered by the pupil's first real textbook in health. With this greater responsibility there may be special emphasis on safety.

In addition to the knowledge items listed for lower grades the pupil may be expected to have some understanding of:

1. What is meant by "healthful living."
2. That physical activities develop skill and that practice in healthful living develops health and strength.
3. What it means to be "a good sport."
4. That practice is needed in forming habits and skills.
5. How to maintain cleanliness of skin, hair, nails, and clothing.
6. That one can give a cold to someone else.
7. The value of regular meals.
8. That cheerfulness aids digestion.
9. That vitamins promote health and growth.
10. That milk, eggs, whole-grain cereals, fruits, and vegetables contain vitamins.
11. How to conduct oneself at the table.
12. How to take care of the teeth.
13. How to stand and sit correctly.
14. How and when to relax and rest.
15. How to get ready for bed.
16. How long to sleep.
17. The best conditions for sleep.
18. How to avoid common accidents.
19. How to care for the ears.
20. How to care for the eyes.
21. That sunlight promotes health.
22. How to get enough sunlight.
23. How to avoid sunburn.
24. That exercise promotes growth and strength.
25. That cool moving air refreshes the skin.
26. How to adjust clothing to comfort.
27. Some harmful effects of alcohol and tobacco.
28. How to help in keeping the home clean and tidy.
29. Some of the practices demanded by good sportsmanship in being fair to other people.
30. How to play some good games involving big-muscle activity.
31. The meaning of words commonly used in a simple vocabulary of health terms, such as abdomen, appetite, blood vessel, bowel, circulation, digestion, heart, intestine, laxative, lungs, nutrition, perspiration, pores, relaxation, saliva, skeleton, stimulant, temperature, ventilation, and vitamin.

Teaching units commonly found in courses of study include such topics as safety, cleanliness, teeth, foods, dangerous substances, posture, sleep, and rest.

In **Grade V** for the first time the child's study centers around the "why" of health practices. This "why" is drawn in large measure from experiences, illustrations, and comparisons familiar to the child, not from the details of anatomy and physiology, for which he is not ready. The child learns more about keeping well and strong and there may be special emphasis on food.

In addition to the foregoing items, the children, by the end of the fifth grade, may be expected to have some understanding of:

Growth and health

1. Why growth is a sign of health.
2. Which practices retard growth.
3. The general nature and function of the important parts of the body.

Physical defects

4. The kinds of physical defects that exist among the members of the class as a whole and what needs to be done to correct these defects. (No reference should be made to the defects of individual children.)

Foods and digestion

5. Which foods contribute to growth and repair.
6. Which foods are used primarily for fuel.
7. Why water is needed in the diet.
8. The sources of the vitamins.
9. Some of the foods that provide roughage and why such foods are valuable.
10. Why iron and calcium are needed in the body.
11. Some of the foods that are important sources of iron and calcium.
12. Why milk is a good food.
13. The general nature of the digestive process.
14. The general functions of the stomach and intestines.
15. What constitute good menus for breakfast, lunch, and dinner.
16. Why good table manners are an aid to health.
17. The emotional and routine habits which help to maintain good digestion.
18. Why fried foods are hard to digest.
19. Why it is best to eat meals at regular times and what is the effect of eating between meals.

Elimination of body waste

20. How to prevent and correct constipation.
21. Why cathartics should be avoided.

Teeth

22. The difference between the first and second teeth and when the second teeth appear.
23. The value of fluoride and of certain foods to the health of the teeth.
24. Why the teeth should be brushed properly.
25. Why regular dental service is needed.

Cleanliness

26. Why bathing is needed.
27. Why nails should be kept clean and trimmed, and why they should not be bitten.
28. Why it is valuable to stimulate the scalp by massage.

Posture

29. How to judge correct standing and sitting posture.
30. Why good posture is desirable.

Feet

31. How to keep the feet in good health.
32. Why these procedures are useful and necessary.
33. The proper kind of shoe.

Nervous system

34. The relation between a healthy mind and a healthy body.

Stimulants, medicines, and drugs

35. Why tea and coffee are poor foods for growing boys and girls.
36. Some facts about patent medicines.
37. Some reasons why alcohol and tobacco are injurious.

Sleep, rest, and relaxation

38. Why sleep benefits the body.
39. The relation between sleep and growth.
40. The similarity between relaxation and sleep.
41. The effects of too little sleep, and the effects of sufficient sleep and rest.
42. Some of the causes of sleeplessness.
43. Why proper conditions for sleep are important.
44. That night air is healthful.

Circulation and breathing

45. That the blood is a clear fluid containing red blood corpuscles and white blood corpuscles.
46. What the red blood corpuscles and the white blood corpuscles do.
47. How oxygen reaches all parts of the body.
48. The nature of the heart and its action.

Exercise

49. Why exercise contributes to health and growth.
50. Why exercise is of value for other reasons.
51. Why outdoor play is better recreation than the movies.
52. Other values of games as well as the health value.

Clothing

53. What constitutes proper clothing and its care.
54. Why it is desirable to wear light clothing indoors and put on extra clothes when going out in cold weather.

Eyes

55. The general structure of the eye and how it functions.
56. How to prevent eye strain.

Ears

57. The general structure, function, and care of the ears.

Body temperature, fresh air, and sunshine

58. How the body reacts to different temperatures and how it keeps the same temperature.
59. The effect of warm and cold baths. (See "Cleanliness.")
60. What constitutes good ventilation.
61. Why sunshine is healthful.

Safety

62. The safety procedures that are important to children of this age.

Instruction includes units about foods and digestion, dental health, senses and the nervous system, blood and circulation, harmful substances, and safety.

In **Grade VI** the child is competent to take further responsibility for his health behavior. A new theme is introduced—the biological approach to cleanliness. A detailed consideration of the nature of soil, dirt, mold, and harmless bacteria starts the pupil on an interesting program of discovery relative to the importance of personal cleanliness and cleanliness in the home. New facts regarding body functions and health are developed in this connection. The special emphasis is *bacterial cleanliness and health in the home.*

In addition to the foregoing items, the children by the end of the sixth grade may be expected to have some understanding of the following ideas:

Health

1. What health is.
2. That health depends upon the kind of body one has and the way he takes care of it.
3. That health is not an end in itself.

Cleanliness

4. What cleanliness really is.
5. The difference between living dirt and nonliving soil.
6. The nature of mold.
7. Why food molds.
8. Where mold grows.
9. Some of the uses of mold.

Bacteria and viruses

10. The nature of bacteria.
11. Some of the things bacteria do.
12. That yeast and bacteria cause dissolved sugar to ferment.
13. That bacteria cause the spoiling of foods and liquids.
14. Something of the work of Pasteur.
15. Some differences between bacteria and viruses.

Teeth

16. Why cleanliness helps to prevent tooth decay.
17. The general structure of the tooth.
18. The nature of tooth decay.
19. How tooth decay is prevented or reduced to a minimum.

Body structure

20. The principles of body structure and how the body keeps in working order.
21. That the body is made of cells and cell products.
22. That the cells are supplied with food by the circulatory system.
23. The nature of the circulation of blood and lymph.
24. What the kidneys do.

Digestion

25. The work of the digestive tract and how to keep it healthy.
26. That starch digestion begins in the mouth.
27. The structure and work of the stomach.
28. The general structure and work of the intestines.
29. What is meant by the absorption of digested food material from the intestines.

Maintaining a healthy digestive tract

30. That there are harmless bacteria in the digestive tract.
31. What happens when constipation is present.
32. What happens when harmful bacteria get into the digestive tract.
33. How to keep the digestive tract healthy.

Skin

34. The structure of the skin and the principles of cleanliness applied to it.
35. The general structure and function of the skin.
36. What a clean skin really means and how to keep it clean.
37. How to keep the hands clean.
38. How to care for the complexion.
39. The effects of bathing upon the skin.
40. How to take care of injuries of the skin.

Breathing structures

41. The relation between the care of the breathing structures and the common cold.
42. The general structure and work of the breathing passage and lungs.

Common cold

43. What "catching cold" really means.
44. How to avoid colds.
45. How to take care of, and break up, a cold.
46. How to protect others when one has a cold.

Avoiding disease

47. The importance of cleanliness and of other factors in preventing disease.
48. The relationship between cleanliness and tuberculosis and what the latter really is.
49. How the body overcomes tuberculosis.
50. The general process of disease prevention—bacteria and viruses.
51. The facts about vaccination against smallpox.
52. The possibilities of protection against typhoid fever, measles, tetanus, and diphtheria.
53. The principles of sanitation.

Animal friends and enemies

54. Some of our animal friends and enemies.
55. How rats and mice may be kept away from the home.
56. That certain kinds of mosquitoes spread yellow fever and malaria.
57. The life history of mosquitoes and how to get rid of them.
58. In what ways houseflies are unclean.
59. How the breeding of flies may be prevented.
60. The important facts in the control of bedbugs, lice, and the hookworm.

Care of food

61. How to care for food in the home.
62. How to care for milk.

63. Why milk sanitation is necessary.
64. Something of the nature of the common processes of food preservation.

Household cleanliness

65. How to maintain household cleanliness.
66. How to keep dishes clean.
67. How to care for the kitchen, refrigerator, pantry, and other parts of the house.
68. The proper methods of washing, cleaning, and dusting.

Harmful substances

69. The effects of harmful drugs.
70. The injurious effects of alcohol and tobacco.

Units present new knowledge about molds and bacteria, health heroes and their discoveries, cleanliness of the individual and the surroundings, the care of the body, and prevention of disease.

Types of learning experiences. We reach our objectives in education by *how* we teach as well as by *what* we teach. Let us review some of the teaching procedures used in direct health instruction, in connection with either long teaching units or individual lessons. How can each be used most effectively? Of course, the use of any teaching technique will vary at different grade levels.

Class discussion. In developing interest in a new topic, in checking and deepening understanding, and in exchanging experiences, class discussion is of increasing value at advancing grade levels. The discussion is usually in the hands of the teacher and questioning is the chief tool by which he accomplishes his objectives. Questions should be clear, definite, thought-provoking, and adapted to the age and grade level. The form and wording of the question should not suggest the answer. Some of the types generally to be avoided are "yes-no" questions, catch questions, and "either-or" questions. Except in scattered types of reviewing, a series of questions should have some continuity.

The following points should be kept in mind when using the discussion method in health education.

1. Each child should be encouraged to participate.
2. Respect for the contributions and opinions of others should be developed.
3. Permit opportunity for leadership.
4. Help pupils distinguish between fact and opinion.
5. Challenge misconceptions and misinterpretations.
6. Insist upon courteous forms of speech.
7. Ask questions whenever necessary to assist a child to make his contribution more meaningful.
8. Acknowledge helpful contributions to the discussion.
9. Direct attention to the techniques of successful discussion, such as: keeping to the point, not repeating, speaking clearly, listening attentively.
10. Keep a record of the important points discussed, on the blackboard or in a notebook.

The problem-solving approach. Recognizing a clear-cut health problem of daily living and taking logical steps toward a solution are important to both individuals and groups, both now and as a preparation for adult life.

Logical thinking and a sharing of ideas take place. Action should follow. For example, the problem of reducing accidents stimulates a class to study types of accidents, causes, and preventive measures. Specific preventive steps and safety practices follow.

Wherever possible, a health problem should be related to a real life situation, clearly defined, and considered in the light of pertinent and properly evaluated data. Periodic evaluation of progress and tentative conclusions are helpful.

Direct experiences. We refer here to firsthand experiences involving actual participation in the activity concerning which learning is to take place. They are highly desirable wherever possible. We use them in driver education and in food selection at the cafeteria. A good medical examination provides such a learning experience. Permitting the child to weigh himself, to check another's height, and to work with plants and animals in the classroom are all direct and practical experiences.

Demonstrations. Demonstrations of simple processes and relationships visualize, clarify, and vitalize health facts. Hand-washing and tooth-brushing may be demonstrated, then practiced in Grade I. Good body mechanics, phases of food preparation, or artificial respiration may be effectively demonstrated in higher grades. The fact that calcium may be present without being seen may be demonstrated by blowing through a glass tube into some plain water and then into some water in which a little lime has been dissolved, thus changing the calcium into visible form. The presence of bacteria and mold in air or water may be demonstrated if sterile bacterial media are available. Even though demonstrations in the elementary school are relatively simple, it is important to:

1. Plan in logical sequence the various steps to be taken.
2. Avoid trying to develop so many steps as to cause confusion.
3. Set up materials in advance.
4. Begin the demonstration by indicating its relationship to the problem to be solved.
5. Be sure the students can see and hear.
6. Make sure, by discussion, that the demonstration was understood.

The use of films. (See also page 281.) The classroom film, either silent or talking, is used in three fundamentally different ways: (1) as an introduction to present a general background of the subject, (2) as a review to summarize previous study, (3) as a teaching lesson to carry the main instructional burden.

There is one type of situation in which the use of the film to introduce a unit is extremely valuable. This is in the teaching of skills in such fields as home nursing and safety. Here the motion picture is an ideal method of demonstrating the technique before pupils attempt to execute it.

The use of a film carrying extensive scientific information is not generally recommended as a means of introducing a unit of instruction, however. Its rapid presentation is too likely to develop confusion.

Using a film to review a problem that has been extensively studied will supply visual concepts where none may have existed, will clear up many misunderstandings, and will add reality to newly acquired information in a way to assure retention. It would seem better, however, to use the film where possible in connection with the study of the unit in order that visualization may assist in the natural development of the concepts.

It is ideal to use a film step-by-step in unfolding the study of factual subject matter in physiology, sanitation, or biology. The teacher indicates what the next section will show, and, after it has been shown, the film is stopped for class discussion. To do this, however, the teacher must be very familiar with the film content. Any film for classroom use should be previewed by the teacher before the lesson plan is prepared, and the class should be oriented by advance questions to look for the significant information to be presented.

Field trips. Field trips in health education are organized visits which bring pupils and teachers into direct contact with existing situations important in health teaching. For children of different grades, they may include trips to farms, zoos, animal hospitals, food markets, local health clinics, health departments, water-purification plants, and voluntary health agencies. It is possible to organize a trip within the school itself, as in a study of the safety conditions.

The following factors contribute to making field trips valuable educational experiences in the areas of health and safety:

1. All senses can be used in providing for pupil learning.
2. They stimulate new interests and increase appreciation.
3. Such trips bring pride in community achievements.
4. They may serve as an excellent introductory or culminating activity for unit teaching.

The following are points to be considered by the teacher in planning a field trip:

1. It should be a purposeful activity, preceded by careful planning and followed by class discussion.
2. It should be an integral part of the classroom activities, being both timely and needed.
3. The teacher should be familiar with the place to be visited.
4. A discussion of things to see and the purposes of the trip should take place in advance, sometimes with the listing of questions for which the field trip will furnish the answers.
5. Clear arrangements, such as permission from parents, means of transportation, expenses, and needed supervision should be made through the administration office.
6. Discuss in advance the desirable patterns of conduct expected of the pupils.
7. Invite parents to help conduct the trip when practicable.
8. While on the trip, children should be encouraged to stay together in order to complete the visit on schedule.
9. Help the pupils interpret and evaluate the trip through discussion, writing, or drawing, and through relating it to the original unit or problem.
10. Write letters of thanks to those people who made the trip possible.

Dramatization or role playing. Dramatics are the natural avenue of expression on the part of pupils. In education, dramatization seeks to orient the child's instincts, impulses, and interests, and to enrich his experiences and concepts through the interpretation of ideas. It permits the expression of emotions and the release of tensions in satisfying and acceptable ways. It encourages poise, self-reliance, self-confidence, cooperation, mutual sharing, and courtesy among all members of the group. It provides lifelike situations which are very important in presenting some phases of health education.

In the primary grades, the role playing of a simple meal or safety situation may be used. Dramatization involving somewhat more complicated situations may be carried out with puppets or as health playlets in grades four, five, and six.

There are some limitations to consider in using this method in health education. Dramatization involves imagination, and, at times, imagination clouds realities. Moreover, pupils with special talents may monopolize such an activity. So much emphasis may be placed on the performance that the health and safety facts are overlooked and the entertainment phase of the activity overshadows the amount of information conveyed.

The teaching of skills. The acquisition of a skill—"an ability performed with great facility"—often occupies part or all of a health lesson, and frequently more than one class period may be spent in perfecting a single technique, especially in such fields as home nursing, first aid, and safety.

For a lesson of this type to be effective, the pupil must first be cognizant of the purpose of the lesson. Conscious effort toward the goal is a vital factor in determining the extent to which exercise and repetition will be effective. The skill should be broken down into its various parts, and those of greater difficulty should be stressed. Demonstration of the activity before the pupils actually undertake it is valuable. After an understanding of the fundamental operation has been achieved, ample opportunity for practice should be allowed. Proficiency in carrying out the activities should be recognized in order that pupils may derive satisfaction from the realization of their progress. For complete satisfaction and fullest learning, the newly acquired skill should be used as soon and as frequently as possible in natural life situations. The creation of such situations can sometimes be subtly effected by the teacher.

Stories. In the lower grades especially, teachers use stories to present ideas and desirable health practices. There are many good health stories from which to select, or the teacher may prepare his own story, being sure that it has a pertinent health message understandable by the class in both vocabulary and concepts. The *open-end story* is of special value. It stops after a situation has been developed, and the class decides through discussion how it should be finished.

The use of the textbook. The basic textbook in health occupies a strategic position in class instruction. Information that is necessary and valuable for an intelligent comprehension of the health problems found at the different grade levels is concisely and accurately summarized in the modern textbook. The best texts present a program of health education,

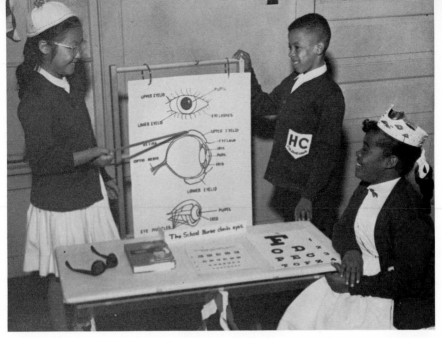

Fig. 54. Role playing in studying the care of the eyes. (Courtesy Los Angeles City Schools.)

and not a mere accumulation of facts. (See also page 274 for the character-istics of modern textbooks.)

The advantages of a good textbook are that it: (1) gives an accurate presentation of essential facts; (2) presents an orderly and comprehensible arrangement of the material; (3) furnishes a common core of content for the class; (4) contains such teaching and learning helps as references, questions, summaries, reviews, exercises, pictures, maps, and diagrams; and (5) saves time.

The textbook can be used in various ways, and in connection with almost any method. The teacher does occasionally teach a lesson in which the mastery of certain materials in the textbook is the immediate objective of the entire class period.

The inexperienced teacher or the teacher with a weak informational background is inclined to use textbook lessons too often. The constant use of this, or in fact any other one type of lesson, is likely to result in lack of interest. Variety in the use of methods and procedures is stimulating to both pupil and teacher.

The textbook is used in solving problems or as reference reading in studying questions that arise out of units. It is desirable that the basic text be supplemented by other suitable texts and additional reading materials.

If a course of study, consisting of a series of teaching units, is used, the textbook will supply the supporting material. If the school system does not have its own course of study, a complete modern series of health text-books with a book for each grade may be used as such, the sequence of material being changed to such an extent as may be necessary to meet the particular needs of the individual class. When this is done, the teacher selects from the suggested pupil activities those that are most useful to his pupils.

Fig. 55. The relationships between the teacher and the individual pupil are most important to health.

(H. Armstrong Roberts)

Objective tests based upon the textbook or taken from it may well be used. They should not replace entirely the use of questions to be answered in narrative or essay form.

Individual health instruction and guidance. One of the most important facets of health education is the person-to-person relationship between the child and the teacher or health specialist. In the kindergarten and first grade, a major health education activity is the development of skills in hand-washing, the adjustment of clothing, and other *simple procedures of daily living.* From grade to grade, health education becomes increasingly a group activity; but the informal relationship between teacher and pupil and the incidental help which the pupil gets from the teacher in matters of routine hygiene remain important. Throughout the elementary school, the teacher has health conferences with individual pupils regarding routine problems of healthful living, such as lack of sleep, failure to get an adequate breakfast, or overfatigue.

In the case of children who appear to show some *departure from normal health,* the teacher works closely with the health specialists. The most direct contact is the school nurse. Teacher observations are supplemented by reference to health records and reports and perhaps a conference with the child in regard to his daily schedule. Where medical or dental problems are involved, the child is referred to the physician or dentist. In the field of mental health, minor worries, anxieties, and emotional upset can usually be handled by the teacher. If the condition is more serious, the help of the psychologist or psychiatrist may be needed. We have discussed in Chapter 5 the educational problems of children with departures from physical or mental well-being. In these more serious conditions, the teacher functions as a member of the health team and helps the child to carry out whatever modified school program is prescribed.

Adolescence sometimes brings emotional problems in which guidance from the teacher may be very helpful. Pubescence more commonly appears at the beginning of junior high school, but it sometimes appears in grade six and the teacher or nurse may be helpful to the girl in removing anxieties related to the physical changes involved.

Special adjustments are also needed for *gifted children.* They present more of an educational problem than a health problem, although it is sometimes far from easy to safeguard their mental health. The country needs to develop and use its gifted citizens to the maximum, in spite of the tendency to glorify mediocrity in the democratic process. The gifted do not always find acceptance, and their very superiority may lead to personality difficulties.

Two groups of children are commonly regarded as gifted: (1) those with a high I.Q. (over 130) and (2) those with special talents in such fields as music, art, mechanics, science, social relations, leadership, or organization. Various educational proposals have been made for them, including accelerated promotion, separate grouping, and either special or enriched programs of study.

The gifted child who is interested in a health topic needs individual guidance in extending his study beyond that of the class as a whole. According to his grade level he may extend his reading, carry out some simple inquiry, or contact a health specialist for additional information.

Health counseling is an important activity in the secondary school, and teachers in the upper grades of the elementary school may wish to refer to this subject on page 339.

We should keep in mind that guidance is organized and scientific friendliness for adjustment and direction. It is not telling someone what to do; it means helping the child to act for himself. Individual guidance is an essential part of the health program providing assistance to the individual child. It is important to:

1. Show respect and consideration for the child in order to win his confidence.
2. Avoid prying into his family or personal affairs.
3. Analyze his personal health problems (mental, emotional, and physical) in a careful, objective manner.
4. Recognize his needs and try to assist him in being aware of them.
5. Encourage the child toward self-direction and facing up to his problem, through friendly advice, encouragement, and a positive approach.

The use of correlation. In higher grades subject matter areas become more distinct and training in skills becomes sharper. Broad integration is still possible but it is difficult to integrate all subjects. It is possible to correlate health with other individual subjects in many ways.

It must be kept in mind that correlation is a teaching device, not an end in itself. It can be overdone. Wherever it is natural to do so, the use of the health theme in other areas of instruction enriches the values of both learning activities for the child.

We should not strive for the greatest possible number of correlations. Successful correlations must be pertinent. There must be a real relationship between the ideas that are being correlated. The integrity of both subjects involved in the correlation must be preserved, with respect to the accuracy of the factual material and the quality of the pedagogical method.

There are really three different types of correlation:

1. Health facts may be shown to apply in life situations. For example, in social studies the child sees that health has been and is an important factor in the progress of groups of people in different times and in different places. He sees that health is not a fad but a part of life. He sees that health principles have applied, and do now apply, to the maintenance of health in real life. In the study of biography he sees the place of health in the life of the individual. He finds ideals of mental and physical health expressed in art and literature. Not infrequently health may be correlated with other subjects of instruction in a way to add interest to the subject receiving primary consideration and at the same time to help the pupil to see that health is an aspect of living that demands attention in many and varied situations.

2. Certain subjects supply facts supporting health principles. By pointing out these health relationships hygiene is better understood and a proper relationship between otherwise isolated facts is established. Subjects presenting such material are more commonly found at the higher grade levels. Thus, general science gives supporting health information through the study of light, air, and other topics. Biology gives further basic facts concerning life processes.

3. The teaching of fundamental skills, like language, arithmetic, and handwork, may often be made interesting by selecting health facts, experiences, or situations as the basis of teaching. Thus children are likely to be interested in subtracting two numbers that will show how much they have gained or in writing a story of their own experiences. There is little health promotion in using health ideas for pure drill, but the solving of a real health problem involving skill subjects is of value.

There is no excuse for debasing the arts of drawing, music, sculpture, or literature by parodies in the name of health. It is poor policy to destroy the enjoyment of children's classics by trying to read into them a score of health preachments. A distinction should be made, however, between original contributions of children that represent their best attempt to do something in an artistic way and the debasement of the classics by the teacher. The original work of the child may be poor in the quality of its English or art, and yet the pupil may be growing through a form of self-expression that is worthy of encouragement. On the other hand, study material that is placed before the pupil should always represent good English or good art.

Correlations with arithmetic. These correlations are of the third type mentioned. Life situations related to health furnish problems for which the children really desire answers. Situations involving arithmetical problems are found in connection with records of growth, the serving and purchase of milk, oranges, apples, or other food sold in school for the mid-morning or noon lunch, the planting of gardens ,and the selection of food. Examples of such correlation are *counting* milk bottles, *comparing numbers* to see the pupils' gain in weight, determining *average* gains, finding the *cost* of toothbrushes, and measuring sleeping *time.*

Correlations with art. Many opportunities exist to idealize some phase of health through crayon, papercutting, plasticene, or posters. These should have a place in purposeful units of work. There is no health value in drawing or modeling in the study of hygiene unless care is taken to develop attitudes or knowledge in connection with this activity. The importance of maintaining high standards in teaching both health and art has already been mentioned. The teacher should be careful to see that the health ideas represented are correct and that the educational values are developed through discussion.

In addition to the poster expressing the single idea, older children may sometimes make charts that present a series of health facts or an appreciable amount of health information.

Correlations with geography. Many situations that have a health significance occur in the regular geography work. The study of a region may bring out *dietary needs, habits,* and *customs* related to health and particular *health problems.*

Correlations with history. We may well make use of situations having health significance as they occur in connection with the regular history work. Some examples are these:

1. *Life among the Greeks*—The Olympic games, training of the Spartan soldiers, trained runners, daily bathing after games, Greek clothing, idealized bodily perfection.
2. *Life among the Romans*—gymnasia, training of the Roman soldier, hero worship.
3. *Life among the Pilgrims*—food and living conditions during the first winter, the introduction of cows and goats from Europe.
4. *Habits in individual lives*—Washington, Lincoln, Daniel Boone, Theodore Roosevelt, Franklin Roosevelt.

Correlations with language. We may use health activities and experiences for practice in oral and written language work. Dramatization in playing mealtime, playing house, reproducing family situations, or playing store clarifies concepts and furnishes opportunity for drill.

School experiences in health furnish the basis of compositions. Original limericks, riddles, and rhymes are produced. Letters are written to health departments, to school classmates, or to organizations supplying source material. Older children do library or encyclopedia research upon health topics, put health experiences into the school newspaper, write reports of health field trips, compose original stories with health ideas, or give health talks to younger children.

Suggested correlations are indicated in the following:

Grades I-III

1. Pictures that have health significance may be used for *picture study.*
2. Make use of the health significance of such *poems* as "The Friendly Cow," "The Land of Counterpane," and "The Wind."
3. *Dramatize* health stories and various health practices. Children like to act the health practices appearing in such stories as "The Three Bears." They slept with windows open, aired their beds, ate cereal and drank milk for breakfast, were tidy and neat in their eating, and spent part of every day outdoors.
4. Children may give occasional *reports of their health practices;* e.g., what they did during vacation (on the Monday following a vacation week), what they did to get ready for school this morning, what they ate for breakfast this morning, or what they did to get ready for bed last night.
5. *Oral reproduction of health stories,* either read or told by the teacher or read aloud by individual children, may be used to secure free oral expression.

Grades IV-VI

1. *Compositions* may be based on topics of health behavior, such as "What Helped Me to Gain in Weight," "Why I Eat a Good Warm Breakfast," or "My Favorite Outdoor Sport." Pictures that have health significance may be used as subjects of short compositions, either oral or written.
2. *Original stories, jingles, and slogans* may be written. These may be assembled in a "health reading book" or a "health newspaper."
3. *Original health plays* may be developed and dramatized by the class to present health ideas and practices that the class has agreed upon as desirable.
4. *Health information may be reported* by the children, especially what they have gathered from magazines or library books.
5. *Letters* may be written by the children to ask for health pamphlets or for information regarding health materials. Letters may be written occasionally to parents, reporting some health accomplishment. Letters may also be used to invite parents to attend special health activities at school or to inform them of health plans in which the school would like their help.
6. Health values may be stressed in reading and *writing about the lives* of such persons as Theodore Roosevelt, Wilfred Grenfell, Florence Nightingale, Clara Barton, and Louis Pasteur.
7. *Health "radio" or "television" programs* may be given by pupils to develop careful organization and presentation of ideas. Four-minute speeches on health subjects may be used in a similar way.

Correlations with music. It should be recognized that music itself makes a direct contribution to both physical and mental health. It teaches a proper use of the voice to produce pleasant tones in both speaking and singing without strain or fatigue. The pupils are taught good posture and correct breathing in learning to sing. The importance of keeping the throat and nasal passages in a state of good health is emphasized. Songs of joy contribute to mental health by stimulating a cheerful attitude. The restful and quieting effect of soft, sweet music contributes to the peace and happiness of the individual. The enjoyment of music is a constructive element of personality. Music is enjoyed for its own sake. It helps to develop a taste and enjoyment of the beautiful, provides a fine use of leisure time, and often aids in making friends. We shall do well to recognize the direct contribution of music to health.

Health songs should be acceptable to both the music supervisor and to the supervisor of health education.

Correlations with nature study. There are a limited number of opportunities for health and nature study correlations; but nature study cannot serve as a vehicle of health teaching to any appreciable degree at this grade level. The teacher should be certain of the soundness of relationships that are pointed out. The care of plants and simple animal-feeding experiments have been fairly successful in classes where expert supervision and direction were maintained. With good teaching there is a contribution to health education in connection with the keeping of pets.

Correlations with reading. Health readers that are good readers as such and that contain constructive health material are useful; more of them are becoming available. The essential correlation with reading lies in the use of approved reading materials in the health field which develop understanding of health problems and contribute to improved reading comprehension.

Fig. 56. Music contributes to voice hygiene and the enjoyment of life.

Grades I-VI

1. Make use of stories and situations related to health as they appear in the *reading books* of the grade.
2. In the first grade, develop *reading lessons on the blackboard* made up of sentences expressing concepts which the children are using in the health program.
3. In the second and third grades individual children may *read health stories* aloud from books not commonly used by the class.
4. In the fifth and sixth grades, the health textbook is used for *silent reading.* Thought questions may be asked to determine the child's understanding of the content.
5. *Supplementary health books and pamphlets* are read in solving health problems.

Correlations with spelling. Children learn to spell the words they meet and use in health education.

Motivational activities

Whatever methods of health teaching are used, the teacher seeks to motivate pupils toward more healthful living. Neither cold facts, the voice of experience, the command of authority, nor theories of health as a means of enriching life present concrete and vital reasons to the child for hygienic living. The activities through which the teacher attempts to stimulate the development of health practices, therefore, are exceedingly important.

The school may properly develop a program that maintains the child's natural interest in growth and in physical activities. These are evidences of health. The child realizes that he reaches these objectives through good food, adequate rest, and other hygienic practices. The school may well give the child a chance to measure success and observe progress. The life of the child, both in school and out, provides limitless real situations upon which health motivation may be based. Natural motivation is more desirable and more effective than that which is forced or artificial. All the health services and many routine procedures are activities upon which appropriate behavior may be built.

If attractive teeth are desirable, it is commendable for a class to improve from year to year in the percentage of children who have had all necessary dental work completed. It is a source of justifiable pride for a class to stand well among all the classes in the school system in the degree of success it attains.

Many health practices, such as cleanliness, win social commendation. There would seem to be no harm in the child's learning that his practice of cleanliness wins teacher commendation and class approval. The mirror in the classroom is a motivating device, because it serves as an aid, a reminder, and a means of measuring progress.

Keeping records serves as a reminder to carry out some regularly recurring health practice which the child has undertaken. Observing improvement in one's record, as in one's skills, is always a satisfying experience.

Rewards in the nature of special group celebrations in which all children participate may be given when goals set for the group as a whole are reached. These goals include such activities as going to bed on time or eating good breakfasts. It is not necessary that the goal for which the reward is given should be 100 per cent class achievement. Certain rewards, such as stories, carrot parties, and excursions to dairy farms or food stores, have a health education value in themselves, in addition to the enjoyment which they contribute to children.

These considerations suggest certain feasible types of activities. On the other hand, we should be careful to avoid "hiring" the child to live hygienically by special rewards or special privileges. Father may decide that the end justifies the means when he gives John a dollar to have his tooth out. There is perhaps some difference of opinion as to whether father was right or wrong, but certainly the procedure was not an educational one. Neither do we want competitions which offer prizes and rewards of such intrinsic value that they become the center of attention.

In short, one would approve watching improvement in growth and other specific evidences of health, providing appropriate social approval for those health practices which truly merit it, and recognizing the satisfactions which may be derived from improving one's record in worthwhile activities. One would disapprove, as educationally undesirable, the practice of stimulating health behavior through artificial and unrelated rewards.

If competition is used at all, it should be primarily for the satisfaction of successful achievement. Competition against previous performances should be preferred when possible. Group competition (rows, teams, or classes, not boys vs. girls) is to be preferred to individual competition. The child should not be asked to compete in activities over which he has no control.

Some degree of motivation may be secured by using graphic material to make concepts more definite. For example, we may use a clock face with hands set to show proper bedtime, or food models to aid in selecting a good breakfast.

Such devices as we have been discussing may include:

Grades I-III

1. *Records of class accomplishment* in specific health habits may be kept on the board to stimulate interest and give a measure of the results obtained. These records may show, for instance, the number (not the names) who went to bed at the proper time or who brushed their teeth before school. Habit records may use pictorial or graphic features; e.g., an automobile race with an automobile of different color for each row or a ladder for each row, with a figure of a child climbing to the top.
2. *Individual records of health habits* may be kept by each child in his desk in a small booklet with pages ruled especially for the records or on cards or sheets of paper ruled for the purpose.
3. *Pictorial charts or large drawings on the blackboard* may be used as records of important health accomplishment; e.g., a "health train" for the children who have gained in weight for the month or a "health airplane" for the children whose dentistry is completed. The name or a cut-out doll representing the pupil is put on the "health train" or in the "health airplane" to record successful accomplishment.
4. *A drawing of a clock face* with hands at the desired bedtime for the class may be put on the board, with the words, "We go to bed on time," and a record may be made each morning to show the number who went to bed on time. An

alternative device is the use (in Grades III and IV) of a clock face with movable hands on the desk of each child. Just before school closes the hands are moved to indicate the proper bedtime. The next morning pupils move the hands, if necessary, to indicate the time they did go to bed. This provides a ready check for the teacher.

Grades IV-VI

1. *Individual graphs* may be used to show gains in weight. Such a graph shows by a single line the changes in weight from month to month.
2. An interesting *circle graph to show the distribution of time* throughout the day in relation to health activities can be made by dividing a circle into sections to show the periods spent in sleep, eating breakfast and getting ready for school, the time in school, noon meal, evening meal, play and relaxation. The sections may be developed in different colors, with a key to the colors given below the graph.
3. A *single-line graph* may be made to show the *temperature* record of the classroom for the month.
4. *Samples of foods* or *food models* may be used for grouping foods for a good breakfast, a good dinner, a good supper, growth and repair foods, fuel foods, regulator foods, or mineral foods.

    The food models may be prepared by cutting out pictures of different foods and pasting each on thin cardboard. Boys in the class may be able to make wooden blocks with a groove in the top in which the food models can be stood up straight. The models can be kept and used in a variety of ways in the study of foods.
5. *Individual records of particular health habits* may be kept on papers ruled for the purpose. A system of scoring adds interest because it enables the pupil to measure his own improvement.
6. A *vegetable chart* may be used on the chalkboard to stimulate the eating of vegetables. Let pupils select several common vegetables and place pictures of these across the top of the chart. Keep a daily record to show how many children eat each particular vegetable or those which they have not liked before. A similar record may be used for cereals or for fruits.
7. A *relay race* on posture may be held by having each row of children walk around the room, each child carrying a beanbag on his head. The teacher disqualifies any who assume poor posture. The group finishing with the largest number retaining the bag on the head wins.
8. *Safety councils* may be formed through which pupils may develop plans and activities to prevent accidents on and near the school grounds.

References

Banks, M. A., and Dunham, M. A.: *Teaching Nutrition in the Elementary School,* Washington, D. C., 1959, American Association for Health, Physical Education and Recreation, 32 pp.

Beck, R., Cook, Walter, and Kearney, N.: *Curriculum in the Modern Elementary School,* ed. 2, Englewood Cliffs, N. J., 1960, Prentice-Hall, Inc.

Blough, G. O., Schwartz, J., and Huggett, A. J.: *Elementary School Science and How to Teach It,* rev. ed., New York, 1958, Holt, Rinehart and Winston, Inc.

Grout, R. E.: *Health Teaching in Schools,* ed. 4, Philadelphia, 1963, W. B. Saunders Company.

Humphrey, J. H., Johnson, W. R., and Moore, V. D.: *Elementary School Health Education,* New York, 1962, Harper & Brothers.

Irwin, L. W., Cornacchia, H. J., and Staton, W. M.: *Health in Elementary Schools,* St. Louis, 1962, The C. V. Mosby Company.

Kilander, H. F.: *School Health Education,* New York, 1962, The Macmillan Company.

Martin, E. A.: *Nutrition in Action* and *Nutrition Education in Action,* New York, 1963, Holt, Rinehart and Winston.

National Education Association and American Medical Association Joint Committee: *Health Education,* ed. 5, Washington, D. C., 1961, National Education Association.

National Education Association: *Schools for the Sixties,* a report of the Project on Instruction, New York, 1963, McGraw-Hill Book Company.

Oberteuffer, D.: *School Health Education,* ed. 3, New York, 1960, Harper & Brothers.

Peterson, D. G., and Hayden, V. D.: *Teaching and Learning in the Elementary School,* New York, 1961, Appleton-Century-Crofts, Inc.

Schneider, R. E.: *Methods and Materials of Health Education,* ed. 2, Philadelphia, 1964, W. B. Saunders Company.

Turner, C. E.: *Planning for Health Education in Schools,* 1966, UNESCO and WHO. Available through UNESCO Publications Center, 317 East 34th Street, New York, N. Y.

Willgoose, C. E.: *Health Education in the Elementary School,* ed. 2, Philadelphia, 1964, W. B. Saunders Company.

Chapter xvii

Health education in junior and
senior high schools

H ealth education in the secondary schools deserves a separate discussion. There is a sharp difference in organization with the introduction of a completely departmentalized program. To be sure, the fundamental objectives and educational principles underlying health education remain the same, but there are differences in emphasis and procedure because of the differences in pupil age level and in school organization.

The problem

During the secondary school period, pupils are undergoing those important physiological changes and emotional adjustments incident to adolescence. The pupil is less ready to accept the dictates of authority. This means that he must make a readjustment of relations with the parent in the home. He is less willing to follow the health practices that have been prescribed by the school. He is a nonconformist who is likely to reject a program of behavior reflected in the health rules of earlier years until he realizes more keenly that these same practices are demanded for athletic success, for social approval, and for employment. Health supervision in connection with athletics becomes more important; personality maladjustments are more numerous and more serious.

Perhaps the greatest disadvantage in the health program of the secondary school as compared with that of the elementary school arises from departmentalization. The teacher is no longer an "alter parens," interested in the whole child, confining his attention to forty children or less. The secondary school teacher is a "subject" teacher, meeting scores of children every day. The pupil has no one to whom he can turn for advice as readily as the elementary school pupil turns to his classroom teacher.

The "homeroom" teacher has an opportunity to develop teacher-pupil health relationships; but too often he is more of an attendance officer and record-keeper for the pupils assigned to sit in his room while waiting for academic class sessions. At best he can make a considerable contribution to health attitudes and practices.

The secondary school is an institution of limitless diversities—diversities in the kind of schools and in the study programs followed by different groups, and diversities among the pupils themselves. Planning a health program is a complex task.

Most elementary school pupils now continue through high school. The importance of the secondary school in preoccupational training is increasing. Both the youths who take a job and establish a home directly after high school and the large number of young people going on to junior college and to college must be considered in planning the high school health program. The different kinds of schools and the varied types of curricula make it impossible to set up a single model high school program in health education. Each pupil is in the hands of many teachers, and interrelationships in health subject matter must be definitely arranged by the teachers of different departmentalized subjects. Cooperative planning for both indirect health learnings and direct health instruction is needed.

This planning is often done by a *faculty health committee.* In small schools, such a committee may consist of only the principal, the health teacher, and one or two other persons. In any case, all of the teachers who include some health instruction in their subjects need to be members of such a committee. Teachers of biology and other basic sciences, social sciences, home economics, and physical education would ordinarily be included. The committee may include representatives from school health personnel, such as physician, nurse, and director of the lunchroom. In addition to laying out the program of direct health instruction, a committee of such broad membership can plan for health education in connection with health services and school sanitation, and for other activities involving health and health education. It may initiate special school-wide health projects or campaigns.

Opportunities for indirect health learnings

Home and school cooperation is usually less intimate in the secondary school. Teachers are not so likely to visit the home, but parents come in contact with health programs through the physician and the nurse, and through visits to school exhibitions, where health instruction and physical education are demonstrated. School nurses, health educators, and guidance counselors have a direct relationship with the home in their work with individual students.

At least one, and preferably two, *health examinations* should be provided at the junior-senior high school level. Here is an opportunity to give most welcome health guidance. In some cities pupils are encouraged to secure examinations from the family physician, bringing to school the doctor's report on a standard form. The nurse, the health coordinator, the physical educator, and the homeroom teacher have important responsibilities in securing the *correction of physical defects.* It is desirable that cumulative health records be continued in use in the high school.

The opportunities for incidental health teaching involved in *communicable disease control, school sanitation, school health services,* and the *hygienic regimen* have been discussed elsewhere. Every member of the

Fig. 57. A student council plans health activities.

school staff—not merely the health specialist—has a responsibility to help make the school day a sound health learning experience for the student.

There are certain *special activities* involving cooperative effort which are not commonly found in the elementary school, but with which the high school health education program may be profitably interrelated.

1. The *student council* in most high schools can cooperate in promoting the health program and in handling the publicity connected with special activities and campaigns. The activities may include encouraging neatness in students' lockers and desks; discouraging the careless disposal of wastepaper and food, the marking of walls, and the defacing of property; prohibiting smoking on or near school premises; discouraging standing in the aisles or in basement rooms while eating lunches; and discouraging activities likely to cause accidents.

2. *High school newspapers* can contribute to the health program by publishing health news and timely information. A special health column may be developed in which health information, slogans, and answers to health questions are included. There may be occasional editorials on health activities. Quotations from health department reports, special bulletins, and other health publications may properly be printed from time to time. Health projects, surveys, special drives, contests, or excursions may be described.

3. *Bulletin boards* may be made to contribute to health, particularly if a large share of the material posted is put there by the students themselves. The progress of special campaigns may be recorded there. Posters, original sketches, illustrations, slogans, quotations, publicity materials from national and community health organizations, and attractively mounted clippings of special health interest all have their place. A definite plan should be developed for the assignment of space and for the regular changing of materials.

4. *Assemblies* afford an opportunity for special lectures, auditorium

films, student discussions of health problems, and the presentation of plays that have special health significance.

5. The *lunchroom* offers opportunity for health education. The lunches are carefully prepared under sanitary conditions and are of high nutritive value. It is well worthwhile to make the lunchroom itself attractive. Occasional better-lunch campaigns are effective. In addition, the student council and the teachers of hygiene, home economics, and physical education cooperate with the lunchroom by encouraging the selection of desirable food and by developing an appreciation of the scientific and efficient service which the lunchroom renders. They encourage the use of the school lunchroom in preference to less desirable eating places in the vicinity of the school.

In the lunchroom, specially desirable combinations are promoted by low prices and catchy names. Candy may be kept off the counter, at least until after the whole line has gone through. Special foods, like fruit, milk, salad, and whole grain bread, are sold at very attractive prices. Food trays may occasionally be checked by a nutritionist or seniors in home economics and "A-1" cards placed on trays carrying a well-balanced lunch. Lunch suggestions may be shown on a poster. The promotion or serving of a standard lunch is not entirely popular, but it can provide a lunch of good dietary balance.

6. *Weighing and measuring* take place less frequently than in the elementary school. Interest in growth has, to a considerable degree, been supplanted by interest in athletic accomplishment and personal appearance. Some pupils of high school age, especially girls, prefer not to increase in weight, and indulge in injudicious dieting frequently injurious to health.

7. The *homeroom* is now the place where the beginnings of a communicable disease or lapses in personal appearance can be observed. The homeroom teacher is on the alert to detect pupils showing signs of illness and refer them promptly to the doctor or nurse. Teachers should also refer to the health counselor, nurse, or doctor any pupils whose continuing health status appears to be unsatisfactory. The homeroom teacher can aid in seeing that all his students get dental attention during the year.

One homeroom activity which has been used widely and successfully is the individual *health appraisal*. When these appraisals take place at the beginning of the school year, they provide valuable information for planning health instruction. An appraisal form or blank is prepared by the curriculum committee or by a representative of that committee working with a group of students. These forms ask specific questions, answerable by "yes" or "no," relating to appearance, health practices, and freedom from defects. Structures and conditions considered include skin, hair, nose and throat, mouth and teeth, posture, nutrition, eyes, hearing, immunity, and mental and social health. Under "posture," for example, the question may be, "Do I stand correctly (with head well back, chin in, shoulders level, arms relaxed, back straight, abdomen flat, chest the part of the body furthest forward, and weight mostly on the balls of the feet)?"

9. Regular *rest and relaxation periods* are unnecessary for most students because of the change of work provided by the schedule. Provision should be made, however, for adequate rest facilities to meet the special needs of individual children.

Direct health instruction

In the departmentalized program for the junior and senior high school, health knowledge is presented (1) through health instruction introduced into other subjects and (2) through health courses.

Health instruction through other subjects. Through the planning of the previously mentioned faculty health committee to strengthen interrelationships and avoid undesirable duplication, various subjects can make important contributions to health education.

Home economics commonly provides important and valuable instruction for girls in the field of health, including units of instruction upon such topics as laundering; food preservation; menu planning; individual menus; cleanliness in the kitchen; the sanitary condition of stores and markets; the care of clothing; the nature of textiles and weaves; the relation of clothing to the weather; the selection and use of different types of clothing, shoes, stockings, footwear, underwear; care of the scalp and the hair; the use of cosmetics; the care of the home; the selection of food; making meals attractive. In some school systems home nursing and child care are taught in connection with the work of the home economics department.

General science and separate courses in physics, chemistry, and biology contribute to health instruction through the discussion of air and its relation to health; safe drinking water and its health values; the effect of weather upon health; ventilation and heating; sunlight; chemical elements in the human body; the nature of light and vision; sound and hearing; kinds of plants and their relation to the well-being of man; animals as a source of food and as a source of disease; and selected problems in sanitation.

The percentage of high school students who take *biology* is not large, but those who do take this subject learn much about life processes and their relationship to health. The student studies growth, nutrition, respiration, movement, fatigue, reproduction, and responses to stimuli. He studies the nature of cells, protoplasm, immunity, disinfection, and sterilization. As the class in *physics* discusses new uses of atomic energy and the exploration of outer space, many health considerations arise. In *chemistry,* the growing problem of air pollution is discussed, as is the conversion of sea water to fresh water. Laboratory experiments sometimes include the study of urinalysis and other chemical diagnostic processes.

Social science considers the adjustment of the individual to the community and within the family; the interdependence of people; the interpretation of health and social data by means of graphs; the effect of changing economic conditions upon health; transportation in relation to health; social health agencies; occupation and health; immigration; housing; civil service; community planning; health responsibilities of government; medical care; taxation for health purposes; standards of living in relation to health; the importance of health in national development and in community planning; the choice of a vocation; and the qualities which make for success. The development of sound personality and the health aspects of occupations are very personal matters. These topics are so intimately related to the hopes and ambitions of the pupil that they lead directly to a consideration of health values.

Physical education makes an important contribution to both health and health education. Stamina, neuromuscular coordination, and good body mechanics are developed. The desire for athletic achievement is an outstanding motivating force and stimulus in the development of sound health practices. The teacher of physical education finds many opportunities for giving needed health advice to individual students. Helpful learning experiences develop with reference to the importance of exercise, group leadership, and the wholesome use of leisure time. The importance of adequate nutrition to athletic capacity and the dangers of alcohol, tobacco, and narcotics are pointed out. Safety relationships are effectively taught in relation to the different sports.

Opportunities for contributing to health education in the study of *English* occur in the study of books that set forth health ideas, in the study of biography, in the analysis of characters in novels, and in the use of health topics for panel discussion, socio-drama, and debates. "Feature stories" for the school newspaper may deal with health subjects.

In the study of *history*, students see the influence upon world health of the invention of the microscope, the automobile, and the airplane and of the development of anesthetics, refrigeration, electric power, and fluoridation. They see the effects of industrialization and of war upon the health of nations. They note the effects of loss of health by world leaders.

The contributions to health by *art* and *music* have already been described. (See pages 317 and 318.)

Foreign languages are related to health through occasional health topics that arise in connection with reading and study.

Mathematics may use health material as data for graphs, percentages, space requirements in dwellings, or tax rates for health purposes.

Manual arts contribute to health education by requiring clean hands and materials, proper clothing, correct posture, good ventilation, safety precautions, and habits of concentration and industry.

Most subjects of instruction in the high school can make some contribution to health, and in every course due consideration should be given to mental and physical health in developing the schedules and methods of instruction.

Health courses. Direct health instruction must vary in different high schools because problems, teacher training, and educational resources vary. Certain *characteristics of good health teaching,* however, are generally recognized.

It is based upon analysis of needs and interests, determined not only by a study of the (1) public health findings and (2) the health problems of school and community, but also by (3) pupil observation, (4) parent conferences, (5) habit, attitude, and knowledge tests, and (6) student interest surveys. An increasing number of studies in recent years have given us research findings upon the health needs, health interests, misconceptions, health attitudes, and health practices of secondary school students and some evaluation of motivational factors related to behavioral change.[1]

Good health teaching is adapted to the maturity of the student. It has a scientific approach and separates health facts from health fallacies, establishing sound basic knowledge for individual health guidance. It involves pupil planning and pupil action. There are plenty of challenging health problems. Students make surveys of sanitation (at home, at school, or in the community); visit the activities of official and voluntary health and hospital agencies; study health advertising, community recreation, child guidance programs, and any number of other health-related activities. Health teaching is directed toward the development of sound concepts, attitudes, and behavior and is not limited to the memorizing of health facts.

The *scope* of health education is broad. The Joint Committee report on "Health Education"[2] suggests the following ten major subject areas: (1) the human body; (2) the balanced regimen; (3) mental health; (4) preparation for marriage, family life, and child care; (5) communicable and noncommunicable diseases; (6) consumer health education; (7) accident prevention and emergency care; (8) protection from hazards of poisons, drugs, and narcotics; (9) community health; and (10) health careers.

Successful instruction in health and hygiene in junior and senior high schools requires resourcefulness as well as a broad scientific knowledge on the part of the *teacher.* The health teacher needs a good background in personal and community health, communicable disease, school hygiene, educational psychology, modern teaching technique, and secondary education, with a good understanding of the programs of physical education, home economics, student counseling, first aid, and health service. Only the big high schools, however, can use the full time of a teacher in health courses. In the smaller high schools the teacher must teach some other subject, such as for example, biology or physical education.

---

[1]An excellent summary of such research is to be found in *Synthesis of Research in Selected Areas of Health Instruction,* 1963, a publication of the School Health Education Study, sponsored by the Samuel Bronfman Foundation. Available from Publications-Sales, National Education Association, 1201 Sixteenth Street, N.W., Washington 36, D. C., 192 pp., price $2.00.

[2]Joint Committee on Health Problems in Education of the National Education Association and the American Medical Association: *Health Education,* Washington, D. C., 1961, National Education Association, p. 234.

Adequate teaching facilities include a classroom providing an instructional area with furniture which can be arranged for individual or group work, a demonstration desk at the front of the room, storage space for supplies and apparatus, bulletin board display areas, and source materials in the form of supplementary printed matter, charts, films, and models. Projection equipment and space for library and reference materials should be available. It is desirable that a small committee room should be available for the use of working groups of students. The office of the teacher or a small conference room is needed for regular hours set aside for health counseling.

Practices and opinions have varied with respect to the *grade distribution, course organization, and time allotment* of health teaching in the secondary school. One procedure has been to teach health one period a week throughout the secondary school on the basis that the student would have a continuing stimulus toward more healthful living. It is now generally agreed that the health course must meet more often than once a week if interest is to be sustained.

Another procedure has been to make the health course a part of the course in physical education and to have the class meet for health education once or twice a week. In some cases a teacher of physical education will be the health teacher, but experience indicates that the health course should be an entity in itself.

Another procedure has been to try to put all of the health teaching into the science course. There is too much health subject matter to be presented through incidental teaching or as an occasional science unit. Where health is taught by the science teacher, therefore, experience has led to the grouping of health units together into a health course which represented the instruction in science for a semester.

Authoritative opinion now supports the policy of concentrating health instruction into courses which meet four or five times a week and insisting upon one such course in the eighth or ninth grade and another in the eleventh or twelfth grade.

School Health Policies, issued by the National Conference for Cooperation in Health Education, states:

Specific courses in health should be provided for all pupils in both junior and senior high schools. The minimum time allotment for the junior high school health course should be a daily period for at least two semesters, during the seventh, eighth, or ninth grades. The minimum time allotment for the health course in the senior high school should be a daily period for at least two semesters, preferably during the eleventh or twelfth grades. Health courses should receive credit equal to that given for courses in other areas. Health courses should be given in regular classrooms, adequately equipped. The classes should be comparable in size to those in other subject matter areas.

Home nursing is often taught by a school nurse with the required preparation in health education, as a separate subject or unit of instruction in the program of ninth or tenth grade girls. *First aid* likewise is given to girls and boys as a separate unit. The importance and nature of driver training is discussed in the chapter on safety.

The intensive *health problem course* given in grade eleven or twelve deals with all the major health problems of effective living. It is adapted to the current health needs of the students; but it also recognizes that these young people are soon to be confronted with new health problems as they become workers, citizens, and parents. There is an increasing demand for instruction that is related in a practical way to the after-school life of the great group of boys and girls whose formal education terminates with the senior high school. The value of practical health instruction in enabling a boy or girl to secure and hold a job is being increasingly appreciated. Employers desire young people of good health and good personal appearance. They also wish the employe to possess the poise, emotional balance, and social adjustment that accompany good mental health.

The following statement is quoted from *Planning for Health Education in Schools,* published jointly by the United Nations Educational Scientific and Cultural Organization (UNESCO) and the World Health Organization (WHO).

It may be helpful to curriculum committees to see a list of the subjects of instruction found in secondary school health curricula. The scope of the different topics varies and the sub-topics listed below are distributed differently in different outlines. The following pages do not suggest what should be taught in secondary schools of any specific country, district, or community. The choice will be based upon the important health problems and health needs of the students involved, upon the available time and facilities and upon the beliefs and practices which may need to be changed.

There follows an inclusive list of major subjects and minor topics found in health curricula, designed for grades 7, 8 and 9 and a separate list of topics found in curricula for grades 10, 11 and 12. It is not suggested that all of the topics should be taught at both levels. What is actually taught at each of the two levels will depend upon plans for health instruction at the other level and upon the extent to which major topics are included in both courses. These lists are inclusive and are not proposed for adoption in toto. They are for use in selecting the topics your committee decides to propose. The sequence of subjects as listed here is not significant. The reader will find some sub-topics repeated under different major subjects.

Areas and topics of instruction found in health curricula for grades 7, 8, and 9

1. *The care of the body* (based on an elementary knowledge of structure and function of the human mechanism)

The digestive system, the circulatory system, the sense organs, the nervous system, the excretory system, the skin, physiological development related to adolescence, growth patterns, individual differences.

2. *Food and nutrition*

Food and growth, food groups, food values, adequate diet, food selection, the handling and care of food, preservation of foods, habits of eating.

3. *Hygienic regimen* (health maintenance, or healthful living)

Exercise and rest, sleep, study, relaxation, recreation, the use of leisure time, values of physical activity, individual health needs, daily schedule.

4. Mental health

Emotions, understanding one's self, personality, getting along with others at home and at school, accepting reality, interrelationship of physical, emotional and social factors, personal appearance, grooming, posture.

5. Communicable diseases

The cause, transmission and prevention of the most common communicable diseases.

6. Health protection

Health examinations, correcting defects, alcohol, tobacco, narcotics, dental care, care of the sense organs, dangers of self-medication.

7. Education for family living (familial hygiene, or family-life education)

Instruction in this area varies sharply between different countries. This is because family structure and the authority within the family varies; and because beliefs vary as to what should be taught to young adolescents. Most curricula emphasize the importance of the family, the relationships within the family, the care of the children, and the care of the sick. Differences in instruction are found in what is taught regarding maturation, sex hygiene, population growth, boy and girl relationships, and social customs of engagement and marriage. In some countries rather extensive instruction is given in those matters, in other countries very little is given. Curricula recognizes that health instruction in this area must be carefully related to the customs and culture of the people and so organized and put into operation as to meet the approval of parents and society.

8. Safety

Safety at home and at school, safe transportation, safe recreation, bicycles, steps in the prevention of accidents.

9. First aid

Here the Red Cross Course is often used. The instruction covers such topics as bruises, cuts, burns, fractures, sprains, dislocations, sunstroke and heat prostration, sunburn, frostbite, fainting, electric shock, poisons, snake bites, insect bites, foreign bodies in eye, nose and throat, nose bleed, drowning and suffocation.

10. Home nursing

The Red Cross Course is often used. Topics cover the selection and care of the sick room, bed-making, care of the sick, feeding the sick, medicines, treatment, communicable diseases, convalescence, household emergencies, "mothercraft" or "homecraft," and the care of the infant.

11. Community health

Food control, safe water supply, waste disposal, air pollution, housing, work of health authorities, health at school, community safety.

12. Occupational hygiene

Hygiene related to the kinds of occupations which most students will enter.

Areas and topics of instruction found in health curricula for grades 10, 11, and 12

1. The human body in health and disease

Normal functions of the systems of organs, defects and diseases of these systems, endocrines and hormones, abnormal function, hygienic practices.

2. Hygienic regimen

Individual health needs, sleep and rest, recreation, exercise, body mechanics, study, daily schedule, grooming, dress.

3. Mental health

Emotional maturity, stress, intelligence, personality adjustment, social relationships, emotional disorders.

4. Familial hygiene

Family living, child care, heredity and eugenics, choosing a mate, preparing for marriage, marriage and the establishment of a home, housing, medical care for the family, dental services, needs and costs of health maintenance. (Here as in teaching outlines for the earlier years of the secondary school, there are wide differences in different countries as to what is taught.)

5. Communicable and non-communicable diseases

Consideration of the most common diseases in the area, their cause and prevention with special reference to the communicable diseases and such organic diseases as cancer, heart disease, diabetes, alcoholism, and mental illness.

6. Safety

Community programs of accident prevention, work accidents, home accidents, public accidents, safety in sports and recreation, fire prevention, disaster relief, emergency care, school safety, distribution and cost of accidents, automobile driver training.

7. Food needs and digestive hygiene

Nutritional needs, metabolism, vitamins, carbohydrates, fats, proteins, meal planning, food values, nutritional deficiencies and diseases, school gardens and the cultivation of desirable foods, food conservation, food preservation, food adulteration, food sanitation, food additives, digestive hygiene and digestive disorders, diarrhea and other intestinal infections, indigestion, colitis, appendicitis.

8. Consumer hygiene

Expenditures for health, adequate health care, fads, quackery, consumer protection and truth in the advertising of health products, sources of information about health, distribution of health expenses, insurance against sickness and accidents, the evaluation of advertising appeals.

9. Community health

Water supply, waste disposal, drug control, radiation, air pollution, insect control, rat control, governmental health agencies, voluntary health agencies, individual responsibility for community health.

10. Careers in health

Consideration by students who are in a position to go on to professional education in such professions as medicine, public health, dentistry, nursing, teaching, nutrition, dietetics, hospital administration, occupational therapy, physical education, laboratory services. There may be consideration of the health aspects of other professions such as law, the clergy, journalism, architecture and the arts.

The topics listed above are taken from curricula planned for general secondary schools. There are various special schools and special programs which need adapted courses of study. Some developing countries have mentioned the importance and value of the "écoles ménagères" and their special preparation for homemaking. Agricultural schools and other vocational schools which prepare boys for specific occupations may need their own outlines. It is not possible to consider here these various special situations.[3]

Teaching techniques

We have discussed various types of learning experiences in the elementary schools (Chapter 16). Many of the methods used in the upper grades are used with little modification in the secondary school. We may well consider here, however, the use of some of the teaching techniques of special value in teaching health in the junior and senior high school.

The lecture. A good lecture presents information efficiently and quickly. The higher the educational level, the more effectively it can be used; but even at the college level, a series of lectures is usually supplemented by discussion and quiz sections. In the secondary school, the teacher gives few full-period lectures, but he commonly talks to the class at some length in introducing or summarizing a unit of study or in presenting a demonstration or in outlining an experiment.

A lecture does not have to be any given length. Lincoln's Gettysburg Address was a talk of about three minutes. The teacher commonly gives three or four short "lectures" interspersed with discussion in a class period. These presentations need careful planning.

The quality of a lecture-type presentation is so important to its acceptance by the student and its contribution to learning that some thought may be given to the method of making it as useful as possible. There is an old saying that the lecturer should tell his audience what he is going to tell them; tell them; then tell them what he has told them. In other words, the lecturer should have an attention-getting beginning, with an introduction telling what he is going to try to do and how he expects to do it. The basic framework of the lecture should be simple, with a few main points. Visual materials should be drawn upon when they are useful. Quoting from experience, from research, or from some authority gives support for what is said. The summary should restate the essentials.

The teacher must be careful not to assume that the class knows something that it does not. On the other hand, he must not underestimate the knowledge of the class and bore it with detailed repetition.

A few suggestions or reminders may be offered regarding presentation. The good teacher has the kind of natural enthusiasm which goes with a friendly talk. He does not use oratory. Effective speech is for communication, not for exhibition. Great art in any field is marked by simplicity, sincerity, directness, spontaniety, and effortlessness. The teacher's appearance before the class is important. Impressions are derived from the manner in which he stands and walks, his muscular tensions, his eye movements, his gestures, his voice, and his inflections.

From your study of public speaking, you learned many things about

---

[3]The above statement is reproduced, by permission, from *Planning for Health Education in Schools,* a work prepared for UNESCO and the World Health Organization by C. E. Turner. Copies are available in the U.S.A. through the UNESCO Publications Center, 317 East 34th Street, New York, N. Y.

the mechanics of public address. Here are some things to remember in talking to students:

1. *Being properly dressed* for the occasion will help you feel at ease.
2. *Speaking directly to the class* gives a much stronger presentation than reading.
3. *Stand straight, stand at ease, and (for the most part) stand still.* If you feel awkward standing still, it is because you are not used to it. Practice talking while standing still with your arms comfortably at your side until the position becomes natural and no longer disturbing. The speaker who is standing still seems perfectly natural to the audience. It is constant motion which they notice.
4. *Concentrate on what you are saying.*
5. *Look your audience in the eye.* Look at one person and then another. It is the mark of direct communication.
6. *Speak so you can be heard easily,* but do not let your volume go higher than that.
7. *Purity of tone* gives the voice a pleasing quality and aids its carrying power.
8. *Pitch is important.* See that you do not speak at too high a pitch. Drop your voice.
9. *Flexibility makes for a pleasing voice.* One can increase the range of tone by practice. Speaking continually on the same pitch is highly monotonous. Practice particularly to develop the lower tones in your voice.
10. *Distinct enunciation is essential* if one is to be clearly understood. Many persons suffer from lip laziness or tongue laziness. They do not pronounce their consonants distinctly and neatly.

Small group discussions. Variety can be added to class discussions by the use of different organizational procedures such as are used by adults in community meetings. In *"buzz" groups,* small clusters of six or eight students are given a topic or questions upon which to report, following 10 or 15 minutes of discussion within each group. A *panel* of three to six students, presenting different points of view, sits at a table and discusses a proposal under the direction of a leader. Following the discussion, the rest of the class participates in both questioning and discussion. Sometimes, a formal *debate* is organized regarding the desirability of some health proposal. In a *"meet the press"* procedure, a student is asked questions upon a specific topic or situation by selected "reporters."

Surveys. There is an unlimited number of possible special projects of interest to secondary school students, including surveys and special investigations in the community and in the library. These activities are time-consuming, but some of them may be made by small committees or working groups. Other special investigations may be assigned to individuals who have time and ability to undertake them.

Surveys may be made of student interests in health, of accident hazards, of sanitary conditions, of dental health, of voluntary health agencies in the community, of clinic and hospital facilities, of morbidity and mortality rates. Investigations which can be carried out in the library include a study of state laws and regulations regarding safety in hunting or boating, problems of world population growth, and activities of international health agencies.

Field trips. While certain principles and values are to be found in field trips at all grade levels (see page 311), the secondary school has its own problems and limitations in the use of this educational tool. Classes are large, and it may be better for a small group or an individual with special interests to make the trip and report to the class.

High school students are sufficiently mature to seek somewhat detailed information. Careful advance planning is needed with the students and with the host establishment to make sure that the trip is not merely an excursion or an outing. At its best, the field trip allows the community to serve as a laboratory in which the student clarifies his concepts, gains skill in observation, and learns how to report observations clearly and accurately. Profitable visitations are made to health departments, public health laboratories, hospitals and clinics, food processing plants, museums, traffic courts, and many other places. However, the number of visits for any one group or individual must be limited because they are time-consuming.

Speakers from outside the school. Stimulating enrichment in the study of some health topics can be brought to high school students by members of the health professions and representatives of health-related occupations, speaking at a school assembly or to students enrolled in health classes. The contribution of such speakers is integrated into the program of study and is not substituted for units of work on important themes. The speaker should be advised as to the age group, what will be expected of him, and the exact time and place of meeting. He should be asked whether he is willing to answer questions and to talk with individual students. Merely asking an important person to give a talk to students is likely to result in disappointing learning experiences.

From the health department, the health officer himself may be available to present public health programs or special health problems of the community. The public health educator may discuss health education campaigns with the adult population. The sanitary engineer or director of sanitation and the director of public health nursing may help with health problems in their respective fields. The county medical society and county dental society are usually ready to provide speakers on special medical and dental topics, such as mental health, alcoholism, the dangers of drugs, narcotics and self-medication, dental caries, and the fluoridation of water supplies. An industrial physician may discuss health in industry. A nutritionist may discuss weight control, special diets, and the relation of nutrition to general health. The police chief may discuss safety ordinances; a beautician may discuss beauty practices; a milk inspector may discuss the sanitary control of the milk supply. In larger communities, voluntary health agencies can supply experts in their special interests, such as tuberculosis, diabetes, arthritis, epilepsy, safety, first aid, and home nursing.

A note of thanks and appreciation is always sent to the speaker.

Setting codes and standards. In the legislative activity of cities, states, and nations, regulations, standards, codes, and laws are set according to the same basic procedures. A committee brings a proposed ordinance, code, or law to the legislative body, which discusses the proposal and

(H. Armstrong Roberts)

Fig. 58. A student committee prepares a proposed health code.

takes action upon it. In the health class, a small group may be assigned the task of drafting a proposal and presenting it to the class as a whole for class discussion. This procedure might be used, for example, in the development of standards for safety and courtesy in driving an automobile, hygienic standards for athletic training, daily dietary requirements, the responsibility of the citizen for public health, training requirements for babysitters, standards for sanitary housing, safety practices in bathing and swimming, requirements of an ideal recreation, desirable procedures in consumer hygiene, the control of quackery, and the criteria of emotional maturity.

Demonstrations and experiments. Somewhat advanced demonstrations and experiments form a useful part of health instruction in the secondary school.

Demonstrations need careful planning and effective execution if maximum educational results are to be achieved. It is usually desirable for the teacher to rehearse the presentation in advance. This enables him to make sure that all necessary equipment is at hand and to discover any particularly difficult element in the processes to be demonstrated. It also gives him a check on the timing. The teacher makes sure that everyone can see the different steps of the demonstration as he explains them. He is careful to give the demonstration at its proper place in the unit of instruction and to develop such supplementary study and discussion as is needed.

The following are examples of some of the demonstrations carried out by the teacher:

Coagulation of protein by heat.
Digestion of starch by saliva.
Mechanics of breathing with a bell jar, rubber balloons, and a rubber sheeting bottom for the jar.

Demonstrations of fats, starch, protein, mineral salts, and water in foods.
Tests for sugar in urine.
Tests for color blindness and peripheral vision.
Measurement of lung capacity with a spirometer.
Tests for blood pressure.

Experiments which can be performed by students include a study of the following:

Changes in heart rate due to exercise.
Multiplication of insects, using the fruitfly.
Effects of insecticides.
Growth of bread mold and prevention of its growth through refrigeration.
Growth of bacteria using sterile culture media from the health department.
Animal-feeding experiments.
Plant-feeding experiments.
Relation of oxygen to burning by depriving a lighted candle of oxygen or by rolling it in a blanket.
Increased need of oxygen during exercise as shown by increased breathing rate.
Incubation of hen's eggs to show embryological development and hatching of chicks.
Studies of inheritance by crossing different strains of fruitflies or plants, or crossbreeding rats or hamsters.
Measurement of lighting in the school building with a light meter.

Health counseling. In the secondary school, the students need expert health counseling in physical and mental health and in social adjustment. In the early years of junior high school, students are going through the physical changes of pubescence. They are adjusting to a new type of school schedule. Parental and social relationships may become strained. In the senior high school, there are problems of future careers, athletic achievement, and mating, as well as departures from normal health.

Physical examination of the high school student is the place for wise health counseling by the physician. In it, the previous health records of the student are reviewed. The examination brings to light any important defects or signs of illness, and there is an opportunity to discuss the health of the individual. In many schools, there is also a plan for systematic counseling which is carried out by the health teacher, the teacher of physical education for girls, the director of physical education for boys, the school nurse, or some other person.

Basic to such counseling is the *interview,* the preparation and conduct of which deserves special consideration. In preparing for the interview, it is important to know as much as possible about the student in terms of his health record, his academic record, and his special interests. This information can be supplemented during the interview itself.

With a good background of information, the interviewer will give thought in advance as to just what he may expect to accomplish during the interview. He makes sure that his own attitudes toward the student are friendly and unprejudiced and that he is ready to help him make an objective approach to problems rather than to prescribe a preconceived program of what he, the teacher, thinks should be done. A fixed appointment is set for the interview to be conducted in surroundings which provide privacy so that the student feels free to talk without being overheard by others.

In the conduct of the interview, the first step is the establishment of rapport. One must gain and deserve the confidence of the interviewee. Pleasant associations are established, and direct questions are not asked until the interviewee feels at ease and ready to talk. A discussion of common interests unrelated to the interview may help to establish the desired relationship.

The second step is to listen—to let the interviewee tell his story. The teacher keeps the interview on the subject, but he allows it to develop easily and naturally. The teacher is straightforward and frank rather than shrewd or clever. He takes pains to phrase his questions so that they are easily understood. He avoids implying the answer to his questions. He helps the interviewee to realize his responsibility for facts. He gives the interviewee an opportunity to qualify his answers. He checks the answers where possible and is careful to get the full meaning of each statement. In listening, the teacher often learns much from the emotional tone of the replies and the mannerisms and facial expressions of the student. Enough time is allowed, but the interviewer should not dawdle. From the interview, he separates the problems with which he can deal from those which should be referred to others.

When a situation or problem has been stated and clarified, the next step is the decision as to what action will be taken. In some cases, the next step may be clear, as, for example, the need for medical attention. Most problem situations are not to be solved by specific directions from the teacher as to what should be done. More constructive is the indirect approach, in which the teacher, with sympathetic recognition of the situation, thinks through the best future steps with the student. He recognizes the problem. Perhaps he asks the student what is his own idea of the best procedure. The discussion may be summarized by reviewing the facts which have now become clear. The summary may help to suggest future steps.

The interview explores the essential facts, discovers the needs, focuses the greater knowledge and experience of the interviewer upon the situation, and aids the self-guidance of the student. The teacher turns to the health team as necessary for their respective contributions and is careful not to invade their respective fields of professional competence. Counseling is a combination of person-to-person health instruction and joint planning for the solution of specific health problems.

Role playing. Role playing provides a device for exploring the responsibilities and feelings of individuals in professional and social relationships. It is the unrehearsed acting out of a situation in which different members of the class are assigned essential roles. Each one tries to put himself into the frame of mind of the person he is representing. He tries to think what that person would say in that situation. The students are cautioned against attempting to entertain rather than give a realistic representation of the character. Each other member of the class is asked to select one of the roles and identify himself with it. He tries to think what that person might say or do.

Role playing may be used, for example, to reflect the planning of a program of immunization by the health officer, the president of the county medical society, the school physician, the school nurse, a school principal, and a parent. Other possible situations might be planning a school lunch program, or planning a community campaign in health education on some specific project, or a discussion presenting opinions for and against the fluoridation of the water supply—in each case with a cast of characters made up of the persons most naturally concerned with the problem.

References

Alberty, H. B., and Alberty, E. J.: *Reorganizing the High School Curriculum,* ed. 3, New York, 1962, The Macmillan Company.

Anderson, C. L., and Langton, C. V.: *Health Principles and Practice,* ed. 4, St. Louis, 1964, The C. V. Mosby Company.

Hansen, K. H.: *High School Teaching,* Englewood Cliffs, N. J., 1957, Prentice-Hall, Inc.

Harnett, A. L., and Shaw, J. N.: *Effective School Health Education,* New York, 1959, Appleton-Century-Crofts, Inc.

Irwin, L. W., and Mayshark, C.: *Health Education in Secondary Schools,* St. Louis, 1964, The C. V. Mosby Company.

Jewett, A. E., and Knapp, C.: *The Growing Years; Adolescence,* Washington, D. C., 1962, American Association for Health, Physical Education and Recreation.

Kilander, H. F.: *School Health Education,* New York, 1962, The Macmillan Company.

National Education Association and American Medical Association Joint Committee: *Health Education,* ed. 5, Washington, D. C., 1961, National Education Association.

National Education Association: *Schools for the Sixties,* a report of the Project on Instruction, New York, 1963, McGraw-Hill Book Company.

National Health Council: *Health Careers Guidebook,* New York, 1955, National Health Council.

Nemir, A.: *The School Health Program,* ed. 2, Philadelphia, 1965, W. B. Saunders Company.

Schneider, R. E.: *Methods and Materials of Health Education,* ed. 2, Philadelphia, 1964, W. B. Saunders Company.

Todd, F.: *Teaching About Alcohol,* New York, 1964, McGraw-Hill Book Company.

Turner, C. E.: *Planning for Health Education in Schools,* 1966, UNESCO and WHO. Available through UNESCO Publications Center, 317 East 34th Street, New York, N. Y.

Part six

Improving school, home, and community relationships

Chapter XVIII

School, home, and community relations in health and health education

The child's learning experiences in health while he is at home and during his extra-school hours in the community are a part of his total health education. They support, extend, or negate what he has learned at school.

The home controls the child's nutrition, clothing, rest, and many other hygienic factors. It secures or permits immunization and such medical or surgical care as may be needed for the correction of defects. Obviously the school health program needs to be interpreted to the home. New developments in the school health program and new discoveries in the field of health which are being taught at school need, especially, to be presented and interpreted to parents.

The school is part of the community. Teachers are citizens. Children are future citizens. The school clearly recognizes the importance of the home, the department of public health, and the voluntary health agencies in promoting hygienic living.

In many communities the health department provides nursing and medical services, communicable disease control, and sanitary supervision in the schools. It usually provides clinical and hospital facilities for the correction of physical defects under certain conditions. In communities where many of these activities are administered by the school department, the city health department comes into the schools for tuberculin testing, diphtheria immunization, vaccination, or other specific procedures.

All of these activities provide vital health experiences for school children, and it is important that they should be conducted in such a way that their educational possibilities are developed. From the standpoint of the health department, school cooperation in health education is important in raising the general standard of hygienic living, in developing an appreciation of public health services, and in developing community support for special immunization programs and health control measures. Communities have found, for example, that the promotion of a tuberculin case-finding program through the health education channels of the higher elementary grades and secondary schools has greatly contributed to the development of favorable public acceptance and wide public participation.

345

Private health agencies and voluntary health associations in the community furnish source material and conduct community-wide educational programs which supplement the child's health experiences at school. These community activities stimulate the pupil's interest and his desire to participate in the solution of health problems.

The official and voluntary health agencies are actually solving the health problems of the community. No phase of health education can be more interesting to the child than some participation in this process. The integration of the pupil's health interest and learning experiences inside the school with those outside the school is also good educational practice.

There are many reasons why the school staff should know both the public health activities and the health education activities in the community. They influence the pupil through the home. Some of them influence the pupil directly through his contracts with clinic service and other forms of medical care. The schools may wish to secure speakers, visual material, and printed matter from these outside agencies. As an educator the teacher will naturally be interested in public health education as a phase of adult education. When school children and parents are both interested in solving the same health problem, health education is almost sure to be satisfying and effective.

For these reasons, the home and the school have come closer together in the health education of the child, and, to an increasing degree, schools have joined in community-wide efforts to improve various aspects of the public health. The school health program has become a more integral part of the community health program. Closer coordination between school health education and public health education is under way.

Let us look more closely at the possibilities and procedures in the schools' relationships with the home and the community.

School and home cooperation

There are several activities through which school and home understanding and cooperation develop.

The visit of the teacher to the home. Parents, as well as the schools, participate in planning the child's day. It is very important that each understand the other and the requirements which the child must meet in the school and outside it. Many school systems advise and some school systems require teachers to visit the homes of their pupils early in the school year. Such a visit (1) establishes a friendship with parents which makes the year's work easier and more pleasant, and (2) helps the teacher to understand the child. In the home visit such factors as the nature of the neighborhood and the type of parents—their racial stock, economic and social status, occupation, health, and emotional stability—are observed. As the teacher sees the child's family group and learns more of his activities and behavior while at home, he is helped to understand the personality traits which are displayed at school. Joint planning may take place to give the child a program of adequate and leisurely meals, out-of-door

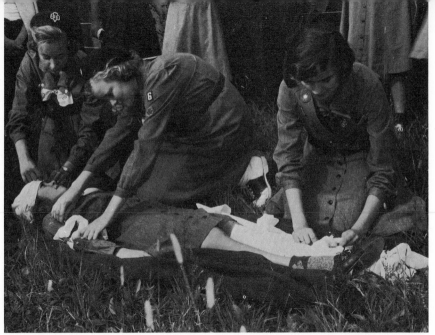

Fig. 59. Skills are learned in scouting and other voluntary organizations outside of school.

activities, sleep, and rest. The child's activities are balanced against his energy and capacity. Extra demands upon his energy, such as music lessons, are taken into consideration. Study hours are planned to be free from interruptions. Time is provided for the high school girl for personal grooming. Children are given time for family relationships, the pursuit of their own hobbies, and participation in community activities.

Teacher and parents may discuss the avoidance of excessive emotional stimulation of the child by radio, television, and motion pictures, by excessively harsh discipline, and by extra-curricular activities. The abilities, limitations, capacities, and special interests of the child become better understood. The pupil is given opportunities in fields where he has special ability and is not forced into undertakings and situations with which he is unable to cope.

Home visits by the school nurse. The school nurse provides a most important health contact between the school and the home. She understands the classroom program and often explains it to parents. Confidential information concerning economic and social problems in the home is often given to the nurse. She helps the parent with health problems. She brings back to the teacher a knowledge of health conditions in the home, which makes it possible for the teacher to deal more easily and effectively with individual children.

Parents visit the school. Parents are invited to attend health conferences at school; pupil demonstrations of the classroom program of health work are arranged; and special health talks to parents are occasionally provided. Parents have conferences with the teacher, often with the nurse and/or the physician present. When one or both parents attend the health examination of their child, they learn the health problems and needs of the child, and they increase their understanding and appreciation of the school health services.

Communications to the home. Many kinds of communication are sent from the individual school or the school system to parents to inform them in matters of health and to seek their cooperation. Letters from the head of the school or the department of education are sometimes sent to parents, describing health policies and activities. Bulletins are used, for example, to describe the school policy regarding health examinations, the parents' part in preparing the child for school entrance, or the results of the dental examination of school children with suggestions for dental hygiene and needed dental attention.

Questionnaires have been used with parents to secure community opinion regarding health activities or parents' judgments concerning the status or improvement of health practices of children. Some years ago, in carrying out school health studies, the author wished to find out what results of an experimental school health program had been observed by parents. A questionnaire was sent to each home. A copy of the questionnaire follows, with the "yes" and "no" answers from the 233 questionnaires returned.[1]

Is your child:

Going to bed earlier? Yes, 129. No, 104.
Spending more time out of doors? Yes, 198, No, 35.
Keeping himself more clean? Yes, 196. No, 37.
Brushing teeth more regularly? Yes, 146. No, 87.
Drinking more milk? Yes, 169. No, 64.
Eating more vegetables? Yes, 176. No, 57.
Eating more fruit? Yes, 194. No, 39.
Eating less candy between meals? Yes, 156. No, 77.
Eating foods which he had refused before? Yes, 141. No, 92.
Standing and sitting in better posture? Yes, 149. No, 84.
Has your child improved in health appearance as shown by bright eyes, clear skin, good color? Yes, 177. No, 56.
Do you think there has been a real improvement in health? Yes, 186. No, 47.
Have you noticed improvement in any of the following ways as result of better health:
　More cheerful and good natured in disposition? Yes, 151. No, 82.
　More completely rested in the morning and willing to get up promptly?
　　Yes, 150. No, 83.
　Better appetite? Yes, 171. No, 62.

Parents' meetings. Many types of public meetings are useful in presenting programs or activities in school health and health education. The meeting may be:

A *film showing.*
A *lecture* in health or health education.
A *forum* in which a lecture is followed by a general discussion from the floor.

---

[1]From Turner, C. E.: "Malden Studies in Health Education and Growth," *American Journal of Public Health* 18:1217–1230, 1928.

A *symposium* where several speakers present their views briefly, after which there is a round table discussion with questions from the audience.

A *panel* where three to six persons, presenting different points of view, sit at a table and discuss a subject informally under the direction of a leader, usually allowing the audience to raise questions and join in the discussion.

Role playing or dramatization involving a health problem. There is a preliminary description of an incident, and the members of the group volunteer to act it out as a real-life situation. Role playing is particularly useful in allowing parents and teachers to explore and understand the feelings and relationships involved. The dramatization is usually summarized by a leader.

The parent-teacher association, school health council, or health committee. An association of parents and teachers in some form of association, council, or committee is of great value in the promotion of pupil health. It has a wide range of activities. Such meetings as we have just discussed may be organized by the school health council instead of being organized by the school itself. Members of parent groups have assisted with such practical matters as improving the playgrounds, providing some needed facility, source material, or equipment in the field of school health, or improving school sanitation or lunchroom facilities.

One activity frequently undertaken by such groups is aiding in securing the examination of pupils who are to enter school within a few months. Mothers visit the homes, acquaint parents with the plans, and assist in various ways at the examination clinics. Such parent cooperation increases the number of children who secure their health examinations and the number of children who receive correction for the defects found.

One parent-teacher association carried out a project for the establishment of neighborhood policies regarding health and safety practices. Parents noted that many children felt that their parents were unfair because they were not allowed to do what other children in the neighborhood were doing. The parents agreed upon what the policies should be with respect to attendance at movies, listening to radio, watching television, bedtime hours, and various home responsibilities. A code was developed regarding the use of the family automobile by teenagers.

Various study groups have been organized by parents, dealing with such topics as growth and development, nutrition, and mental health. Sometimes the group studies under the leadership of a professional person. Sometimes the study is based upon the reading of a book selected by the group.

Health education outside of schools

Programs of health education directed to the community at large, but primarily to adults, are developed by official or governmental agencies and also by nongovernmental or voluntary health organizations. The citizen meets public health education in many forms and in many places. He finds it in:

1. *Contact with the medical and paramedical professions.* Practicing physicians and private-duty nurses contribute extensively to the health education of the people they serve. Members of the public health profes-

sion and workers in closely allied fields are constantly educating people in health. This group of persons includes the health officer, directors of various public health activities, public health nurses, sanitarians, nutritionists, medical social workers, and farm bureau extension workers. In fact the contact of the public health nurses with the home represents one of the most important and extensive health education activities outside the public schools.

The information from these workers goes to persons seeking advice. It is authoritative, personal, applicable, and direct. It is expensive but it is most effective, since it instructs people in the correct manner of living at a time when they are most amenable to advice. Usually the citizen contacts these professional workers as an individual, but in other instances the contact is at a public meeting.

2. *The health activities of clubs, associations, and labor, social, or religious groups.* Many service clubs, women's clubs, societies, lodges, and churches have health committees and a health program. In these groups the citizen learns more about health problems and helps to solve them.

3. *Programs of adult education.* Courses in nutrition, child care, mental hygiene, social hygiene, and other subjects reach large numbers of the most alert citizens.

4. *Newspapers, periodicals, and books.* Health is constantly in the news. Health officials have regular press conferences. Some papers occasionally print a special health edition or health section in which attention is given to the many health activities current in the community. Most newspapers carry a syndicated health column. New scientific discoveries are reported in the press and in popular magazines.

The deeds and lives of the great men and women in the health field find their way to the printed page. Libraries and other agencies in the community often call attention to new and desirable publications in this field.

5. *The printed and visual material of official and voluntary health agencies.* There is a wide variety of reports, pamphlets, booklets, posters, models, exhibits, films, and other types of visual media. Some of this material is very timely. Letters are sent by the health department to expectant mothers. Infant welfare booklets are sent to the homes following birth registrations. Information is distributed concerning the control of communicable disease at the time the house is placarded. Press releases warn the public in times of threatened epidemic.

6. *Radio and television programs.* The malicious effect of undesirable health propaganda through the commercial radio and television is serious. Food fads are propagated, unreasonable claims for patent medicines are advanced, self-treatment is urged where medical attention should be secured, and a confusion of fact, near-fact, and error is carried into the home. On the other hand, we receive some helpful health instruction by radio and television from health authorities.

7. *Campaigns.* All of these instruments for public health education are

Fig. 60. Camping is both a school and a community activity.

(H. Armstrong Roberts)

often used together in a campaign with respect to some particular disease or public health activity. Community leadership and community organizations and agencies unite in an effort to inform the people and arouse them to action. A school-initiated community campaign for the eradication of hookworm disease is described later in this chapter.

Public health educators. We have seen that all professional workers in the health-medical field contribute to public health education, whether in private practice or employed by health agencies. Health departments and voluntary health agencies also employ professional health educators.

The public health educator does not take the place of any of these other public health workers. His work does not conflict with the health education activities of public health nurses or any other professional group. In fact, he facilitates their work by developing appreciation and support for it, by helping to produce printed and other visual material, and by aiding in the development of educational techniques.

His work is mainly with groups, not individuals. His function, however, is not to address the groups himself on all the various phases of health or hygiene, either by word of mouth or by the printed page. His job is to seek the best authority available on the topic in question, help to develop from him the strongest possible message, and help that message to reach the largest number of people in the most effective way possible.

The health educator in the community, like the health educator in the school, is primarily an educator. With a background of culture, he studies chemistry, biology, anatomy, physiology, bacteriology, psychology, hygiene, sanitation, public health statistics, public health organization and procedures, behavioral science, community organization, and various techniques of health education in school and community.[2] He assists the health department or other employing agency in developing cooperative relationships with other groups in health and education for an organized community health education program.

He studies the need for and possibilities of health education in the area served. He takes part in many or all the phases of public health education mentioned. He has special skill in the organization and conduct of campaigns and in measuring their results. He cannot be an expert in journalism, radio techniques, exhibit techniques, the production of amateur health films, and all the other skills utilized in public health education; but he is sufficiently familiar with these tools to work effectively with the newspaper editor, the printer, the radio or television program director, and other specialists. He is especially skilled in working with councils, committees, conferences, and similar groups.

Community organization for health education

The trend toward community organization for health education and close coordination of school health education and public health education has been both desirable and inevitable. It is almost as valuable and important for the director of public health education and the director of school health education to work closely together as for the school superintendent and the health officer to do so. If there is not a public health educator and a school health educator, then the health and education authorities most directly concerned have the responsibility for relating the two programs. If there is not a director of health education in the schools and if the public health educator has a school background, he can serve teachers as a valuable resource person.

An example of cooperation between the schools and other forces in the community is seen in the following story of a campaign for the control of hookworm disease.

A school-community project. The activities next described took place in Greensboro, Florida, as part of the Florida School-Community Health Education project, sponsored jointly by the Florida State Department of Education and the Florida State Board of Health. The Greensboro High School, a large, consolidated high school with grades one through twelve, was selected as one which would be interested in seeing what could be done through a school-community health education program. It had a progressive principal and stable faculty concerned about the community in which they lived.

The first step was a visit during the summer by the Health Educator

---

[2]*Report of the Committee on the Educational Qualifications and Functions of Public Health Educators,* 1957, American Public Health Association, 1790 Broadway, New York.

from the state level to get acquainted and to discuss with the principal the possibilities and interests of the school. During this first visit, the Health Educator also met the County School Superintendent, the General Supervisor of Education, and the County Health Officer. At this time, the principal arranged a later meeting for the Health Educator with the entire faculty of the school to discuss what was involved in a school-community health education project and why this approach to health problems might prove of special value.

The faculty decided that four committees would be appointed, namely, a Fact-Finding Committee, a Committee on School Health Services, a Committee on Sanitation, and one on the Instructional Program in the School. These committees were (1) to survey the present status of the health program in Greensboro schools and (2) to determine the health problems. The Fact-Finding Committee studied the reports of the local and state departments of health. The members also conferred with the personnel in the County Health Department and with a physician who had been in general practice in the community for some time. The Committee on Health Services studied the school health records. The Committee on Sanitation investigated environmental conditions within and about the school. The Committee on Instruction reviewed the over-all program of instruction in relation to health within the school.

These committees reported at a subsequent meeting of the staff, and a list of problems which might well receive attention was put on the chalkboard. Criteria to help decide which problems should be selected were established. The first criterion was urgency, pointing to selection of the problem which represented the greatest health need. The second criterion was that the problem be one about which some definite action could be taken. The third was that the problem should be sufficiently simple and clear-cut to give a good chance of solution within the available resources and within the time allotted for the project, which was a two-year period. It was unanimously agreed, following a discussion, that the problem to be undertaken should be hookworm control.

Some members of the staff felt disturbed at the selection of this problem because they said children in this school had been examined and given hookworm medicine for several years, and it still remained a major problem. This provoked a discussion of reasons why hookworm disease had not been controlled and what further steps would be necessary to reduce its incidence. Clearly, hookworm was indeed a school-community problem, and it seemed certain the school would have to work with parents and with the whole community if the problem were to be solved.

The teachers pointed out that they were busy all day with a heavy teaching load, and the question was raised as to how community participation could be developed. It was suggested that perhaps there were other people in the community who could help with this phase of the program. The faculty decided to call in the County School Superintendent, the General Supervisor of Education, the Supervisor of Public Health Nursing, the County Health Officer, the Sanitarian, the President of the P.T.A. and the Chairman of the P.T.A. Health Committee, the County Home Demonstration Agent, and the County Farm Agent to discuss this problem with them. It was also recognized that the State Department of Health had an experienced expert in hookworm control, and it was decided to ask him to meet with the group. The Health Educator from the state level continued to meet with the group also. This enlarged group really functioned as a School-Community Health Council, but it did not bear that name. It was called a Planning Committee and functioned quite informally.

At the first meeting of this new and enlarged group, the principal presided. He explained what the faculty had done previously and pointed out that hookworm seemed to be a major problem of the children in this school. He briefly reviewed current knowledge of this disease and the facilities for fighting it. It was agreed that the following four major steps were involved: (1) the discovery of persons who had hookworm disease, (2) securing treatment for them, (3) the sanitation of the environment, and (4) the education of the community for the prevention of hookworm in the future. The hookworm specialist spoke, reviewing his experience in other communities in fighting this disease. After his statement, the question "What do you think we can do in this community?" was proposed. The meeting was then thrown open for general discussion.

The question was soon asked, "Who will do what?" The different members of the group indicated the steps which they could take in carrying out the project. The Director of Public Health Nursing said that she could secure bottles for the taking of specimens and arrange for the examination of specimens in the State Public Health Laboratory. The nurse assigned to this particular school said that she would secure treatment for children found to have hookworm, by taking medicine to the individual homes and discussing needs and procedures with the parents. The Sanitarian agreed to make a sanitary survey of the community and find out which homes did not have satisfactory sanitation facilities. The Home Demonstration Agent said that she had health committees and could arrange for these committees to take on hookworm control as their major project, and the Farm Agent agreed to discuss this problem with the groups with whom he had contact.

The teachers in the various grades from one to twelve said that they would help the children understand the giving of specimens, and, within the maturity level of the class, they would discuss the procedures for hookworm control. The biology teacher said that he would teach the life cycle of the hookworm. The social studies teacher said that she would discuss hookworm from the socioeconomic viewpoint, particularly the economic loss to the community in production. The nutrition teacher said she would discuss the nutritional problems involved. The health teacher, teaching the course in "Effective Living," agreed to consider hookworm as a health problem. The General Supervisor felt that he was in a position to work with all teachers in the development of the best possible health education program in relation to hookworm. The Superintendent was interested in this factual approach to an educational and health problem. The President of the P.T.A. and the Health Chairman agreed that they would like to have the hookworm expert discuss this problem at the next P.T.A. meeting.

The faculty at a later meeting discussed how it would be possible to contact those families that were not ordinarily reached by educational and public health services. It was decided to have a minstrel show, because the people liked minstrels; and it was felt that all of the children could take part. The County Superintendent agreed to assist in getting the people to the show by allowing the school busses to bring those persons who did not have their own transportation.

Everybody came and the minstrel was a huge success. At the beginning of the show, the school principal explained that the minstrel would be followed by an educational part of the program. At that time, the hookworm expert talked to the audience about the nature of the disease, its spread, and its control. He had a blackboard, visual materials, and a specimen of human intestine showing hookworms attached.

The next day, specimen bottles were given out to the children, and there was a 100 per cent return of the specimens. The specimens were sent to the state laboratory, and the reports showed that approximately 56 per cent were positive.

The principal sent a card to the fathers of the children with positive specimens, explaining the situation and inviting them to come to a special meeting. At this meeting, the County Sanitarian showed a film on hookworm and a film on how to build sanitary privies. He discussed the economic aspects of the problem and explained how the families could get help in constructing such a unit. He subsequently visited the individual families to ascertain what types of sanitation facilities were available and to discuss plans for improving conditions, if necessary.

At a later time, the planning committee came together to evaluate progress to date and to plan future steps. Incidentally, this was not the only health education activity. While this project was under way, other things were also taking place. The nutrition program was expanding. The P.T.A. equipped a small room for emergency care of sick children. Vision and hearing were tested. Hand-washing facilities were established in individual classrooms through the provision of funds by the County Board of Education. The faculty evaluated the program at the end of the first year and planned a further extension of its health education program the next year. During the summer the school building was painted inside and out. This development was made easier because the success of the hookworm project had attracted state-wide attention to the school. The whole community was enthusiastic about the success of the project and the part they had played in it. The children were retested for hookworm in the fall, and it was discovered that the incidence of the disease had decreased 53.4 per cent. Twelve families had installed flush toilets and eight had installed sanitary privies.

Five significant elements in the project may be mentioned: (1) The school-community group grew out of a felt need on the part of the school, and achieved highly satisfactory results. (2) The people themselves, with suitable consultant help, worked out the solution to their problem. (3) The people who carried leadership were involved in planning from the beginning. (4) The leaders evaluated progress from time to time, replanned, and, at the end of the project, made a final evaluation. (5) The leadership from the state level was a submerged leadership. It was the people's project, planned and carried out by them.

This splendid project of community health education was initiated by the schools. But could you imagine wide-awake schools remaining aloof from the program even if some other agency had initiated it? The pupils in those schools will be ready to tackle other health problems when they are adults, because they have found that community efforts will bring results. They have seen the democratic process successfully at work. Had their health education been limited to the memorizing of facts and to classroom discussion, their adult reaction would probably be "Oh, well, you can't do anything about hookworm and the other health problems. They always had hookworm where I grew up, and nobody ever did anything about it."

There are various plans for coordinating health education activities in the community. In some communities the two governmental agencies jointly employ a *health education coordinator* whose training allows him to meet the professional requirements for a health education supervisor in the school and a health educator in the health department.

School departments, health departments, and private health agencies all recognize that health education can be made more effective by coordination. The teacher who understands the public health education program as it exists in his community has added to his sources of professional assistance and to his sources of material. The use of some organized plan for coordinating health education activities in each community is desirable.

School participation in community health planning

Schools commonly and desirably participate in the activities of community health councils. Some councils have a membership from governmental agencies only. More commonly, the health council includes both official and voluntary health agencies. In some cities, a health division of the Council of Social Agencies or of the Welfare Council provides for joint planning and cooperation in public health and school health. Such councils are concerned with the improvement of sanitation, the prevention and control of communicable disease, and the maintenance and improvement of school and community health services as well as with health education.

The best health promotion and the best opportunities for health education occur where there is effective coordination between school and community health programs.

Principles of community organization. The following statement of observations, values, and principles concerning community planning is based upon a study of various programs of community organization for health education.

1. Modern health education is concerned primarily with learning on the part of the individual rather than with teaching by the health educator.
   Individuals are being helped to discover, analyze and provide solutions for the problems of health that face them. These are problems of the individual, the class, or the neighborhood. In true learning situations the pupil or citizen discovers his own needs, capabilities and limitations. He further learns how to draw upon his own resources and those of his community.
2. Community organization for health education teaches principles of democracy, and gives experience in the practical working of democracy. Democracy, itself, is thus strengthened.
3. Various types of community organization for health education have originated locally and spontaneously in many parts of the country.
4. Community organization for health education is also being encouraged by state programs for health education.
5. A community program of health education substitutes sound professional study and an educational approach to local needs for less desirable, separate, discrete and sometimes overlapping health education programs based upon individual and special interests.
6. There is no single best plan for community organization. Local factors and available personnel will determine the type of organization.
7. In successful joint programs, persons and organizations subordinate their individual desires and interests to the purpose of the joint project.
8. When the joint committee type of action is successfully used, those agreeing to the plans made must make no mental reservations about their agreement.
9. If the plan for cooperation is well made, it sets up good administrative procedures and sound supervision. It defines the functions of agencies and of staff members. This facilitates joint relationships. If the mechanism of cooperation does not do these things, friction ensues which may disrupt the harmony of the program.
10. While the mechanism of cooperation is important, the people who operate it are even more so. A good mechanical plan can succeed only when the people who operate it are broad enough to see its values, are compatible personally, and are not antagonistic professionally.
11. In all the programs studied, it seems to have been the policy to make the teacher responsible for the health of the child while at school. She is recognized as the individual through whom the health education of the child is primarily secured.
12. Plans of community organization for health education often move in the direction of using the services of an individual as a health education coordinator.
13. Continued, patient and persistent effort is needed to develop community cooperation in a democratic society. Cooperation must not be expected to operate with the speed of dictatorship.

Physical education and community recreation. The school recreation program should be regarded as part of the total community recreational activity program. The various recreational agencies in the community offer opportunities for the continuation and extension of the activities to which the child has been introduced in the school. Both the school and the outside agency contribute to his total development and the same standards for the conduct of activities should prevail in both. Joint planning and sharing of leadership and facilities is the ideal for which a community should strive. Many communities have made great strides toward this goal, but in others little has been accomplished.

Obviously, interest in the community aspect of recreation should be encouraged on the part of boys and girls. Bringing the leaders of the community agencies into the school is one way of bringing about an effective tie-up in the mind of the child. The school should publicize community opportunities for summer and after-school hours. On the other hand, the community should seek to provide facilities which will make possible the continuance, during leisure hours and after graduation, of the various skills offered by the schools. Supervised swimming, little leagues, and ski clubs are a few of the opportunities offered.

Secondary school students are encouraged to give play-leadership to younger groups. They will enjoy participating in community surveys and studies for improving recreational situations. Such activities help them to develop permanent interests and desirable attitudes toward community recreation. They will understand its value not only as a means of continuing healthful, enjoyable activities but also as a phase of constructive citizenship.

Care should be taken that athletic boys or girls do not get an unbalanced program by playing a single sport, like basketball, on a high school team and a community team at the same time.

Sharing community camping facilities will serve to give school camping greater impetus.

References

American Association of School Administrators: *Health in Schools,* rev. ed., Washington, D. C., 1951, American Association of School Administrators.

Byrd, O. E.: *School Health Administration,* Philadelphia, 1964, W. B. Saunders Company.

Grout, R. E.: *Health Teaching in Schools,* ed. 4, Philadelphia, 1963, W. B. Saunders Company.

Hanlon, J. J., and McHose, E.: *Design for Health,* Philadelphia, 1963, Lea and Febiger.

National Committee on School Health Policies of the National Conference for Cooperation in Health Education: *Suggested School Health Policies,* ed. 3, Washington, D. C., 1956, National Education Association.

National Council of Chief State School Officers and the Association of State and Territorial Health Officers: *Responsibilities of State Departments of Education and Health for School Health Services,* rev. ed., Washington, 1959, National Council of Chief State School Officers, 1201 Sixteenth St., Washington, D. C.

National Education Association and American Medical Association Joint Committee: *Health Education,* ed. 5, Washington, D. C., 1961, National Education Association.

Nemir, A.: *The School Health Program,* ed. 2, Philadelphia, 1965, W. B. Saunders Company.

New York State Interdepartmental Health Council: *Coordination of School and Community Health Services,* Albany, 1949, Office of Public Health Education, New York State Department of Public Health, 95 pp.

Turner, C. E.: *Planning for Health Education in Schools,* 1966, UNESCO and WHO.

Available through UNESCO Publications Center, 317 East 34th Street, New York, N. Y.

University of North Carolina: *Community Development Seminar*, Chapel Hill, N. C., 1963, Department of Public Health Education, School of Public Health, 110 pp.

World Health Organization: *Expert Committee on Health Education of The Public*, Technical Report Series, no. 89, Geneva, 1954, 41 pp. (Copies may be ordered from Columbia University Press, International Documents Service, 2960 Broadway, New York 27, New York.)

World Health Organization: *PAHO/WHO Inter-Regional Conference on the Post-Graduate Preparation of Health Workers for Health Education*, Technical Report Series, no. 278, Geneva, 1964, WHO.

World Health Organization: *Teacher Preparation for Health Education*. Report of a Joint WHO/UNESCO Expert Committee, Technical Report Series, no. 193, Geneva, 1960, WHO.

Part seven

Appraising the school health program

Chapter xix

Evaluation

T o evaluate is to appraise something on the basis of a definite set of values. We evaluate programs, and we measure progress or change. In the evaluation of programs as to scope, philosophy, and methods, we find out whether the activities and the way in which they are being carried out meet an approved standard. If we wish to measure the extent of a change in educational or health status due to some specific activity or program, we must carry out at least two evaluations. The first of these establishes a base line or picture of conditions which we shall need to improve. For example, if we are to measure an increase in knowledge, we must pretest for knowledge. If we are to measure an improvement in nutritional status, we must know the previous state of nutrition. Subsequent evaluations allow us to measure changes in those conditions.

If we are to present scientific evidence of change, we must have not only a soundly established base line but also statistically reliable data. You have learned in your study of tests and measurements that the reliability of such findings depends upon the size of the sample, the consistency or variability of the initial data, and the maintenance of conditions which make it clear that the changes were brought about by the forces or activities under investigation. Data presented in research findings are subjected to tests for statistical reliability.

Teachers and school health personnel are constantly engaged in the appraisal of conditions and programs. We shall discuss here the three types of evaluations most commonly carried out in the school health program. They are: (1) the evaluation of the school health program, (2) the evaluation of the educational status (knowledge, attitudes, skills, and behavior) of pupils or students in respect to health, and (3) the evaluation of health status.

Evaluation of the school health program

The classroom teacher is interested in evaluating the health program in his own classroom and in participating in the evaluation of the total health program. All of the professions involved in the respective activities should have a part in evaluating them. The nurse or educational psychologist may evaluate home visits. The physician may evaluate the way in which the health examination of the child is carried out. Only clinicians can evaluate clinical procedures, and only the physician can profit from such evaluation. If the Board of Health and the local medical society have a part in the health service program, they should have a part in its evaluation. Sometimes evaluation is carried out by a committee. Sometimes a consultant or a team of consultants is brought in from the outside in order to increase the effectiveness and objectivity of the evaluation. The activities are evaluated in terms of a standard or ideal program.

Limitations in the evaluation process are obvious. Many of the measurements we use are inexact. Different school systems have different problems and need different emphases. Even if schools were much more similar than they are, it would not be easy to agree upon a standard of perfect practices. Nevertheless, it is profitable for a school system to study what it is doing in the light of what could be done and to evaluate its procedures in terms of the best approved practice. A measurement of results is helpful to the school staff and to the community even though it is not precise or exact.

We may evaluate the entire school health program, or we may evaluate major phases of the program, such as:

1. The maintenance of a teaching staff which is well, competent, cooperative, professionally qualified, and concerned with the physical, mental, and social health of the child.

2. The provision of administrative and professional leadership to direct the various phases of the program.

3. The maintenance of sound and effective community relations in the field of health.

4. The maintenance of a safe and healthful environment.

5. The provision of a daily program at school, which is conducive to the health of the child.

6. The maintenance of school health services which will provide adequate examinations, records, follow-up, and communicable disease control.

7. The maintenance of a broad and cooperative program of health education which will provide sound, consistent learning experiences adapted to the needs and age levels of the pupils.

Over the years, many check lists have been developed for evaluating the school health program. A pioneer development was the Massachusetts Institute of Technology School Health Appraisal Form of 73 pages, which made its appearance in 1926. It was prepared as a "constructive and suggestive guide in the study of a school health system rather than as a precise scoring plan." It contained 243 evaluative items under the following headings:

Health protection

A. Sanitation	100 points
B. Physical examinations	125 points
C. Communicable disease control	125 points

Correction of defects

A.	Special classes	50 points
B.	Clinics	30 points
C.	Follow-up	70 points
D.	Results of follow-up	100 points

Health promotion

A.	Hygienic arrangement of program	75 points
B.	Physical activities	125 points
C.	Health training and instruction	200 points

Total score	1000 points

Appraisal forms. There follows a list of presently available and widely used appraisal forms.

American Journal of Public Health Yearbook: *Suggested Standards for Health Services in Secondary Schools*, **42:**5 May, 1952.

American Public Health Association: *Guide to a Community Health Survey* (includes sections on school health), Committee on Administrative Practice, APHA, 1790 Broadway, New York, N. Y., price $1.00.

California State Department of Education: *Elementary School Health Education Program Inventory*, Bureau of Health Education, Physical Education and Recreation, Sacramento, 1960; also, "Check List for a Healthful and Safe School Environment," 51 pp., 1957; "Criteria for Evaluating the Elementary School Health Program," 20 pp., 1962; "Criteria for Evaluating the High School Health Program," 24 pp., 1962.

Dearborn, Terry H.: *A Checklist for the Survey of Health and Physical Education Programs in Secondary Schools*, Stanford, California, 1951, Stanford University Press, 23 pp.

Grout, Ruth E.: *School Health Inventory*, In *Handbook of Health Education*, New York, 1936, Odyssey Press, Inc. Prepared primarily for rural schools.

Indiana University: *School Health Program Surveys*, Bloomington, Indiana, School of Health, Physical Education and Recreation.

LaPorte, William A.: *Health and Physical Education Scorecard No. 1 for Elementary Schools*, Parker and Company, 241 East 4th Street, Los Angeles 13, California.

Los Angeles City Schools, Division of Educational Services: *Evaluation of the Health Program in the Los Angeles City Schools, 1954–1961*, School Publication No. 673, 1962.

Michigan School Health Association: *Appraisal Form for Studying School Health Programs*, 1962.

National Commission on Safety Education: *Checklist of Safety and Safety Education in Your School*, Washington, D. C., 1953, National Education Association.

Oregon State College: *A School Health Program Evaluation Scale*, Corvallis, Oregon, 1955 (School Health Services 350 points, Health Instruction 400 points, Healthful School Living 250 points). Also included on pages 432-441 in *School Health Practices* by C. L. Anderson, The C. V. Mosby Company, St. Louis.

Paper Cup and Container Institute: *Survey of School Lunch Operation—Part I and II*, Public Health Committee, 250 Park Avenue, New York 17, N. Y.

Phelan, Annette M.: *A Study of School Health Standards*, Menasha, Wisconsin, 1934, George Banta Publishing Company.

Smith, Sara Louise: *Evaluation of School Health Program by Classroom Teachers*, rev. form, Tallahassee, Florida, 1959, Florida State University.

Superintendent of Public Instruction, Lansing, Michigan: *A Checklist for Surveying the Secondary School Health Program*, Bulletin No. 346, 1946, 16 pp., free.

Texas Education Agency: *A Checklist Appraising the School Health Program,* Bulletin 519, Austin, Texas, 1955, State Education Department.

University of the State of New York, The State Education Department, Division of Health and Physical Education: *Inspection and Supervision of the Health Aspects of the School Plant,* Sanitary Survey Form, revision, Albany, New York, 1948, 12 pp.

Weatherby, Harold R.: *A Check List for School Health Services,* Stanford, California, 1952, Stanford University Press.

Evaluation of health education activities

Teachers, administrators, and health specialists in the school are all concerned with the quality of health education and with means of evaluating it.

In the elementary school, some of the topics for consideration in determining the efficacy of health education in a classroom are:

I. *Personal qualifications of the teacher*

1. Health—as shown in appearance, energy, regularity of attendance
2. Mental outlook—as shown by poise and cheerfulness
3. Neatness of appearance
4. Posture
5. Appropriate dress—shoes, extra clothing for bad weather
6. Attitude toward health teaching
7. Amount and accuracy of health knowledge

II. *Health teaching*

1. Use of natural interests and incentives of children
2. Skill in teaching subject matter of health
3. Scientific accuracy in presenting health facts
4. Skill in interesting children to follow health habits
5. Skill in developing desired attitudes in pupils
6. Amount and kind of illustrative material and source material made available for pupils
7. New projects developed by teacher during current school year

III. *Related activities*

1. Regularity and accuracy in weighing and measuring
2. Care in keeping records—completeness and accuracy
3. Cooperation with nursing, dental, and medical service
4. Cooperation with physical education service
5. Integration of health with other subjects
6. Follow-up of individual children
7. Ability to secure cooperation of home in regard to individual children
8. Use of life situations as they occur to develop attitudes, habits, and knowledge related to health
9. Conduct of daily inspections for cleanliness

IV. *Hygienic control of school environment*

1. Ventilation of room
2. Proper seating for pupils
3. Attention to lighting
4. Removal of outdoor clothing

5. Attention to proper use of drinking fountains and toilets
6. Attention to hand-washing
7. Sanitary methods of serving milk (if mid-morning lunch is served)
8. Arrangement of program to avoid undue fatigue

V. *Measurement of results*

1. Results shown in weight gains of children
2. Results shown in correction of physical defects
3. Results shown in improved habits as measured by inspection
4. Results shown in improved habits as measured by health habit questionnaires (or other devices)
5. Results shown in improved posture
6. Results shown in increase of health knowledge as measured by health knowledge tests
7. Results shown in attitude and general appearance of class

Let us see some of the questions which should be raised if we wish to test the adequacy of (1) administrative provision for health education, (2) indirect learnings, and (3) direct instruction.

1. *Administrative provision for health education. Health in Schools,* the Twentieth Yearbook of the American Association of School Administrators, states:

The organization of a school system for health education requires an integrating, directing head if the health program is to be developed properly, and successfully related to the other activities of the school program. In the smaller schools the superintendent must accept this immediate responsibility. In others he may rely upon the services of a supervisor or director of health procedures throughout the schools. In the larger systems, such a director will rank as the head of a department or division or as an assistant superintendent. In either case he will serve as an active member of the group which confers with the superintendent concerning policy-making and administration.

Here we are concerned with such questions as the following:

1. Is the health education program recognized and actively supported by the school administration?
2. Do school principals accept administrative responsibility for the health education program in their respective schools?
3. Is the administration of the program of general education in accord with the principles of hygiene?
   a. What is the average class size?
   b. What is the length of the school day at different grade levels?
   c. How much outdoor recess is allowed for each grade?
   d. What is the daily pupil schedule?
   e. Is pupil health considered in the amount of home work required at each grade level?
   f. Is there a satisfactory plan for grouping pupils on the basis of health needs and learning abilities?
   g. Are the health interests of pupils considered in school policies relating to examinations, grades, and reports?
   h. Is the mental health of the pupil considered in the school policy relating to discipline?
4. Is the supervision of health education activities adequately carried out?
   a. Is there a qualified supervisor of health education responsible to the superindent of schools?

    b. Are suitable health education materials provided for teachers and pupils?

    c. Are adequate facilities provided for the in-service education of teachers?

5. Is there provision for home and school cooperation through such activities as those of the parent-teacher association, parents' visits to the school, and home visits by the teachers?

2. *Indirect learnings.* We wish to determine whether the health experiences of the pupil outside of direct instruction are desirable and effective. We wish to know whether the school health services are so conducted as to be of maximum educational value. Does the child find satisfactory standards of safety and sanitation at school? Does the child have a hygienic regimen which accustoms him to a healthful mode of living?

We shall want to ask such questions as the following:

1. Does the school environment meet the satisfactory standards of sanitation?
2. Do pupils and teachers assist in the maintenance of hygienic conditions in the school building?
3. Is the school environment used as a basis for teaching?
4. Are satisfactory educational experiences provided for the child in connection with the periodic health examination and the correction of physical defects?
5. Are desirable health education experiences provided by a sound program of communicable disease control carried out with effective cooperation between the school health service and the teaching staff?
6. Is the daily regimen of the child contributing to the formation of desirable habits and attitudes in the field of health?
7. Are satisfactory health education experiences provided for the child through the physical education program?
8. Is adequate use made of those routine procedures which have excellent health education possibilities in the elementary school?
   a. Is monthly measuring and monthly weighing by teachers or under teacher supervision carried out properly and with sufficient accuracy in the elementary school?
   b. Is educational use made of weighing and measuring?
   c. Is the morning observation of health status and cleanliness carried out effectively?
   d. Are school lunches satisfactory from the standpoint of:
      (1) Time allotment?
      (2) Conditions under which the lunch is served?
      (3) The educational values derived from it?
   e. Is adequate use made of suitable relaxation periods?
9. Are satisfactory standards of safety maintained at school?

3. *Direct instruction.* Here we are concerned with such questions as the following:

1. Is there some form of course of study or teacher guide?
2. Did the techniques used in building the curriculum include:
   a. Teacher participation?
   b. Classroom experimentation?
   c. An analysis of pupil needs?
3. Does the instructional plan give evidence of well-articulated sequences and progression from grade to grade?
4. Is there provision for constant revision of the curriculum plan in the light of scientific research and educational experimentation?

5. Does the health instruction serve the present and future needs of the pupils?
6. Does the schedule provide adequate time for health education?
7. Is the primary responsibility for health education in the elementary schools in the hands of the classroom teacher?
8. Does the health instructional plan recognize, in scope of objectives, the mental, emotional, and social aspects of health, as well as the physical?
9. Does the instructional plan provide for critical thinking in health matters on the part of the pupil?
10. Is the health education program carried out with special recognition of the interests, needs, and capacities of the individual, as well as of the group?
11. Are the assigned health periods used to formulate and crystallize health experiences and to promote health attitudes and practices—not merely to present factual information?
12. Are motivational devices adequate and sound?
13. Are the plans and methods of health teaching sufficiently varied?
14. Is the instructional program sufficiently broad in its inclusion of:
    a. An adequate consideration of desirable health practices?
    b. A working knowledge of body needs, structures, and functions?
    c. A working knowledge of those factors in the environment that should be controlled in the interest of health?
    d. A working knowledge of the means of controlling such factors?
    e. Sufficient knowledge to make clear the value of such control to the individual, the group, and the nation?
    f. A knowledge of the sources of reliable health advice and information?
15. Do teachers use evaluated and sound health instruction materials?
16. Does the school system use the facilities for health education that are available through governmental and social agencies in the community?
17. In the curriculum plan and in classroom practice is health education both direct and integrated with other subjects of instruction?
18. Is there an effective and coordinated program of health instruction in the secondary school?
19. Do teachers use school and community situations in the teaching of the topics concerned?

Desirable criteria for *health education in the secondary school* are reflected in the following evaluative criteria from the National Study of Secondary School Evaluation.[1]

I. ORGANIZATION

1. A planned program of sequential topics or units in health education is provided in appropriate courses in grades 7 through 12.
2. At least one course in health education is provided for pupils in grades 7, 8, or 9.
3. At least one course in health education is provided for pupils in grades 10, 11, or 12.
4. Provision is made for staff members to plan the health education programs cooperatively.
5. A school health coordinator or committee charged with the responsibility of coordinating health education is provided.
6. Planned instruction in health is given in each subject area of the secondary school when such instruction is appropriate.

---

[1] Quoted from "Evaluative Criteria, 1960 Edition" by permission of the National Study of Secondary School Evaluation, 1785 Massachusetts Avenue, N.W., Washington 6, D. C.

II. NATURE OF OFFERINGS

1. Emphasis is placed upon the need and desirability of having students develop positive attitudes toward safe and healthful living.

2. Experiences are provided which contribute to an understanding of the personal and environmental factors affecting health.

3. Students investigate the causes and methods of prevention of important communicable and noncommunicable disease.

4. Emphasis is placed on the individual's responsibilities both for his own health and for the health of others.

5. Effort is made to acquaint students with reliable sources of health information and with developments in health research which affect their lives.

6. Experiences are provided for the study of safety as it affects life in the home, school, and community.

7. Experiences are provided for each student to gain understanding of the growth, structure, and function of his own body.

8. Experiences provide for the study of nutritional needs.

9. Emphasis is placed on helping students to plan and participate in a balanced daily program of work, recreation, activity, rest, and relaxation.

10. Experiences provide for the study of factors affecting mental and emotional health, including a study of personality and adjustment.

11. Experiences are provided which are designed to develop knowledge, understanding, and attitudes concerning health which are necessary for effective family and community living.

12. Students are assisted in developing knowledge of procedures to use in emergencies, sickness, injury, or disaster and developing skill in applying them.

13. Experiences are provided which show contribution of personal appearance to mental health and which lead to ability to maintain or improve one's appearance.

14. Experiences are provided which aid students in understanding heredity and its sociological implications.

15. Education is provided to assist students in making satisfactory adjustments in adolescence and to develop desirable understanding concerning marriage and family life.

16. Experiences assist students in studying public and professional health services of the community.

17. Opportunities are provided for the development of understanding of the need for care in selecting health services and health products.

18. Attention is given to the study of the emotional, social, and physiological effects of the use of drugs and alcohol.

19. Attention is given to the effects of irritating and poisonous substances on the human body, including pollen and other allergens, chemicals, gases, and tobacco.

III. PHYSICAL FACILITIES

1. Adequate classroom space is provided for health education classes.

2. Classroom furniture can be arranged for individual and group work.

3. Tables are available for conduct of experiments and demonstrations.

4. Space is provided for library and reference materials.

5. Display space and storage space is provided for models, exhibits, charts, and other instructional materials.

6. Projection equipment is available and there is provision for its use.

IV. DIRECTION OF LEARNING

A. *Instructional staff*

All staff members who have responsibility for organized courses in health education:

1. Have had preparation in general liberal education.
2. Have had preparation in biological sciences (e.g., bacteriology, anatomy, physiology, biology).
3. Have had preparation in social sciences (e.g., anthropology, sociology).
4. Have had preparation in psychology (e.g., child growth and development, educational psychology, mental health).
5. Have had preparation in physical sciences (e.g., chemistry and physics).
6. Have had preparation in professional health courses (e.g., school health education, personal and community health, safety education, first aid, nutrition, sex education, methods and materials in health instruction).
7. Maintain acquaintance with current developments in health and safety education.
8. Aid in coordinating the instructional activities with community health and safety activities.
9. Are thoroughly acquainted with the health service program.
10. Maintain active participation in inservice education through formal study and other professional activity.
11. Maintain an active interest in professional advancement, including participation in educational organizations.

B. *Instructional activities*

1. Instruction in health education contributes to the school's objectives.
2. Instruction is directed toward clearly formulated, comprehensive objectives in health education.
3. Specific instructional activities contribute to the comprehensive objectives of the health education program.
4. Careful planning and preparation for instruction is made.
5. Instruction is readily adapted to new and changing conditions.
6. Students have a part in planning instructional activities.
7. Individual needs of students are considered in planning, conducting, and evaluating activities.
8. Instruction is centered around health problems of daily living.
9. Instruction includes a study of community health problems.
10. Models, charts, and exhibit materials are used.
11. Movies, slides, recordings, demonstrations, and other audiovisual teaching materials and methods are used.
12. Physicians, nurses, dentists, policemen, and other resource people are used in instruction.
13. Instruction is coordinated with the health service program of the school.
14. Instruction is coordinated with activities in physical education and other related subject-matter fields.
15. Students are motivated to read current articles on health and safety.
16. Community resources are used when appropriate to enrich and vitalize the instruction.
17. Individual and group projects are used.

C. *Instructional materials*

1. A variety of textbooks adapted to the reading levels of the students is available.
2. A variety of reference materials is available.
3. Current periodicals pertaining to health and safety instruction are available.
4. Films, slides, models, charts, recordings, and other audiovisual materials are available for classroom use.
5. Teaching materials from voluntary agencies and reputable commercial sources are provided.
6. Curriculum guides, study guides, and resource units are provided.
7. Splints, bandages, and first aid materials are available.
8. Materials for home nursing are provided.

D. Methods of evaluation

1. Evaluation is an integral part of instruction.
2. A variety of testing techniques is used (e.g., standardized tests, teacher-made objective tests, essay-type tests).
3. Interpretation of test results is used in planning instruction.
4. Both teachers and students recognize that tests are used to reveal strengths and to point out areas for improvement.
5. Health practices and attitudes of students are studied to determine the effectiveness of instruction.
6. Parents cooperate in the evaluation of health and safety practices and attitudes of students.
7. Students engage in self-evaluation activities (e.g., keep records of diets, sleep and rest, and growth, and collect data on accidents in school and community).
8. Health appraisal data are considered in determining the effectiveness of health instruction.

Evaluation of habits, attitudes, and knowledge

A variety of methods is used to determine behavior, attitudes, and knowledge relating to health. The information these methods yield is valuable but, in most areas, far from exact. Through day-to-day observation and through direct discussion, the teacher in the elementary school comes to understand the individual child in relation to health. To a less extent, the teacher in the secondary school secures detailed information through observation and conferences with individual students. Instruments of measurement give us less detailed information for groups. So far as an appreciation of health education is concerned, improvement reflected in individual *case studies* is more convincing to parents than group statistics.

Changes in habits. It may be well to remember, in studying changes in habits or in comparing habits at different age levels, that the child's health behavior tends to become better in some respects and worse in others as he grows older and becomes more mature.

Several kinds of measurement may be suggested.

1. *Direct observation.* The status of certain health habits may be determined by direct observation, as, for example:

(a) Observation of cleanliness each morning, under standard conditions (see page 133).

(b) Occasional class surveys under standard conditions, such as the determination of: (1) the number of children in proper sitting position when checked, without their own knowledge, at weekly or less frequent periods while engaged in the same form of activity, such as writing or silent reading (the standard requirements to be met in this checking might involve: hips back in the chair, back straight, shoulders even, and feet flat on the floor); (2) the number of children who put fingers, pencils, or other such articles into their mouths during a three-minute period while engaged in a standard type of activity; or (3) the number of children taking milk at recess; (4) the number of children who have fruit for lunch; (5) the number of children who are holding the book from which they are reading in a proper position; or (6) the number of children who follow some specific safety practice.

(c) A sanitary survey of the school environment, reflecting the extent to which children and teachers cooperatively are succeeding in maintaining satisfactory classroom ventilation, the cleanliness of toilets and washrooms, the adjustment of seats, the maintenance of satisfactory lighting, and the condition of cleanliness facilities, such as those for hand-washing.

2. *Reports and questionnaires.* Very valuable though somewhat less precise data can be obtained from the following types of reports concerning health practices:

(a) Health-habit *questionnaires* may be used from time to time to determine the health behavior of pupils with respect to particular items during the preceding twenty-four hours. They should be unsigned. Children should understand that the questionnaire is not asking what they *usually* do, but rather what they happened to do on a particular day. Questions such as these are asked:

> How many hours did you sleep?
> How many times did you brush your teeth?
> Did you eat candy between meals?

(b) The individual health-habit *conference,* in which the teacher reviews with a single pupil the activities of the preceding twenty-four hours, gives certain specific information concerning the health behavior of an individual child.

(c) Questionnaires to parents have been useful in securing information as to which habits are being improved and which habits are in need of further improvement (see page 348). Occasional indications of improvement in health habits are obtained in *conversations* with parents.

3. *Health records.* We may also regard as evidence of improvement in health practices, data showing an increase in the percentage of physical defects corrected, in the percentage of pupils immunized, or in the percentage of children receiving regular dental attention or private health examinations.

4. *Case studies.* We may get evidence of improved habits from detailed records of individual children. Some of these may be autobiographical records or diaries.

Measurement of attitudes. Attitudes are extremely difficult to measure by pencil and paper tests. This is because children, as well as adults, find it very easy to indicate how they know they ought to feel instead of making the critical analysis of how they actually feel toward a health practice or situation. Attitudes determined in this way have been found to be more closely related to knowledge than to health behavior.

Some indication of attitudes may be obtained from the reaction of pupils toward health as a subject of instruction and toward the development of health behavior. We may observe the attitude of pupils toward the school nurse, physician, dentist, family physician, the correction of physical defects, cleanliness and sanitation of the school building, and toward public health activities in the community.

It is probably fair to assume that an improvement in health attitudes accompanies any marked improvement in health practices, provided the improvement was not brought about by an attempt to earn some special award. Parents often have a better opportunity than teachers to observe improvement in the child's health attitudes.

Better procedures for determining health attitudes will doubtless be developed. Several tests for the measurement of health attitudes or health awareness will be found in the accompanying list of objective tests.

Measurement of knowledge. The teacher's expert skill in the measurement of knowledge can be utilized in this field, as well as in the others. Teacher-made tests are constantly used in connection with class instruction, as measures of progress in learning and as a means of discovering individual children who need special attention. Standardized objective tests are used to measure the strength and weakness of health instruction, to get a comparative picture of pupil knowledge, and to evaluate the factual learning which has taken place.

The teacher develops and uses both essay-type and objective tests. The former explore the knowledge of the pupil or student effectively, but they are difficult to grade and do not give easily measurable comparisons between pupils.

In large secondary schools, the size of classes makes the use of objective tests almost necessary. *Multiple-choice tests* are the most widely used in the upper levels of education and in the professional examinations and placement examinations outside of academic life. A direct question, statement, or situation is presented, and the student indicates which of several responses is the correct or best answer. For example, the student puts the letter "D" in the blank space in the following question:

```
_____  Gallstones are formed from substances in:
          A. Gastric juice          D. Bile
          B. Saliva                 E. Pancreatic juice
          C. Lactase
```

Matching-type tests are somewhat more complicated. One list of statements is to be matched against another by indicating opposite the first set the number of the appropriate item in the second set. For example:

Indicate by Roman numeral which vitamin listed on the right is associated with each activity or condition listed on the left.

```
_____  1. Prevention of rickets          I. Vitamin A
_____  2. Prevention of beriberi        II. Thiamine
_____  3. Prevention of night blindness III. Niacin
_____  4. Prevention of pellagra        IV. Ascorbic acid (vitamin C)
_____  5. Prevention of scurvy           V. Vitamin D
```

Completion tests are easy to construct and are useful in checking the recall of specific terms. The student completes the statement by writing in the missing word or by writing it in the space to the left reserved for that purpose. For example,

```
_____  The vitamin that the body stores least and requires daily is vitamin
_____.
```

True-false tests enable one to cover ground quickly, but it is difficult to avoid clues in preparing such questions. They are easy to construct; but a student would get many right answers if he distributed his true and false answers at random. True-false questions are set up as follows:

_____1. The best thing to do in case of abdominal pain is to take a laxative.

Standardized tests have been carefully studied to determine their reliability. Many such tests are now available for both elementary and secondary schools. Their use is essential if objective and comparable data are needed showing the health knowledge status of a school population. Standardized tests for the exploration of both habits and attitudes are listed below. They are used to measure student achievement, to point up strengths and weaknesses in the teaching, to indicate areas needing greater emphasis, to determine changes in attitudes, knowledge, and behavior, to secure evidence as to the need for health instruction, and to determine the desirable placement of students in health classes.

Standardized tests

Byrd, Oliver, E.: *Health Attitude Scale* (suitable for last three years of high school and the first two years of college). Write to Stanford University Press, Stanford, Calif.

Colebank, Albert D.: *Health Behavior Inventory,* Monterey, California, 1963, California Test Bureau. For grades 7, 8, and 9. Has 25 items on behavior, 25 items on attitudes, and 50 items on knowledge.

Crow, Lester D., and Ryan, Loretta C. (edited by Brownell, C. L.): *Health and Safety Education Test* (grades 3 to 6, inclusive). Part 1. Good Health and Safety Habits; Part 2. Cause and Effect in Relation to Health and Safety; Part 3. Facts About Health and Safety; Part 4. Application of Health and Safety Rules. Rockville Centre, N. Y., Acorn Publishing Company.

Dearborn, Terry H.: *College Health Knowledge Test,* Personal Health Form A, Stanford, Calif., rev. 1959, Stanford University Press. For college or senior high school.

Dzenowagis, Joseph G.: *Self-Quiz of Safety Knowledge,* Chicago, 1956, National Safety Council, School and College Department. To measure safety preparedness at the fifth and sixth grade levels.

Johns, Edward B., and Juhnke, Warren L.: *Health Practice Inventory* (for senior high school and college students), Stanford, Calif., rev. 1952, Stanford University Press.

Kilander, H. Frederick: *Kilander Health Knowledge Test* (for high school seniors and college freshmen), 1961, 8 pp., sample set 15 cents. Write to H. Frederick Kilander, 33 Colonial Terrace, East Orange, N. J.

Kilander, H. Frederick: *Information Test on Biological Aspects of Human Reproduction,* Staten Island, New York, 1958, the author, Mimeographed, junior high school through college. Norms are available.

Kilander, H. Frederick: *Nutrition Information Test,* ed. 4, Staten Island, New York, 1959, the author, Wagner College. Mimeographed, junior high school through college. Norms are available.

Kilander, H. Frederick: *Stimulants and Depressants Information Test,* ed. 2, Staten Island, New York, 1958, the author, Wagner College. Mimeographed, junior high school through college. Norms are available.

Kilander, H. Frederick: *Tuberculosis Information Test,* ed. 3, Staten Island, New York, 1957, the author, Wagner College. Mimeographed.

Lawrence, Trudys: *Getting Along: Grades 7, 8, 9.* Temple City, California, 1964, the author 6117 North Rosemead Boulevard. For the evaluation of emotional health.

Le Maistre, E. Harold, and Pollock, Marion B.: *Health Behavior Inventory,* Monterey, California, 1963, California Test Bureau. For senior high school students.

Los Angeles City Schools: *Health Tests* A, A4, A6, Los Angeles, 1958, Associate Superintendent, Division of Educational Services, Los Angeles City Schools, P. O. Box 3307, Terminal Annex. Used in the extensive evaluation of the school district that was completed in 1960.

McHugh, Gelolo: *Sex Knowledge Inventory,* Form Y, Durham, North Carolina, 1955, Family Life Publications, Inc. High school and college.

National Safety Council: *Bicycle Safety Information Test,* Chicago, National Safety Council, 425 North Michigan Avenue. For use at the elementary level.

Neher, Gerwin: *Health Inventory for High School Students* (for grades 9-12; an inventory-type test covering health status, health habits, and health knowledge; reliability for an unselected group for eleventh grade pupils was 0.86). Write to California Test Bureau, Los Angeles, Calif.

New York State Council on Health and Safety Education: *Health Knowledge Examination for the Secondary Level,* developed by a committee of the Council, 1962.

Shaw, John H., and Troyer, Maurice E.: *Health Education Test: Knowledge and Application,* Form A rev. 1956, Form B rev. 1957, Chicago, Psychometric Affiliates. For grades 7-12 and college freshman.

Southworth, W. H., Latimer, Jean V., and Turner, C. E.: "A Study of Health Practices, Knowledge, Attitudes," *Research Quarterly* **15:**118–136, May, 1944.

Speer, Robert K., and Smith, Samuel: *Health Test,* Form A rev. 1960, Form B rev. 1957, Chicago, Psychometric Affiliates. For grades 3-8.

Thompson, Clem W.: *Thompson Smoking and Tobacco Knowledge Test,* Mankato, Minnesota, 1963, the author, Mankato State College. Grades 8 to 12.

Veenker, C. Harold: *A Health Knowledge Test for the Seventh Grade,* Lafayette, Indiana, 1957, the author, Purdue University.

Yellen, Sylvia: *Health Behavior Inventory,* Monterey, California, 1963, California Test Bureau. For grades 3, 4, 5, and 6.

Measuring changes in health status

We are confronted with two difficulties in using changes in health status as a measure of the quality of the school health program. Our first difficulty is to find a satisfactory measure of health status. But even if we had a much better measure than now exists, we would still be confronted with the second difficulty—that of determining whether the school or the extraschool health program was responsible for the improvement. Only where a scientifically controlled experimental procedure is possible can this second difficulty be eliminated.

A medical examination discovers the presence of disease or physical defects; but there is no exact, objective, and quantitative measure of the health of an individual, although an extensive science of testing has been developed to measure growth status, and organic, muscular, and athletic efficiency. We may discuss briefly some of the indications of health status which have been suggested for use in estimating the health of a school population, in determining health improvements within a school system, or in comparing the health of two or more pupil groups.

Tests of growth status.

1. *Underweight.* Studies have shown that underweight cannot be used as an indication of health status. The precision and reliability of the underweight measurement are low and the weight-height ratio is primarily de-

termined by skeletal build rather than by health status. For these reasons former proponents of the use of "below average weight for height and age" as a health index have recommended its abandonment.

2. *Growth.* The Malden Research Studies, mentioned earlier, demonstrated an improved rate of growth in both height and weight among children whose health practices had been improved through health education, as compared with a control group of like children who had not benefited from health education. They did not show a change in body proportions.

A study carried out by the Department of Health of Scotland has confirmed the findings in the Malden Studies by showing that growth is more directly related to the health of the child than is the weight-height ratio. The study showed that an increase in the amount of milk in the diet of certain school children produced an accelerated growth in both the height and weight.[2]

The necessity for the scientifically accurate accumulation of data and their statistical analysis makes possible the use of this measurement of health improvement only in the hands of a research organization.[3]

3. *Intermittency in growth.* Growth studies have shown that children who failed to gain in weight for three successive months have a poorer rating with respect to physical defects, recent illnesses, and hygienic habits than do children who are growing regularly. As yet we are without comparative data to indicate the amount of three-month intermittency in different communities or the degree to which the intermittency can be reduced in the same school population.

4. *The Lucas-Pryor Nutritional Index.* This index uses hip width (the distance between the iliac crests), together with height, to classify the child with respect to skeletal build. Upon the basis his weight is compared with that of his skeletal peers.[4]

5. *The Wetzel Grid.* The basic principle of the grid is related to the constancy of rate of growth which each individual may be expected to follow along his own hereditary channel, provided health and nutrition are good. Recognition of disturbance comes from a change in the individual's growth pattern.

The grid consists of seven paths of growths on a chart for boys and girls of different body builds. When a child moves out of his own growth path for height and weight, his growth status is regarded as unsatisfactory. This may be taken as an indication of a need for medical attention. When

[2]Leighton, Gerald, and McKinley, Peter: *Milk Consumption and the Growth of School Children,* Department of Health, Scotland, published by His Majesty's Stationer's Office.

[3]Hardy, M. C., and Hoefer, C. H.: *Healthy Growth,* Chicago, 1936, University of Chicago Press.

[4]Lucas, W. P., and Pryor, H. B.: "Physical Measurements and Physiological Processes in Young Children," *Journal of the American Medical Association* 97:1127–1133, 1931; also Pryor, H. B., and Stolz, H. R.: "Determining Appropriate Width and Body Build," *Journal of Pediatrics* 3:606–622, 1933.

the chart has been kept for some years it shows at a glance whether the individual is following along his normal growth pattern. It is not always easy to classify the child with respect to the grid until his growth has been observed for some time.

The grid is rather expensive and time-consuming to use; but some schools, as well as many pediatricians, are using it.[5]

Tests of organic, muscular, and athletic efficiency. Various tests of respiratory and cardiovascular efficiency have been proposed. Although progress has been made in the understanding of the facts responsible for physical fitness, we are still unable to recommend cardiovascular or metabolism tests for the objective determination of health status.

Many tests and measurements have been developed in the field of physical education. The tests which have been most directly associated with health are tests of strength, lung capacity, and physical achievement. They are more useful in determining the adequacy of the physical education program than in evaluating health status, as they may reflect improvement in athletic skills rather than in health. Good muscular development is desirable. It is evidence of the fitness of the child or youth to carry out certain physical activities which reflect, in varying degrees, the physical activity requirements of daily living. In recent years some studies have indicated low muscular capacity in children in an urbanized environment with apartment living, motor and elevator transportation, and electrically powered apparatus of all sorts. We wish to provide them with vigorous, stimulating, healthful, and developmental activity. At the same time, so far as "fitness tests" are concerned, we know that health in terms of "complete physical, mental, and social well-being" cannot be measured in its entirety by any set of muscular achievements. We have referred (page 129) to the tests now widely used in the national physical fitness program.

Direct indications of health status. Several indices of this type are available but most of them have serious difficulties and limitations as measures of pupil health status.

1. *The number of physical defects or the number of children free from physical defects.* Experience has shown wide variations in the number of defects reported when different physicians examine the same children. This is due to the fact the physicians have different standards of judgment as to how severe a condition must be to constitute a physical defect. More comparable results are obtained when a group of physicians agree in advance upon specific definitions of the various physical defects, but even then the judgment of the different doctors is not sufficiently objective to make comparisons statistically reliable. The most significant results in the evaluation of pupil health status are obtained when the same school physician examines the children repeatedly, recording changes in nutritional

---

[5]Wetzel, Norman T.: "Physical Fitness in Terms of Physique Development and Basal Metabolism," *Journal of the American Medical Association,* March 22, 1941, p. 1187.

and general health status, and the correction or noncorrection of physical defects.

2. *The percentage of physical defects corrected within a given period.* It is obvious that a change in the amount of free clinic service available within a community or a difference in the amount of clinic service in two otherwise comparable communities might sharply influence the number of corrections secured.

3. *Dental health status.* Various simple dental indices are available and experience has shown that the number of dental corrections can be markedly increased through the school health education program.[6] Data from different years or different communities are comparable only when the amounts of available clinic service are the same.

We have mentioned the most commonly used dental health index, the DMF which gives the number of decayed, missing, and filled teeth. As we pointed out, this is less useful for children than for adults because the loss of the first teeth and their gradual replacement by permanent teeth produces changes in the number of teeth in the mouth at different age and grade levels. The examinations for decayed, missing, and filled teeth must be made by a dentist, dental hygienist, or other person with special preparation for the task.

4. *Sick absenteeism.* Although this is an indication of health status, it is not a safe measurement of the health education program because it is influenced by epidemic conditions outside the school.

Results not directly measurable

It is important to measure results wherever possible, but we should recognize that there are many values arising from the school health program that cannot be measured quantitatively. The benefits of the school health program will be felt by the individual throughout his whole life. It might well be maintained that the school health program contributes enough to the health of the future adult to make it worthwhile even if *no* specific health improvement could be measured during the years in school.

Improvement in the health and nutritional status of the child is often evident to the physician, and sometimes to the teacher, even though this improvement cannot be recorded by an objective health index.

There are also some values in the improvement of home conditions, through the indirect education of parents, that result from the health program in the school. There will be presumably a direct effect upon the health of the next generation through the improved attitudes and health standards of the present group of pupils when they become parents. Attitudes are difficult to measure, yet the contribution of the school to the development of sound health attitudes is one of its most important services.

---

[6]Turner, C. E., Howe, Percy R., and Dick, Marita J.: "A Usable Dental Health Index for Schools," *Journal of School Health,* January and February, 1942.

Health education makes many contributions to vigor, efficiency, contentment, cheerfulness, community health, and human betterment that we can never hope to measure.

References

Bean, K. L.: *Construction of Educational and Personnel Tests,* New York, 1953, McGraw-Hill Book Company, Inc.

Clarke, H. H.: *Application of Measurement to Health and Physical Education,* ed. 2, Englewood Cliffs, N. J., 1950, Prentice-Hall, Inc.

Jackson, C. O.: *Let's Rate Your Health Education Program,* Springfield, Ill., February, 1956, Educational Press Bulletin, Superintendent of Public Instruction.

Johns, E. B.: *School Health Education Evaluative Study, Los Angeles Area, 1954–1959,* Los Angeles, 1964, U.C.L.A., 128 pp.

Knutson, A. L.: "Evaluating Health Education," *Public Health Reports,* January, 1953; also, "Pretesting: A Positive Approach to Evaluation," *Public Health Reports,* July, 1952.

Knutson, A. L., and Shimberg, B.: "Evaluation of a School Health Program," *American Journal of Public Health,* 45:21, 1955.

Larson, L. A., and Yocom, R. D.: *Measurement and Evaluation in Physical, Health and Recreation Education,* St. Louis, 1951, The C. V. Mosby Company.

Los Angeles City Schools: *Evaluation of the Health Program in the Los Angeles City Schools, 1954–1961,* Los Angeles, 1962, 265 pp.

McCloy, C. H., and Young, N. D.: *Tests and Measurements in Health and Physical Education,* ed. 3, New York, 1954, Appleton-Century-Crofts, Inc.

Ross, C. C., and Stanley, J. C.: *Measurement in Today's Schools,* Englewood Cliffs, N. J., 1954, Prentice-Hall, Inc.

Solleder, Marion K.: *Evaluation Instruments in Health Education,* Columbus, Ohio, 1965, Ohio State University. Mimeographed, 16 pp.

Travers, R. M. W.: *How to Make Achievement Tests,* New York, 1950, Odyssey Press.

Wetzel, N. C.: "Assessing the Physical Condition of Children," *Journal of Pediatrics,* January, February, March, 1953.

Willgoose, C. E.: *Evaluation in Health Education and Physical Education,* New York, 1961, McGraw-Hill Book Company, Inc.

Instructions for the control
of communicable diseases in the school[1]

DEFINITION OF TERMS

Carrier. A carrier is a person who harbors a specific infectious agent in the absence of discernible clinical disease and serves as a potential source or reservoir of infection for man.

Communicable. Capable of being transmitted from one person or animal to another.

Cleansing. This term signifies the removal by scrubbing and washing, as with hot water, soap, detergent or washing soda, of organic matter on which and in which bacteria may find favorable conditions for prolonging life and virulence; also the removal by the same means of bacteria adherent to surfaces.

Teach all students the necessity of:

1. Keeping the body clean by sufficiently frequent soap and water baths.
2. Washing hands in soap and water after emptying bowel or bladder, and always before eating.
3. Keeping hands and unclean articles or articles which have been used by others, away from mouth, nose, eyes, and ears.
4. Avoiding the use of common or unclean eating, drinking, or toilet articles of any kind, such as towels, handkerchiefs, hair brushes, drinking cups, etc.
5. Avoiding close exposure of persons to spray from the nose and mouth; as in coughing, sneezing, laughing, or talking.

Contact. A "contact" is any person or animal known to have been in such association with an infected person or animal as to have been presumably exposed to transfer of infectious material directly, or by articles freshly soiled with such material.

Disinfection. By this is meant the killing of pathogenic microorganisms by chemical or physical means.

When the word "concurrent" is used as qualifying disinfection, it indicates the application of disinfection immediately after the discharge of infectious material from the body of an infected person, or after soiling of articles with such infectious discharges, all personal contacts with such discharges or articles being prevented prior to their disinfection.

When the word "terminal" is used as qualifying disinfection, it indicates the process of rendering the personal clothing and immediate physical environment of the patient free from the possibility of conveying the infection to others, at the time when the patient is no longer a source of infection.

---

[1]Thanks are expressed to the Los Angeles City Schools for permission to draw extensively upon their quarantine rules and regulations in the preparation of these instructions.

Fumigation. By fumigation is meant a process by which the destruction of insects, mosquitoes, body lice, and animals such as rats, is accomplished by the employment of gaseous agents.

Isolation. Isolation is defined as separation of infected persons from other persons, for the period of communicability, in such places and under such conditions as will prevent the transmission of the infectious agent. Isolation will be applied as instructed below.

Strict isolation. If the disease is one requiring strict isolation, the health officer shall insure that instructions are given to the patient and members of the household, defining the area within which the patient is to be isolated and stating the measures to be taken to prevent the spread of the disease.

Strict isolation shall include the following measures:

1. The patient shall have a separate bed in a room protected against flies.
2. All persons, except those caring for the patient, shall be excluded from the sick room.
3. The persons caring for the patient shall avoid coming in contact with any other persons within the household or elsewhere until every precaution has been taken to prevent the spread of infectious materials from the patient's room.
4. The persons caring for the patient shall wear a washable outer garment and shall thoroughly wash their hands with soap and hot water after handling the patient or any object he may have contaminated. On leaving the room in which the patient is isolated, the attendant shall take off the washable outer garment and hang it in the room until disinfected.
5. All discharges from the nose and mouth shall be burned or disinfected. The discharges should be received in pieces of soft tissue or cloth and dropped into a paper bag which can be burned.
6. Objects which may have been contaminated by the patient shall be thoroughly cleansed before being removed from the contaminated area.
7. The feces and urine of patients suffering from diseases in which the infectious agent appears in the feces or urine shall be disposed of according to instruction given by the local health offices.

Modified isolation. If the disease is one in which only a modified isolation is required, official enforcement is neither a necessary nor a practicable procedure. But rather, the modified practice should be instituted under the direction of the attending physician, and its duration is to be generally, if not exclusively, at his discretion.

Immune. An immune person is one who is protected from a communicable disease by natural or acquired means.

Susceptible. A person who is not immune to a particular disease by natural or artificial process.

Incubation period. The period between the implanting of the infecting organism and the development of symptoms.

Quarantine. Quarantine is defined as the limitation of freedom of movement of persons or animals that have been exposed to a communicable disease, for a period of time equal to or exceeding the longest usual incubation period of the disease, in such manner as to prevent effective contact with those not so exposed. If the disease is one requiring quarantine of the contacts in addition to isolation of the case, the local health officer shall determine the contacts who are subject to quarantine, specify the place to which they shall be quarantined, and issue instructions accordingly. He shall insure that provisions are made for the medical observation of such contacts as frequently as necessary during the quarantine period. (California Administrative Code, Title 17—Public Health—2520.)

Report of a disease. By report of a disease is meant the notification to the health authorities that a case of communicable disease or other listed condition exists in a specified person at a given address.

Epidemic. Occurring in unusually large numbers in a given locality.

Sporadic. Not widely diffused or epidemic; occasionally occurs here and there.

Endemic. Occurring more or less constantly in a given locality.

Preventive measures (prophylaxis). Measures which reduce incidence of disease. The following preventive measures apply to infectious diseases:

1. Isolation of patient.
2. Quarantine of contacts to certain diseases.
3. Immunization against certain diseases particularly smallpox, pertussis, diphtheria, tetanus, poliomyelitis, typhoid fever, as well as certain other diseases.
4. Prophylactic treatment of contacts to certain diseases; immune sera or chemotherapeutic or antibiotic agents.
5. Disinfection of hands (through soap and water washing) of attendants and everyone before handling food.
6. Individual utensils for patients.
7. Scrupulous care in disposal or disinfection of excreta, respiratory secretions, sputum, etc.
8. Screens to prevent flies from having access to patient, soiled bedding, excreta, etc.
9. Careful observation of contacts during period of incubation, and isolation on first suspicious signs.
10. Pasteurization of milk.
11. Chlorination of water.
12. General sanitation and hygiene.

Schick test. The skin test by which is shown the relative susceptibility (nonimmunity) of an individual to diphtheria.

Mosquito elimination. This is the chief means of control for yellow fever and malaria and is also prophylaxis for other diseases which are transmitted from patient to new host by the bite of that mosquito.

Rodent control (rats, squirrels, etc.). This is the ultimate means of prevention of plague and murine typhus which are transmitted through the bite of an infected rat-flea.

Immunization

Parents should be educated to have their children immunized, beginning in early infancy, by their family physician. In some cities with large numbers in the lower socio-economic levels, it has been necessary, in order to maintain an adequate level of immunization, for health departments to initiate immunization programs not only in well-baby clinics but also in the schools. The programs involve cooperative planning and operation by the local health department and the school administration. Schools are notified of the date set for giving immunizations, and consent slips are provided by the health department and filled out at the school (showing the name and age of the pupil, address, name of school, and room number) before being sent to the pupil's home for the signature of the parent or guardian. Pupils are excused from class for immunization procedures. The school nurse assists with the program, checking consent slips, for example, and is responsible for recording all immunizations on the pupil's health record card.

Exclusion of pupils from school because of illness

Communicable diseases. Any pupil suspected of having a contagious, infectious, or quarantinable disease shall be sent home immediately by the principal. If this is a reportable communicable disease, the name and address of the pupil shall be reported to the local health department. The local health department likewise has a responsibility for notifying schools of all communicable diseases reported to it.

Whenever there is good reason to believe that a pupil exempted from physical examination is suffering from a suspected communicable or infectious disease, such pupil shall be sent home and not permitted to return until the school authorities are satisfied that such disease does not exist.

Readmission of pupils after illness

The readmission of pupils who have been absent from school on account of illness shall be governed by the following provisions:

1. Pupils absent from school because of a nonreportable communicable disease such as chicken pox, German measles, "colds," influenza, pneumonia, skin diseases, or because of noncommunicable illnesses, may be readmitted to school by the principal, providing any health department regulations concerning the period of exclusion have been met and the child appears to have recovered.

   If the principal is in doubt as to whether the pupil is well enough to return, he may refer him to the school physician or nurse for readmittance or request the parent to obtain a readmittance statement from the pupil's personal physician.

2. Pupils who have been absent from school on account of a reportable communicable disease other than a quarantinable disease or ringworm of the scalp must have a permit to return to school issued by the school physician or nurse, the city or county health center, or the personal physician.

3. Pupils with ringworm of the scalp whether under clinic or private care may be readmitted to school without prescribed cap only with written consent from the local health department of jurisdiction for residence of the pupil.

4. Pupils who have been absent from school because of a disease subject to full quarantine or residing in a home in which there is a quarantinable disease (diphtheria, smallpox, cholera, plague) may be readmitted to school only after they have been released from quarantine by the written consent of the local health department of jurisdiction for residence of the pupil.

It should be noted that communicable disease exclusion and readmission regulations apply also to teachers and other school personnel.

Instructions for cleaning after quarantinable diseases

When a case of quarantinable disease such as diphtheria, smallpox, cholera, or plague is suspected or discovered in a school, the following procedure shall be followed:

1. The pupil shall be isolated until school is instructed by the health officer as to transportation.

2. Blankets, pillows, cot covers, or mattresses which have been contaminated shall be removed from use. The principal shall see that such contaminated material is bundled in blanket or sheet, clean side out, as instructed by the school physician or school nurse, and labeled with the name of the school. The Maintenance Section shall be notified immediately to collect for sterilization.

3. The desk of the pupil shall be immediately emptied of its contents and all books, papers, pencils, etc., shall be wrapped in brown paper and tagged.

4. Cots shall be washed with the antiseptic solution issued to all custodians and placed outside to dry for at least six hours before being used again. Direct sunlight when available is preferable.

5. The pupil's personal effects, clothing, etc., shall be wrapped securely in paper and sent home for boiling or sunning, or as directed by health department.

6. The pupil's desk and the four other desks or tables immediately surrounding the contaminated desk, as well as the floor in this area, shall be thoroughly washed with the antiseptic solution. The room shall then be thoroughly aired.

7. The pupil's locker shall be washed inside and out with the antiseptic solution.

8. The principal of the school shall be notified of all cases developing among other pupils from that school. The same sanitation procedure shall be followed with regard to the classroom and the belongings of the affected pupil.

Inspection following quarantinable communicable disease

In case of a quarantined communicable disease, all pupils of the school involved must be carefully observed.

1. In elementary schools, a daily inspection of all pupils shall be made by the school nurse and all those suspected of being ill shall be excluded immediately by the principal.
2. In secondary schools, an inspection shall be made of all pupils who are suspected of being ill and readmission service by a school physician or school nurse provided.
3. Pupils who have been absent for one day or more shall be carefully inspected by the school nurse or physician upon their return to school, and any suspected of having quarantinable communicable disease isolated and reported to the health department.
4. When absentees are suspected of being ill, investigation is made.
5. All contacts who have been quarantined are excluded until readmitted by the health officer.

Isolation room procedures

Every school shall set aside one or more cots for the use of the acutely ill children. These cots shall be covered with blankets. All blankets on these cots shall be covered with clean sheets or large paper towels, which shall be folded over the tops of the blankets for about eighteen inches. All pillows shall be covered with clean pillow-cases or large paper towels. Both sheets and pillow-cases shall be removed for laundering, or if made of paper shall be burned immediately following their use by a sick pupil.

SPECIFIC INFECTIOUS DISEASES

Chicken pox (Varicella)

Description of the disease. An acute disease, with a slight fever, mild constitutional symptoms, and an eruption, maculopapular for a few hours, vesicular lasting 3 to 4 days, leaving a granular scab. Vesicles tend to be more abundant on the covered than on the exposed parts of the body, and usually appear in different stages on the same region of the body. The vesicles may be so few as to escape observation. The lesions appear also on the mucous membranes of the upper respiratory tract and upon the scalp.

Etiologic agent. The varicella-zoster virus.

Source of infection. Secretions of the respiratory tract of infected persons; lesions of the skin are of little consequence and scabs of themselves are not infective.

Mode of transmission. Directly from person to person; indirectly through articles freshly soiled by discharges from the skin and mucous membranes of infected persons.

Incubation period. Two to three weeks; commonly 13 to 17 days.

Period of communicability. Probably not more than one day before nor more than 6 days after the appearance of the first crop of vesicles. Especially communicable in the early stages of the eruption. One of the most readily communicable diseases.

Susceptibility and resistance. Susceptibility is apparently universal among those who have not previously had the disease. An attack confers permanent immunity, with possible rare exceptions.

Prevalence. Universal. Probably 70 per cent of persons have had the disease by the time they are 15 years of age. Not uncommon in early infancy. Winter and spring are seasons of greatest prevalence in temperate zones.

Method of control. Preventive measures—None.

Exclusion. Minimum of seven days after appearance of first crop of vesicles and until exposed parts of body are free of primary crusts.

Contacts. When the case is properly isolated, there should be no restriction of contacts. Unusually severe cases, or cases occurring in persons over fifteen years of age, or at any age during an epidemic, should be carefully investigated to rule out smallpox.

Readmission. The principal may readmit the pupil providing there have been at least seven days after appearance of first crop of vesicles and primary crusts are off exposed surfaces.

Remarks. Complications or death rare. Chief danger is that sporadic cases of small-pox may be mistaken for chicken pox, and so start epidemics of smallpox.

Common cold

Identification of the disease. A highly infectious acute catarrhal infection of the upper respiratory tract, usually accompanied by a slight rise in temperature on the first day and chilly sensations with nasal discharge (coryza), and general indisposition or lassitude lasting 2 to 7 days. The nasal discharge tends to become mucopurulent due to secondary bacterial invasion and it is not uncommon for it to spread to the lower respiratory tract and to the middle ear.

Etiologic agent. 50 or more rhinovirus types.

Source of infection. Discharges from nose and mouth of infected persons.

Mode of transmission. Usually directly by coughing, sneezing, and explosive manner of speech by which droplets pass in the air from the infected person to susceptible persons, especially within short range; and indirectly by handkerchiefs, eating utensils, or other articles freshly soiled by discharges of the infected person.

Incubation period. Probably between 12 and 72 hours, usually 24 hours.

Period of communicability. Nasal washings taken 24 hours before onset and for 5 days after onset produce symptoms experimentally in man.

Susceptibility and resistance. Susceptibility is universal. No immunity demonstrated in volunteers reinoculated three weeks after an attack.

Prevalence. Most persons, except those living in small isolated communities, have one or more colds each year. The incidence does not vary materially according to sex, race, or occupation, but incidence is higher in children under 5 years of age and becomes less after 20 years.

Methods of control. Preventive measures: Education in the niceties of personal hygiene as in covering the mouth when coughing and sneezing and disposal of nose and mouth secretions. It is advisable to have patient use disposable tissue which can be burned or put in the toilet.

The infected individual, contacts and environment:

1. On recognition of the premonitory or early stage of a "common cold" the infected person should avoid direct and indirect exposure of others.
2. Isolation: Such modified isolation as can be accomplished by rest in bed during the acute stage of the disease is to be advised.

Conjunctivitis

1. *Acute bacterial conjunctivitis—pinkeye*

Definition. A very contagious eye infection characterized by a marked inflammation and redness of the conjunctiva with a mucopurulent or purulent discharge.

Cause. Various microorganisms.

Methods of infection. Direct contact with infected persons, and indirectly by contact with articles freshly soiled with the infectious discharges of such persons.

Incubation period. Usually 1 to 3 days.

Symptoms. Itching and smarting of the eyelids, followed by swelling and profuse discharge, inflamed and reddened conjunctiva, abnormal sensitiveness to light.

Exclusion. Patient only until recovery.

Readmission to school. May be readmitted to school by the principal providing patient has no symptoms.

2. *Allergic conjunctivitis*

Sudden onset of redness of the conjunctiva (particularly in the spring or early summer) accompanied by itching, watery discharge, and redness and inflammation (excoriation) of the cheek in chronic cases. Usually a history of mutiple allergies. Non-infectious.

Exclusion. Not excluded.

Points on diagnosis:
  Discharge
    Mucopurulent or purulent in acute bacterial conjunctivitis.
    Watery in allergic conjunctivitis.
  Appearance of mucous membrane of the conjunctiva.
    Reddened and smooth in the acute bacterial type.
    Often raised in multiple patches in the allergic type.
    History of allergy in the allergic type.

Diphtheria

Reportable and quarantinable disease

Description of the disease. An acute febrile infection, generally of the air passages, especially tonsils, throat, and nose, marked by a patch or patches of grayish membranes from which, as a rule, cultures of the diphtheria bacillus may be obtained. Occasionally, especially in adults, there may be a slight inflammation with little or no membrane. Nasal diphtheria is often marked by a one-sided nasal discharge and the nose may be raw (excoriated). Nonrespiratory forms include infection of the skin or wound surfaces. Vaginal infection is rare. Failure to obtain the bacillus on culture in suspected cases of diphtheria is not a valid reason for withholding specific treatment.

Onset may be mild or severe, usually chilliness in young children, sometimes convulsions, pain in back and limbs, temperature 102° to 104° F. Great variations in virulence in different cases, malignant cases proceed rapidly to delirium, stupor, and death in three to five days. Mild cases may recover in a few days.

Cause and method of infection. Klebs-Loeffler bacillus (Corynebacterium diphtheriae). Transmitted by contact with patient or healthy carrier or with articles soiled by the discharges from nose, throat, and lesions. Milk can serve as a vehicle.

Incubation period, 2-5 days, occasionally longer.

Recognition of disease. By clinical symptoms with confirmation by bacteriologic examination of discharges.

Exclusion. Patient is strictly isolated until two cultures from the throat and two from the nose, taken not less than 24 hours apart, fail to show the presence of diphtheria bacilli. Release cultures shall be taken not less than 7 days after discontinuance of antibiotic therapy. Isolation may be terminated if bacilli cultures from the case prove to be an avirulent form.

Contacts. All teachers, students, and food handlers are excluded for seven days from last contact and one negative nose and throat culture not less than 7 days after antibiotic, if given. All releases including food handlers at the discretion of health officer. Carrier released after cultures or other appropriate tests as directed by health officer. Carrier may not be permitted to engage in any occupation which involves handling of foods or close association with children outside his own family.

Methods of control. Early diagnosis and isolation of patient, adequate immunization of school children. During an epidemic or when a case of diphtheria has occurred in a school child, there should be daily observation of exposed school children and employes during the incubation period of five days. Parents and physicians should be notified when illness is recognized in a school.

Readmission to school. By written permission of the city or county health department of jurisdiction for residence of the pupil.

Remarks. Diphtheria may be primary in the conjunctiva (eyes) or extend to the ear (external), or to the skin around the mouth, anus, or genitals, and may occur in wounds.

Occurrence. Diphtheria is endemic and epidemic, a disease of autumn and the winter months. In communities where active immunization has been neglected, approximately one-fourth of the cases and one-half of the deaths occur in children under five years of age. In communities where childhood immunization has been adequate but reinforcing of toxoid was not continued, age distribution tends toward older persons.

All children should be immunized against diphtheria, and reinforcing doses of toxoid should be given at appropriate periods (2, 3, and 4 months, 15 months, 4 years, 8 years, 12 years, 16 years, and during epidemics). School immunization programs should immunize previously unimmunized children and children needing booster doses at any age.[2]

Dystentery (amoebic)

Reportable disease

Description. The disease may be mild, with moderate abdominal discomfort and diarrhea alternating with constipation; or acute, with profuse mucus and some blood; or may take the form of chronic diarrhea, with mucus and some blood.

Occurrence. Infection is worldwide, especially in warm and hot countries and in unsanitated areas.

Cause. Entamoeba histolytica, a protozoan.

Method of infection. Cysts from feces of infected persons, hand to mouth transfer, contaminated water and vegetables, and soiled hands of food handlers.

Incubation period. Five days to several months.

Exclusions. None usually, except food handlers. Food handlers are released after 3 negative stool specimens, not less than 3 days apart.

Dysentery (bacillary)—shigellosis

Reportable disease

Description. An acute bacterial disease of the intestine, characterized by diarrhea and accompanied by fever and often vomiting, cramps, and tenesmus. In severe cases, the stools may contain blood, mucus, and pus.

Release of case. The patient may be released after clinical recovery, unless such patient is a food or milk handler or is engaged in an occupation involving the care of children, in which case the patient shall not be released until two feces specimens (taken at least 7 days apart, and at least 7 days after specific therapy has ended) have been found negative by an approved public health laboratory.

Contacts. Food handlers excluded at discretion of health officers.

Food poisoning

Reportable diseases

    Causes.
1. Staphylococcus intoxication
2. Botulinus intoxication
3. Salmonella infection

Symptoms. Food poisoning is characterized by gastro-enteritis of abrupt evolution, acquired through food, with a characteristic grouping of cases. It occurs either from poisoning or from infection.

1. *Staphylococcus intoxication* is a poisoning of abrupt and sometimes violent onset, with severe nausea, vomiting, and severe prostration, sometimes severe diarrhea. This is probably the most common cause of diarrhea in tourists.

   Incubation period: Interval between taking food and onset is one to six hours, usually two to four.

   Source of infection is the ingestion of food that has become contaminated. Organism grows when food such as chopped meats, custard, and cream fillings, are poorly refrigerated. People handling foods should be free of pyogenic skin infections, especially of the hands. Food handlers should pay strict attention to sanitation and cleanliness of kitchens, refrigeration, and hand-washing.

2. *Botulinus intoxication* is a highly fatal, afebrile poisoning characterized by headache, weakness, constipation, paralysis, and the absence of diarrhea.

---

[2]American Academy of Pediatrics recommendation.

Incubation period: Symptoms usually appear within eighteen hours, possibly longer, after eating food containing toxin, the interval being determined by the amount of contaminated food taken and the content of botulinus toxin.

Report suspected cases by telephone to the local health office.

Remarks: Single cases of botulism are rare. Suspicion or recognition of a case at school should cause immediate search for other persons who shared suspected food.

3. *Salmonella infection* is most commonly characterized by acute gastroenteritis with diarrhea and abdominal cramps. Fever, nausea and vomiting are frequently present.

Etiologic agent: Salmonella of the group pathogenic for animals and occasionally for man.

Incubation period: In epidemics, 6 to 48 hours, usually about 12 to 24 hours.

Methods of control: Thorough cooking of all foodstuffs derived from animal sources, with particular attention to preparation of fowl, egg products, and meat dishes; protection of food against rodent or insect contamination; refrigeration of prepared foods, etc.

Control of infected individual: Report to local health officer; exclude infected persons from food handling until negative feces cultures have been obtained; exclude patient until recovery and two negative fecal and urine cultures, one week apart, beginning one week after discontinuance of specific therapy.

Exclusion of contacts: Food handlers at discretion of health officer.

German measles (rubella). (Not reportable; outbreaks reportable.)

Definition. An acute, communicable disease frequently occurring in epidemics, characterized by a mild onset, very little fever, a diffuse rash, sometimes resembling that of measles, sometimes that of scarlet fever—sometimes both at the same time. Enlargement of the cervical glands (postauricular, suboccipital, and occasionally others) is almost always present.

Cause. The virus of rubella.

Method of infection. By direct contact with the patient, or with articles freshly soiled with the discharge from the nose and throat of the patient.

Incubation period. From 14 to 21 days—usually 18 days.

Communicability. At least 4 days from onset of catarrhal symptoms.

Complications. None usually to the school age child. No attempt should be made to protect female children in good health against exposure to the disease before puberty. Efforts to control rubella are prompted by the hazards of congenital defects in offspring of women who acquired the disease during pregnancy, as from 18 to 20 per cent of living infants born after mothers have had this disease during the first trimester of pregnancy have defects.

Isolation. None except where contacts include a woman in early pregnancy; then under the direction of the attending physician for five days after onset. No isolation of contacts.

Exclusion. The patient only at least 4 days from onset and until clinically recovered.

Readmission to school. By the school principal.

Hepatitis (infectious and serum)

Reportable diseases

Description. Common, acute, systemic virus infection of man involving the liver; commonly associated with jaundice and impaired liver function. Formerly called "acute catarrhal jaundice" and "epidemic jaundice."

Modes of transmission. Intimate person-to-person contact, with respiratory spread possible. Transmission also occurs through injection of virus by way of transfusions of blood, serum, or plasma from infected persons, or accidental contamination of syringes or needles. Epidemics have been related to contaminated water, food, or milk, or ingestion of contaminated material.

Etiologic agents. For infectious hepatitis, the virus of infectious hepatitis.

For serum hepatitis, the virus of serum hepatitis.

Incubation periods. Long and variable. For infectious hepatitis, from 15 to 50 days, commonly 25 days. Period of communicability is from a few days before to a few days after onset, usually not exceeding a total of seven days.

For serum hepatitis, incubation period is from two to six months. Serum hepatitis is not known to be transmitted in nature from man to man.

Exclusion. Modified isolation during the acute symptoms. Patient with infectious hepatitis excluded at least 7 days from onset and until recovery. Contacts are not excluded.

Immunization. Homologous serum globulin gives passive protection even as late as six days before onset of disease, lasting for six to eight weeks, and may be advisable for intimate contacts.

Readmission to school. By school physicians and nurses, the local health department, or by the personal physician.

Impetigo

Definition. A purulent dermatitis, occurring sporadically and in small epidemics, and characterized initially by vesicular lesions which later become crusted seropurulent plaques.

Cause. Staphylococci or (hemolytic) streptococci.

Method of infection. Lesions on the skin of an infected person; possibly discharges from the nose and throat.

Directly by contact with moist discharges of the skin lesions, or indirectly by contact with articles recently soiled by those discharges. The infection may be readily inoculated from place to place on the patient's body by scratching.

Incubation period. Short, usually two to five days.

Symptoms. Purely local. Rapid development of pustules, most commonly about mouth, face, and hands, but may occur anywhere on body. Pustules solitary at first, but may become merged (confluent). Crusting usually conspicuous and often disfiguring.

Exclusion. Patient only until recovery.

Readmission to school. By all regularly licensed physicians and by the nurses of the Health Education and Health Services Branch.

Remarks. Sometimes spontaneous cure after a few days; sometimes continues indefinitely if not properly treated. Easily and quickly curable if treated.

Influenza (Not reportable; outbreaks reportable.)

Description. An acute, highly communicable disease characterized by sudden onset, fever of 1 to 6 days' duration accompanied by chills or chilliness, prostration, aches and pains in the back and limbs, coryza, sore throat and cough. Recognition is ordinarily on the basis of symptoms and the presence of an epidemic. Sporadic cases are difficult to identify. Influenza is important because of the complications that may follow, especially pneumonia.

Cause. Two types of influenza virus, Influenza A and Influenza B, are long recognized; Influenza C and "Asian Flu" have more recently been identified.

Method of infection. By direct contact, through droplet infection, or by articles freshly soiled by discharges of the nose and throat of infected persons; possibly airborne.

Period of communicability. Probably limited to one week after onset.

Incubation period. Usually 24 to 72 hours.

Susceptibility and resistance. Susceptibility is general, although natural resistance or relative immunity appears to protect from one-quarter to three-quarters of persons intimately exposed to the disease even during widespread epidemics. Acquired immunity resulting from an attack of and recovery from the disease may be of short duration (a few months to a year) and is effective only against specific strains of the virus. Artificial immunization with specific strains of influenza virus produces a similarly narrow specific immunity of a few months' duration. Vaccination may be desirable in certain large groups during the winter or when an epidemic appears imminent. Disease occurs pandemically at irregular intervals.

Duration. Usually a few days unless there are complications. Complications may be severe.

Methods of control. Preventive measures: Education of the public as to sanitary hazards from spitting, sneezing, or coughing in the close presence of other persons, and the advantages of so guarding the mouth and nose when sneezing and coughing that the likelihood of spray and droplet infection of others may be reduced. The use of common towels, glasses, eating utensils, or toilet articles should be avoided. The use of disposable paper handkerchiefs and napkins is to be encouraged. The fact that pathogenic microorganisms and viruses are present in the sputum and saliva of healthy persons should be made known.

Isolation. During acute stage of the disease, especially in severe cases. Visiting the patient by others than professional attendants should be discouraged. Proper disposal should be made of the discharges from the nose and throat of the patient.

Epidemic measures. During epidemics efforts should be made to reduce opportunities for direct contact infection, as in crowded halls, stores, and public conveyances. In isolated population groups and institutions infection has been delayed and sometimes avoided by strict exclusion of all visitors. The closing of the public, parochial, and private schools has not been effective in checking the spread of the infection.

To minimize the severity of the disease, and to protect the patient from secondary infections and thus reduce mortality, patients should go to bed at the beginning of an attack, and not return to work without the approval of their physician.

Appropriate antibacterial therapy should be instituted at once if evidence of secondary pneumonia appears.

Large aggregations of young adults unaccustomed to such association create a danger of spread of influenza when it is prevalent, and such aggregations are to be avoided as far as possible especially during epidemics.

Crowding of beds in hospitals and institutions to accommodate increased numbers of patients and other inmates is to be especially avoided. Increased spacing of beds in wards and dormitories should be carried out to reduce the risk of attack, and of the occurrence of pneumonia.

Exclusion. Patient only until complete recovery.

Readmission to school. By the school principal.

Measles (rubeola)

Reportable disease

Definition. A highly contagious viral disease characterized by fever, catarrhal symptoms of nose, throat, and eyes in the prodromal stage (as well as at the height of the disease) and an early eruption in the mouth. This is followed by a rapidly spreading blotchy eruption, sometimes followed by a branny scaling and peeling during convalescence.

Cause. The virus of measles.

Method of infection. Direct contact and droplet spread. Indirectly through articles freshly soiled with the nose and throat secretions of an infected individual. One attack usually, but not invariably, confers permanent immunity. A "measles year" comes at fairly regular intervals, as soon as there is a large percentage of susceptible children in the population. Endemic in large population areas.

Incubation period. Usually ten days from date of exposure to onset of fever, thirteen to fifteen days until appearance of rash. When passive immunization is attempted too late to prevent infection, the incubation period may be as long as twenty-one days.

Symptoms. Invasion marked by chilliness, coryza, redness of eyes, sensitiveness to light, then cough, and fever rising to 103° to 104° F. Eruption usually appears on fourth day during highest temperature; begins on face and forehead and extends over body as rounded or crescentic reddish blotches. Typical spots (Koplik's spots) seen inside mouth in most cases before rash on skin. Rash remains three to seven days.

Complications. The most common are bronchopneumonia, middle-ear inflammation, nephritis, and encephalitis.

Exclusion. During catarrhal symptoms four days before and seven days after appearance of rash. If inspection is available and exposed nonimmune children can be inspected daily they may remain in school. Immune children may remain in school.

Readmission to school. By the health officer, physicians and nurses of the Health Education and Health Services Branch, or regularly licensed physicians.

Remarks. Probably 80 to 90 per cent of all persons surviving to the twentieth year of life have had an attack, and rarely does a person go through life without having had measles.

Parents should be educated about the special danger of exposing young children to others having fever and cold symptoms of any kind, particularly during years and seasons of epidemic or prevalence of measles.

An effective immunizing agent against measles is now available. A single injection of a live attenuated vaccine induces active immunity in 95 per cent of susceptible children for a known 5 years. The majority have mild or inapparent noncommunicable infection with minimal symptoms. Thirty per cent to 40 per cent develop fever of 103 degrees rectal on the fourth to tenth day, lasting 2 to 5 days, but with little disability. Measles immune globulin administered at the same time as the measles vaccine will sharply reduce symptoms.

The passive immunization of children and infants under three years of age with immune globulin (preferably gamma globulin) in families where cases of measles occur should be encouraged by the department of health and by private physicians. Gamma globulin is also utilized for modification of measles in exposed susceptible contacts of any age.

Patient should be isolated during period of communicability to protect the patient against additional infection, as well as to prevent measles infection of other persons in the household, particularly of susceptible contacts of early ages.

During an epidemic there should be daily examination of exposed children and of other possibly exposed persons. This examination should include record of the body temperature. A nonimmune exposed individual exhibiting a rise of temperature of 0.5° C. (0.9° F.) or more should be promptly isolated pending diagnosis.

Schools should not be closed or classes discontinued, but daily observation of the children by physician or nurse should be provided.

Meningitis (epidemic)

Meningococcic infections

Reportable disease

Description. The onset is usually sudden with fever, intense headache, nausea, and often vomiting, signs of meningeal irritation, and frequently a petechial skin rash. Delirium and coma may appear early. Occasionally fulminating cases occur, exhibiting signs of collapse and shock from the onset.

Cause. Meningococcus or Neisseria meningitidis.

Method of infection. By direct contact with infected persons and carriers, indirectly by contact with articles freshly soiled with the discharges from the respiratory tract of infected persons.

Incubation period. Two to ten days.

Symptoms. The commonest clinical type is characterized by an acute onset, with severe headache (throbbing in character), backache, fever, chills, and vomiting. A stiff neck is soon noted. Petechial spots frequently appear on the skin.

Exclusion. Patient is isolated until end of febrile period and until all acute symptoms have subsided.

Contacts. Quarantined at the discretion of the health officer. Intimate contacts should be kept under frequent medical observation for a minimum of 4 days. Prophylactic treatment of household contacts under medical supervision may be required by the health officer.

Adult contacts whose occupation involves the care or supervision of children, or attendance at school where contact with children of age groups under 15 years is involved, must remain away from school or work until completion of the prophylactic course.

Children under 15 years shall be kept under quarantine for four days if taking prophylaxis, or for ten days if prophylaxis is not taken.

Readmission to school. By health officer, school physician, or any regularly licensed physician.

Mumps (infectious parotitis)

Description. An acute specific infection characterized by fever and by swelling and tenderness of one or more of the salivary glands usually of the parotid, sometimes of the sublingual or submaxillary glands. Involvement of ovaries and testicles is more frequent in persons past puberty; not infrequently involvement of the central nervous system is encountered in the course of the disease. Orchitis and meningoencephalitis due to mumps virus may occur without involvement of the salivary glands. Specific diagnosis may be made by serologic methods. The virus may be found in the saliva, blood, and cerebrospinal fluid. The use of serologic tests is of value in recognizing atypical forms of the infection. There are many subclinical cases.

Cause. The virus of mumps.

Method of infection. By direct contact with infected persons, droplet infection, and from articles soiled with discharges from the nose and throat of such infected persons. Period of communicability not definitely established but probably beginning about seven days before development of distinctive symptoms and persisting no longer than the swelling of a salivary gland. Susceptible persons may contract the disease through exposure to persons with inapparent infections.

Incubation period. Twelve to twenty-six days, usually eighteen days.

Symptoms. Onset with slight fever (rarely as high as 102° or 104° F.), and pain just below ear where swelling appears if parotid gland is affected. This enlarges greatly within two days. Some difficulty in chewing and swallowing, but often no real pain. Gradual subsidence after a week to ten days.

Exclusion. For nine days after the onset of swelling and until swelling of salivary glands has subsided. No exclusion for contacts.

Readmission to school. By health officer, physician or nurse of the Health Education and Health Services Branch, or regularly licensed physician.

Remarks. Greatest prevalence among young, and more during winter and spring months.

Pediculosis (Lice)

Definition. The presence of the adult louse, larva, or nit on the scalp, on hairy parts of the body, or on the clothing, especially along the seams of the inner surfaces.

Cause. Head or body louse—pediculus humanus.
Crab louse—phthirus pubis.

Method of infection. Direct contact with an infected person and indirect contact by clothing and headgear of such persons.

Incubation period. Strictly speaking, there is none, as the first adult louse to reach a new host may cause symptoms immediately. Under optimum conditions, the ova hatch in a week, and sexual maturity is reached in approximately two weeks.

Symptoms. Itching, and often lesions due to scratching and consequent purulent infections.

Recognition of lousiness.

Head louse: Ova (nits) in hair. More rarely lice.

Body louse: Inner surface of clothing, especially along seams, about neck, under arms, and along crotch.

Crab louse: Examination of pubic hairs.

Exclusion. As long as either active lice or nits are found in the hair, or until under proper treatment.

Readmission to school. By regularly licensed physicians and by the school nurses.

Treatment. For treatment use 10 per cent DDT dusting powder.

Remarks. Proper, persistent treatment rids one of lice, but recurrences are frequent due to undestroyed nits, or reinfestation from infested associates. Both lice and nits are easily seen with the naked eye.

Pinworm or oxyuriasis

Definition. An intestinal parasite which is more common in children than is generally believed and, though more frequent in the South and rural areas and among low economic groups, it is by no means confined to these limits. The pinworm is the most common worm parasite in man and is most frequently found in children of school age. It is exclusively a human parasite and infection is acquired from other infected individuals.

Pinworms are small white worms ⅛″ to ½″ long. The ova or eggs are ingested and hatch in the small intestine. The young worms mature in the lower intestine, cecum, and upper portion of the colon. Mature worms migrate to the rectum and discharge eggs on the perianal skin.

Symptom. The most common symptom is itching around the anus. If a child exhibits unusual scratching in the anal area, he should be referred for private care or examined by a school physician in the presence of his parent, and if sufficient evidence indicates the probability of pinworms, he should be excluded until under adequate treatment.

Readmission to school. On the recommendation of a licensed medical doctor.

Poliomyelitis (infantile paralysis)

Reportable disease

Description. In its recognizable form an acute illness, usually febrile, with early varying symptomatology, but usually with headache and almost always á characteristic stiffness of neck and spine and tightness of hamstring muscles.

A form of illness presumably poliomyelitis (abortive), presenting only vague symptoms and without signs referable to the central nervous system, occurs during epidemics. Inapparent infections exceed clinical cases at least several hundredfold.

Cause and method of infection. Poliomyelitis viruses. Types 1, 2, and 3 are distinguishable. Usually transmitted by direct contact and droplet spread through close association with infected persons.

Incubation period. From 7 to 21 days, commonly 12.

Symptoms. Early symptoms—moderate fever, usually headache, vomiting, constipation, drowsiness, and stiffness of neck and spine.

Later symptoms—motor weakness and paralysis. Abortive cases are common, with vague symptoms and no paralysis.

Exclusion. The patient for seven days from onset, or for duration of fever if longer and clinically severe. Contacts are not excluded if patient is properly isolated. If isolation of patient cannot be maintained, contacts, who are teachers as well as students, shall be excluded from school for the duration of the quarantine period.

Protection during epidemic. Immunization (Salk or Sabin vaccine). Early diagnosis; isolation of patients. Avoid unnecessary contact of children with other persons during epidemics. Avoid unnecessary traveling and visiting, especially of children. Avoid excessive physical strain. Avoid contact with any child or adult who has a suspicious illness. Isolate in bed all children with fever, pending diagnosis. Make sure that hands are thoroughly washed before eating. Postpone elective nose and throat surgery or dental extractions.

Remarks. Both Salk inactivated polio vaccine and Sabin oral vaccine have been proven effective. Children who have been fully immunized in infancy and the preschool period should have a booster dose on entrance to school and every two years thereafter. If not previously immunized, children should be given a full series at school age in accordance with the recommendations of local medical and public health authorities.

Rabies

Management of animal bites

Purpose.—Prevention of human rabies.

Animal bites of concern.—Bites by any warm-blooded mammal, especially dogs and cats.

Reporting.—All persons bitten and the biting dog should be reported by telephone to local Health Department. Include the following:

  a. Name, age, and address of person bitten. Date and address where bite occurred. Location of bite and description of wound.
  b. Name and address of owner of biting animal. Description of biting animal—breed, color, size, license number if known, other identifying characteristics.

Local treatment of wound. Wounds caused by bite or scratch of an animal with rabies or suspected rabies are thoroughly cleansed and irrigated with a solution of tincture of green soap or other antiseptic detergent; corrosive agents, such as fuming nitric acid, are not recommended. If tincture of green soap is used, it should be diluted one part of green soap to two parts of water. As an alternate, the wound should be washed thoroughly with 20 per cent solution of soap, (1 part soap to four of water) for five minutes. A 1 per cent solution of Zephiran is considered by some the treatment of choice. If used, concentrate aqueous Zephiran is diluted with distilled water according to the proportion of 1 part of Zephiran to 11 parts of distilled water, giving approximately a 1 per cent solution. Three successive swabs dipped in the Zephiran solution should be used for each wound and the deeper wounds thoroughly irrigated. Effectiveness of local treatment is dependent on the early application. Any child bitten by a cat or dog should be referred to the parent for private care or the parent should take him to the receiving hospital for further treatment of the wound.

Anti-rabies treatment.

  1. Carefully evaluate the circumstances of the bite and type of exposure.
  2. Face, head, or neck bite: (Incubation period as short as 2 weeks.) Begin at once prophylactic treatment with daily subcutaneous injections of anti-rabies vaccine. Discontinue treatment if biting animal alive and without signs and symptoms on the fifth day following the bite. If animal rabid, escaped, or unknown, continue treatment for a total of 21 doses.
  3. Extremity bites: (Incubation period 4 to 6 weeks or longer.) Withhold anti-rabies vaccine pending observation of biting animal. If animal alive and without signs and symptoms on the 14th day after date of bite, no vaccine treatment. If animal rabid, escaped, or unknown, begin vaccine treatment as soon as possible and continue for 14 doses.
  4. Hyperimmune anti-rabies serum is now available for use by physicians in the management of severe dog bites. This preparation is designed to provide **immediate** protection against rabies in cases of severe exposure. Thus, a patient can be protected **passively** during the interval between starting a course of Pasteur vaccine injections and the time of establishment of his own **active** immunity.

Disposition of suspected animals. It is important not to kill an animal suspected of rabies until clinical diagnosis has been firmly established. If the animal dies from accident prior to diagnosis, it is important that the head be preserved intact for laboratory examination. If for some reason, the animal must be destroyed, it is important that the procedure avoid mutilation of the head. After the head is removed it should be kept in refrigeration pending delivery to the laboratory if immediate delivery is not possible.

Community control. Anti-rabies vaccination of dogs is an important community control measure.

Ringworm of the Scalp (dermatophytosis, epidermophytosis)

Description. A fungus skin disease taking the form of circular patches, such as tinea or favus (the type marked by round "honeycomb crusts").

Inspection of the scalp for localized round, scaly patches with short, broken-off hairs. The fungus may be demonstrated in infested hairs or skin scales, and the type of fungus should be confirmed by culture. Examination under suitably filtered ultraviolet light (Wood's lamp) to detect characteristic fluorescence. Identification of the species of fungus may be important in determining treatment.

Cause. Various species of fungi. Those listed below are most important in school age children:

1. Microsporum audouini—human type
2. Microsporum lanosum—animal type
3. Tricophyton tonsurans

Method of infection. Directly from person to person by contact with lesions of infected person (or in the case of animal fungi, with infected animals). Possibly indirectly by articles of wearing apparel or by surfaces contaminated by scales or hairs from lesions. Transmission occurs in the home and in schools, especially during games in which personal contact is close, and from barber's instruments.

Articles of clothing, especially hats and caps, containing the fungus or its spores, or infested hairs or scales shed by individuals. In the case of infection with M. canis or other animal fungi, contact with lesions or hair shed by young cats or dogs affected with ringworm.

Incubation period. Ten to 14 days.

Period of communicability. As long as infected lesions are present and viable spores are present on contaminated materials.

Prevalence. Widespread, with epidemics, especially among school children and in institutions for children.

Exclusion. Lanosum: Patient only until recovery or under adequate treatment. Release by health department only.

Audouini and tonsurans infections: As soon as ringworm of the scalp is suspected, the child is excluded from school until he is under adequate treatment. If the patient is found not to be faithfully carrying out instructions, he shall again be excluded from school until there is good evidence that treatment is being followed. Readmission to school without prescribed cap is only upon written consent of the health department of jurisdiction for residence of the pupil. No exclusion of contacts.

Treatment. Children with either type of ringworm must stay under adequate treatment at all times. Adequate treatment of the human type of ringworm consists of keeping the scalp shaved, using the prescribed ointment, and wearing a tight-fitting stocking cap at home and at school. Children with the animal type ringworm may have their hair clipped as short as possible instead of shaved. Girls may wear a turban over the cap and boys may wear an aviator-type cap which ties under the chin over their stocking cap. Stocking caps should be boiled daily and turbans or aviator's caps boiled once a week.

Specific treatment with a fungicide administered under medical direction is recommended. The new fungicide griseofulvin which is administered orally shows promise of helping a majority of those infected and shortening the period of treatment. It is used in combination with local therapy.

Laboratory diagnosis is made by means of culture to determine whether the disease is the animal or human type, but the child may be in school pending laboratory results if he is under treatment. The human type is communicable from child to child.

In the school, nurses or teachers must check the infected child at least two or three times a week to see that the ointment is being applied, stocking caps are being worn, scalps are kept shaved, and that the children visit the health center or private physician as required.

Ringworm of the feet (epidermophytosis, athlete's foot)

Description. Condition is caused by a fungus growth which finds the areas between the toes a favorable place in which to live and grow. There is scaling or cracking of the skin especially between the toes, or blisters containing a thin watery fluid. In severe cases vesicular lesions appear on various parts of the body especially on the hands, and represent an allergic reaction to fungus products. The same towel that is used in drying the feet should not be used for drying the body.

In the care of "athlete's foot," it is essential that:

1. All severe cases of athlete's foot be excluded from the use of dressing-rooms, showers, and swimming pools.
2. The feet be bathed daily, washing carefully between the toes with soap and warm water.
3. The whole foot and in between the toes be wiped absolutely dry.
4. Socks be changed daily.
5. Shoes be wide enough to provide free movement of the toes.

Specific treatment. Fungicides and dusting powders may be needed in resistant cases.

Epidemic measures. Thorough cleaning and washing down of gymnasiums, showers, and similar sources of infection.

Scabies (the itch)

Definition. An infestation of the skin due to the itch-mite, which burrows beneath the skin forming greyish white lines housing the mite and eggs. Papules and vesicles may form. Pustules may form due to secondary infection caused by scratching.

Cause. Sarcoptes scabiei.

Method of infection. Direct contact with infested persons and indirectly by use of underclothing, gloves, bedding, etc., of such persons.

Incubation period. Several days or even weeks before itching is noticed.

Symptoms. Intense itching in vicinity of each burrow. Web of fingers and toes most common sites, although any part of the body surface may be affected. Itching is intensified at intervals of a few days as successive crops mature and start new burrows.

Exclusion. Patient only until recovery.

Specific treatment. A bath followed by application of 20 per cent to 25 per cent emulsion of benzyl benzoate or 1 per cent benzine hexachloride ointment to whole body. Following day repeat bath and change clothing.

Readmission to school. By school physicians and nurses, regularly licensed physician, or school principal.

Smallpox (variola)

Description. A quarantinable communicable disease characterized by one to five days of febrile symptoms which precede the true or focal eruption, which is papular for one to four days, vesicular for one to four days, and pustular for two to six days, forming crusts which fall off ten to forty days after the first sign of the lesion, and leave pink scars which fade gradually.

Cause. The virus of smallpox.

Method of infection. By contact with persons sick with the disease—this contact need not be intimate; also by articles of persons contaminated by discharges of the sick, from lesions of his skin and mucous membranes and scabs. Aerial transmission may occur over short distances.

Incubation period. Seven to sixteen days, commonly twelve days, and three to four days more to onset of illness.

Symptoms. Invasion is sudden with chills in adult or convulsions in children, severe headache and (lumbar) backache, and fever to 103° F.

Exclusion. Until recovery, scabs separated and scars completely healed.

Contacts. Exclude sixteen days after last exposure or immunity established by successful vaccination and release by Health Department.

Readmission to school. By the Health Department only.

Streptococcal infections, hemolytic

I. Scarlet fever

II. Streptococcal sore throat

Reportable diseases

Definition. An acute infectious illness caused by Group A hemolytic streptococci, varying clinically according to tissues affected and the presence or absence of a scarlatinal rash. Scarlet fever is streptococcal sore throat in which a rash occurs. If the rash does not occur, the infection is streptococcal sore throat. Other distinguishing characteristics of these diseases are sore throat, exudative tonsillitis, or pharyngitis, tender cervical glands, and strawberry tongue.

Cause. Group A hemolytic streptococci of which there are 40 types found in respiratory secretions of patient or carriers, or objects contaminated with such discharges.

Method of infection. Directly by contact with an infected person; indirectly by articles freshly soiled with discharges of an infected person or airborne; or through contaminated milk or other foods. Most cases occur in children. Repeated streptococcal infections may occur. Highest incidence is in winter and spring months, usually reaching its peak in April and May.

Incubation period. Usually 1 to 3 days, rarely longer.

Symptoms. The distinguishing characteristics are fever, sore throat (enanthem), strawberry tongue and rash. Injection and edema of the pharynx involves the faucial pillars and soft palate; petechial foci are sometimes seen against the background of diffuse redness. Tonsils, if present, often show the lesions of acute follicular tonsillitis. The rash is usually a fine redness, commonly punctate, blanching on pressure and appearing most often on the neck, chest, in the folds of the axilla, elbow, and groin and on the inner aspects of the thighs. Typically the rash does not involve the face except in Negroes, but there is flushing of the cheeks and pallor around the mouth (circumoral pallor). Fever, nausea, and vomiting accompany severe infections. The peeling and scaling (desquamation) of convalescence is seen at the tips of the fingers and toes and less often over wide areas of the trunk and limbs, including palms and soles.

Streptococcal sore throat is scarlet fever infection without a rash nor does desquamation follow.

Complications and sequelae. Rheumatic fever, otitis media, nephritis, and others.

Exclusion of patient. Patients treated with an effective antibiotic released on clinical recovery. Others are released seven days from onset and on clinical recovery. Peeling and scaling (desquamating) skin is not infectious.

Contacts. Exclusion not required if patient properly isolated and contacts inspected daily at school for one week following exposure. School teachers and school cafeteria workers are referred to school health authorities or to the health department for permission to work or to return to work. Appropriate prophylactic chemotherapy or antibiotic agent is effective in preventing infection of exposed persons.

Readmission to school. Patient and contacts by the health officer, school physicians and nurses, or regularly licensed physicians.

Remarks. Scarlet fever is remarkably variable in different epidemics. It varies from the malignant type with 100 per cent mortality to a mild, hardly recognizable type with practically no mortality. There are many "missed cases" which spread infection. In uncomplicated cases, the probability of spreading infection is ordinarily past a few days after clinical recovery. Individuals with complications resulting in purulent discharges are most capable of spreading infection and for long periods. Even minor nasal and aural discharges may spread the infection.

Tuberculosis

Reportable disease

   Description. Among the most common communicable diseases of man. Susceptibility is general.
   Cause. The tubercle bacillus.
   Method of infection. Inhalation or ingestion of infected droplets, or milk of an infected cow. Discharges from tuberculous lesions are also infectious.
   Types of tuberculosis. Primary tuberculous infection (childhood type tuberculosis): Initial pulmonary and hilar gland infection, usually with few or no symptoms, and usually healing by calcification. The tuberculin skin sensitivity test is positive and the x-ray may show typical calcification. In the early stages it may be infectious.
   Pulmonary tuberculosis (adult or reinfection type tuberculosis): May occur by reinfection from a new exposure or by direct extension of a primary type tuberculosis. In minimal cases there may be few or no symptoms, but far advanced cases are characterized by cough, sputum, weight loss, fever, sweating, and sometimes blood spitting.
   Tuberculosis may be generalized, as in military tuberculosis. It may occur in the bones, skin, or glands. These cases are rare, and unless discharges are present they are not infectious to others.
   Methods of control. Pre-employment and periodic x-ray of all school employees, periodic tuberculin testing of school children with x-ray of all positive reactors, close observation of tuberculin-negative reactors who convert to positive, and a search for their sources of infection should be required. Patients with active tuberculosis should preferably be hospitalized and treated with an appropriate combination of antimicrobial drugs.
   Readmission to school. By local health department or specially deputized school medical authority.

Typhoid fever

Reportable disease

   Description. A systemic infection characterized by continued fever, involvement of lymphoid tissues (especially with involvement and often ulceration of Peyer's patches), enlargement of spleen, usually rose spots on the trunk, diarrheal disturbance, and a variety of constitutional disturbances. There are many mild, atypical, and often unrecognized infections. Typhoid bacilli can be found in blood, feces, and urine.
   Cause. Typhoid bacillus (Salmonella typhosa). Several types are readily identifiable.
   Method of infection. Feces and urine of infected individual and carriers. About 2 to 5 per cent of patients become permanent carriers. Family contacts may be transient carriers.
   Transmission of microorganisms through direct or indirect contact with patient or carrier. Principal vehicles for indirect spread are contaminated water, food (especially raw fruit, raw vegetables, milk, and shellfish) and under some conditions, flies.
   Incubation period. Variable average two weeks, usual range one to three weeks.
   Symptoms (very variable). Typical cases as follows: Onset usually gradual with fever, lassitude, chilliness, constipation, or diarrhea. Sometimes nosebleed or abdominal pain.
   Diagnosis confirmed by specific agglutination test after the first week and confirmed by bacteriologic examination of blood, feces, or urine at any time.
   Exclusion. Until recovery and two negative fecal and urine cultures, at least 1

week apart, and at least 1 week after ending specific therapy. Modified isolation of patient.

Contacts. Restrictions of each case shall be at the discretion of the Health Officer. Food handlers cannot work until released by the Health Officer and under his restrictions.

Readmission to school. By the health department only.

Typhoid carriers. Should be reported to local health department and are released by the State Department of Health.

Salmonella, other than S. typhosa—See Food Poisoning.

Whooping cough (pertussis)

Definition. An acute infectious disease involving the trachea and bronchi and characterized by a typical cough, usually lasting from one to two months, becoming paroxysmal in one to two weeks, followed by the characteristic inspiratory whoop.

Cause. Pertussis bacillus (Hemophilus pertussis).

Method of infection. Usually transmitted by direct contact, by droplet spread or with the discharges from the nose and throat of infected persons.

Incubation period. Seven to ten days usually, and not exceeding twenty-one days.

Immunity. Susceptibility is general; no natural immunity. Children are most affected; one attack usually confers immunity.

Symptoms. Onset gradual. The catarrhal stage begins with catarrhal symptoms in eyes, nose, and bronchi (like a cold). After some days (usually seven to ten) the cough gradually gets worse and the paroxysmal stage dates from the first "whoop." However, young infants and adults may not have the typical paroxysm. Severe or frequently repeated cough often ends with expectoration of thick mucus or vomiting.

Convalescence. Gradual—after three weeks.

Complications and sequelae. Frequent enough to cause considerable mortality, especially in the first two years of life. Bronchopneumonia is the chief complication.

Exclusion. Patient is isolated during the early catarrhal period and for twenty-one days after the appearance of the typical paroxysmal cough.

Readmission to school. By City or County Health Department, school physicians or nurses or regularly licensed physician.

Contacts. Children may attend school if daily inspection is available for fourteen days after last exposure.

Remarks. Approximately 15 per cent of the cases occur in children under two years of age. Children under seven years of age are most susceptible to attack, and those under two years of age to fatal attack.

Educational measures should be undertaken to inform the public of the dangers of pertussis and of the advantages of immunization in infancy. Passive immunity may be conveyed for a short time by hyperimmune or convalescent serum.

First-aid procedures[1]

If the school physician or nurse is in the school, he/she should be notified. Notify the parents at once.

Abdominal pain. Pain in right flank induced by exertion is not appendicitis. Pain in right lower abdomen, irrespective of activity, with tenderness and sometimes nausea and vomiting, is *suspicious* of appendicitis. Parents should be advised to obtain professional advice and care for the child.

Burns

> *Slight (first or second degree).* Apply Petrolatum ointment and sterile gauze after keeping under cold water for 10-15 minutes.
> *Severe (blisters or charred skin).* Apply sterile dressing only. Send to receiving hospital or private physician after notifying parent.

> *Cinder or brush burns.* Cleanse out foreign matter with warm water and soap solution. Apply germicide solution then Petrolatum ointment covered with sterile gauze.
> *Chemical burns.* Immediately flush copiously with water or antidote if external, olive oil or egg white if internal. Refer for immediate medical care.
> *Acid burns to eye.* Flush eye thoroughly with water. Refer for medical care.
> *Acid burns of the skin.* Wash with running water, then neutralize immediately with ammonia solution, wash after. Then apply Petrolatum ointment and sterile gauze.
> *Acid burns of the mucous membrane.* Rinse with water, follow with a solution of sodium bicarbonate.
> *Acid burns internally*
>> 1. Give insoluble magnesia, magnesium carbonate, or lime water.
>> 2. Give milk.
>> 3. Refer for medical care.
> *Alkali burns to eye.* Flush eye thoroughly with water. Refer for medical care.
> *Alkali burns of the skin.* Wash with running water then neutralize immediately with vinegar. Then apply Petrolatum ointment and sterile gauze.
> *Alkali burns of the mucous membrane.* Rinse with water and follow with equal parts of vinegar and water.
> *Alkali burns—internally*
>> 1. Give one pint of a solution composed of equal parts of vinegar and water.
>> 2. Refer for medical care.

---

[1]This material on first-aid procedures is a copy of an eight-page folder distributed to its schools by the Health Services Branch of the Division of Education Services of the Los Angeles City School Districts. It is used here with their permission.

Other burns of eyes. Flush eyes copiously with water. Cover with a loose non-pressure bandage. See that child gets expert care as soon as possible.

Cuts

Arteries. Evidenced by intermittent spurting of blood. If hemorrhage cannot be controlled by a firmly applied pressure bandage and serious loss of blood is threatened, a tourniquet should be used. If soft rubber tubing is not available, wrap handkerchief or towel above wound tightly enough to stop bleeding. The tourniquet should be placed close to wound but not at wound edge. The tourniquet should not be released except by a physician. Notify parents at once. Send to family physician or nearest receiving hospital.

Small cuts and abrasions. Cleanse with clean warm water and soap solution. Apply germicide solution. When thoroughly dry, cover with sterile gauze and tape.

Severe cuts and abrasions. Sterile gauze is the only dressing to be used on wounds of pupils sent to the receiving hospital or private physician, as antiseptics or ointments obscure wound and make proper cleansing difficult. If bleeding, use sterile pressure bandage.

Dog bites

Animal bites, especially dogs and cats. The wound should be washed thoroughly with soap solution (tincture of green soap, 1 part, water, 2 parts; or liquid soap, full strength). One per cent solution of Zephiran may be used if available. The deeper wounds should be thoroughly irrigated. Allow to dry and apply sterile gauze. Refer at once for further treatment to family physician or receiving hospital.

Reporting animal bites. All bites should be reported promptly. In Los Angeles, telephone MAdison 53611 or report bites to the nearest Animal Regulation Center (Shelter) or County Health Office. Give name, age, and address of the pupil, location and description of the wound, description of the animal and name and address of owner if possible.

Drowning. See "Artificial respiration" under *"Respiration."*

Earache. Send child home and recommend medical care.

Electric shock. See "Artificial respiration" under *"Respiration."*

Eyes

Chemical burns of eyeball. See "Other burns of eyes" under *"Burns."*

Foreign body in eye. Use warm water in medicine dropper to try to flush the particle out. If not easily washed out refer to nurse, physician, or receiving hospital.

Convulsive seizure. Let patient lie on the floor. Provide fresh air and keep crowd away. Give nothing by mouth. Loosen tight collar or clothing. Place smooth, firm article, such as two tongue blades, between teeth to keep patient from biting his tongue. Remove hard objects against which he might injure himself. After patient is quiet, remove to the rest room and send for parents to take him home.

Fainting. Keep child lying down. Give nothing by mouth. Open windows; loosen clothing, and keep crowd away. Moisten cotton with aromatic spirits of ammonia and hold under child's nostrils. If unconsciousness is prolonged, call parents or send to receiving hospital.

Fractures. Do not move child from place of injury until emergency splints are applied. Keep child lying down. Notify parents. In minor fracture cases with little or no shock, child may be taken to receiving hospital unless parents desire to make other arrangements. In fractures with severe pain and shock, call receiving hospital.

Suspected spine fracture. Usually caused by fall from great height or a crushing blow. Child may be paralyzed. *Do not move child from place of injury.* Send for receiving hospital ambulance.

Headache. Apply covered ice cap with child in reclining position. Look for signs of contagious disease. If child has rash, fever, cough, sore throat, or nasal discharge, isolate until he can be sent home.

Head injuries. Do not move from place of injury, unless imperative—then move as carefully as possible. Keep child lying down, even if injury appears to be minor. Cover with blanket. Treat for shock.

If mucous is collecting in nose or throat and difficulty in breathing is observed, turn patient on side.

Bleeding from scalp wounds may be controlled by sterile pressure bandages.

If patient is conscious and thoroughly warm, covered ice cap to head may be used if it makes him comfortable.

If unable to locate parents, call receiving hospital for ambulance. Never allow child to walk home, go by bus, or ride bicycle, if there has been shock, disorientation, or convulsion. Notify parent to call for child even if he appears to have recovered.

Head injuries severe enough to cause even momentary unconsciousness should be observed carefully for several days.

Insect bites and stings.

Bee stings. Remove stinger. Immediate application of ice or ice water gives relief, then apply germicide. If marked swelling occurs, refer for medical care.

Insulin shock. Sudden pallor, weakness, sweating, mental confusion, convulsions, or unconsciousness. Give sugar, candy, orange juice, or Karo syrup if conscious. If unconscious, call emergency hospital at once.

Nose bleed. Place child in sitting position with head erect. Apply gauze with pressure to anterior portion of nostrils for at least fifteen minutes, by the clock.

Poisoning—by chemicals. See "Chemical burns" under "*Burns.*"

Respiration.

Stopping of respiration—by electric shock, immersion, etc. Give artificial respiration and send for emergency medical aid at once.

Artificial respiration. The mouth to mouth (or mouth to nose) technique is considered the most practical method for emergency ventilation of a victim of any age who has stopped breathing. This technique is basically the same for both adults and children.

Mouth to Mouth Technique

Clean out the mouth.

With victim on-back, TILT the head as far back as possible (one hand pushing the crown of the head down with the other hand lifting the jaw up)

Open your mouth wide and place it over the mouth of the victim, with your cheek against his nose. Blow into mouth. (With infant or small child it is possible to cover BOTH mouth and nose with your mouth.)

Remove your mouth—gasp in fresh air—and repeat.

"Huff and puff," blowing into victim's mouth about 12 times per minute—20 times per minute for children or infants (think of the lungs as paper bags—small puffs to fill small bags, big puffs to fill big bags).

If you have a blanket, pillow, coat, or towel, fold it and place it under shoulders. This will help further extend head. Don't delay in this. Breath into your victim first—then do this if it can be done without delay.

Splinters. Do not remove if deeply imbedded, or if there is possibility of splinter breaking off.

Notify family to seek necessary care, or if serious, send to receiving hospital.

Sprains or bruises. If seen early, use cold compresses. Follow by supporting bandaging. If seen late, hot compresses give more relief. Rest. Notify family to seek necessary care.

Note: Apply ice only in covered ice bag or with a layer of heavy cloth between ice and skin.

Wounds. Use germicide solution. When thoroughly dry, apply sterile dressing. See "*Cuts.*"

Thermometer technique

Use clean thermometer. After use, clean immediately by washing thoroughly with soap solution and water. Rinse in cold water and place in container of alcohol. Rinse with water again. Put in clean container.

For additional information, see the **American Red Cross Manual of First Aid Instructions.**

Index